STRUCTURAL

GEOLOGY

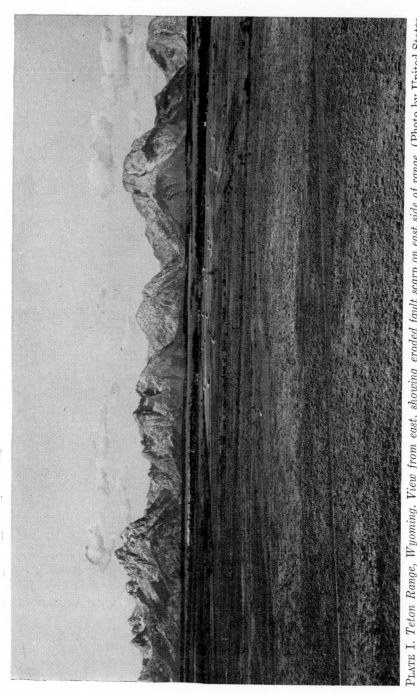

PLATE I. *Teton Range, Wyoming. View from east, showing eroded fault scarp on east side of range.* (Photo by United States Department of the Interior.)

STRUCTURAL
GEOLOGY

by

MARLAND P. BILLINGS

Professor of Geology
Harvard University

SECOND EDITION

Englewood Cliffs, N. J.
PRENTICE-HALL, INC.

LIBRARY OF CONGRESS
CATALOG CARD NUMBER:

54–8507

Current printing (last digit):
20 19 18 17 16 15 14 13 12 11

PRINTED IN THE UNITED STATES OF AMERICA
85382-C

Preface

In the preparation of this new edition I have followed the general policy adopted in the previous editions. As before, the emphasis has been placed on the principles of structural geology. Some consideration was given to the inclusion of several chapters on regional structure and the fascinating subject of mountain ranges and continents. But to treat these subjects adequately would take so many pages that the book would either be greatly lengthened or some of the fundamental principles would be less fully treated.

The usual problem of proper balance has arisen. A definition of the exact limits of structural geology is an academic question of little practical importance. Nevertheless, an author must make arbitrary decisions on this matter. He must decide, for example, which subjects lie within the fields of stratigraphy and sedimentation and which are primarily the concern of the structural geologist. I suggest that the origin of those features related to the processes of sedimentation are not part of structural geology. Thus the origins of bedding and of primary structures (ripple marks, cross-bedding, etc.) are the concern of the sedimentationist. The structural geologist, however, is interested in these features as tools for working out the major structure or as features that may be confused with tectonic structures.

The classification of faults is a perennial problem. As in the first edition, I have followed rather closely the 1912 classification of H. F. Reid and his associates, with the addition of a few worth-while terms. Although this classification may seem unnecessarily involved, all those proposed since then are oversimplified and lead ultimately to confusion. In fact, many of them seem to be based on an incomplete knowledge of the complexities of faulting, and some of them are individualistic schemes that were evolved without any knowledge of the care and effort that went into the Reid classification.

The use of the term "gravity fault" has caused a lot of confusion in geology. Unfortunately, some geologists try to interpret the meaning of a term before they investigate the usage intended by the original author. For example, a geologist with a classical background might discover that the word "batholith" means "depth rock." He might at once decide that it means sedimentary rocks that are deposited in deep water. Even the simple word "anticline" is not always used in its literal sense. Some purist might easily point out that it means "against inclined," referring to the fact that in the simplest anticlines the beds dip away from each other on opposite limbs. Strictly speaking, therefore, the term cannot properly be applied to an overturned anticline or an isoclinal recumbent anticline. "Atom" means "uncut, indivisible." We now know that the word was based on the misconception that the atom was the smallest possible particle in nature. Shall we abandon the word "atom," redefine it, or just recognize that the word no longer means what it says? Similarly, the word "gravity fault," although perhaps based originally in part on a misconception, should be used in the way that the Reid committee considered the best usage.

Although the structural problems at the end of the book follow the same general plan as before, three new exercises have been added, and some of the other exercises have been modified. Moreover, all the numerical data have been changed.

I am grateful to several friends who have made valuable suggestions in the preparation of this new edition. Any failure to follow their advice does not indicate a lack of appreciation on my part. I am particularly indebted for suggestions on the entire manuscript made by Professors John Rodgers of Yale University, Ben M. Page of Stanford University, and C. Noble Beard of Fresno State College. Dr. Eleanora B. Knopf made many suggestions for the chapter entitled "Structural Petrology," and Professor Francis Birch, for the chapter dealing with "Mechanical Principles."

I want to express my thanks to those instructors who since the war have assisted me in my course in structural geology: Clyde Wahrhaftig, Edgar Bowman, Laurence Nobles, and Dallas Peck. In particular, Dr. Wahrhaftig prepared the original draft of Exercise 9 in the Structural Problems, and Dr. Nobles prepared the original draft for Exercise 12. Mr. Peck prepared the new numerical data for the problems.

I am indebted also to Mrs. Constance Schilling, whose efficient and cheerful secretarial work made the task of preparing the manuscript less arduous. To Mr. Edward Schmitz, for his skill in preparing illustrations from rough copy, I extend many thanks.

MARLAND P. BILLINGS

Contents

10. Mechanics of Faulting (*Cont'd*)

11. Thrust Faults 181

12. Gravity or Normal Faults 195

13. Strike-Slip Faults 212

14. Causes of Folding and Faulting 226

23. Geophysical Methods in Structural Geology (*Cont'd*)

CHAPTER 1

Structural Geology

RELATION OF STRUCTURAL GEOLOGY TO GEOLOGY

Structural geology is the study of the architecture of the earth in so far as it is determined by earth movements. *Tectonics* and *tectonic geology* are terms that are synonymous with structural geology. The movements that affect solid rocks result from forces within the earth; they cause folds, joints, faults, and cleavage. The movement of magma, because it is often intimately associated with the displacement of solid rocks, is also a subject that lies within the domain of structural geology.

Structural geology is closely related to many other branches of geology, and in field work the solution of the structural problems is often only one phase of a broader investigation. It is futile to try to study the structure of folded and faulted sedimentary formations without a knowledge of *stratigraphy*, that phase of geology treating of the sequence in which formations have been deposited. *Sedimentation*, which deals with the deposition of stratified rocks, may offer much evidence on the tectonic events in areas adjacent to the basins in which the stratified rocks accumulate. *Paleontology*, which is the study of fossils, is indispensable to the structural geologist who works in rocks containing organic remains. *Petrology*, a subject that includes the systematic description of rocks and the study of their origin, sheds much light on the structural history of igneous, metamorphic, and sedimentary rocks. A knowledge of *physiography*, the study of the surface of the earth, is particularly important to the structural geologist who investigates regions of recent tectonic activity, where the topography is a rather direct expression of the structure. Even in those areas where the tectonic evolution ceased long ago, physiography may furnish important clues to the structural geologist. *Geophysics*, the application of physics to terrestrial problems, has been successfully employed in solving many types of structural problems. Moreover, it is one source of our information on the interior of the earth, the source of tectonic energy. *Seismology*, that branch of geophysics dealing with earthquakes and the propagation of elastic waves through the earth, gives us our most tangible information about the vast interior of the earth that lies beneath the thin surface shell visible to the structural geologist. *Geochemistry*, the application of the principles of chemistry to problems of the earth, is especially significant to the structural geologist who is concerned with the subject of metamorphism. *Oceanography*, especially that phase known as *submarine geology*, is discovering many exciting facts about the topography and composition of the floors of the oceans, facts that are already revolutionizing our thinking about the structure of the crust of the earth.

It is apparent, therefore, that structural geology is intricately interwoven with other phases of geology and, in some instances, with other sciences. Thus the structural geologist must be familiar with the range and subject matter of these related fields. A systematic treatment of these fields, however, is beyond the scope of this book.

OBJECTIVES OF STRUCTURAL GEOLOGY

The structural geologist is concerned with three major problems: (1) What is the structure? (2) When did it develop? (3) Under what physical conditions did it form? [1]

In general, the first question must be answered first. It is essential to determine the shape and size of the rock bodies. Are they great flat-lying tabular masses covering scores of square miles? Or are they tabular masses that have been thrown into folds with a wave-length of several miles and an amplitude of thousands of feet? Or are they great cylindrical bodies thousands of feet in diameter and a mile or two deep?

Geological field work is indispensable to many such investigations, and it is this fact that distinguishes most phases of geology from many of the other sciences. Because the correct location of outcrops is of the utmost importance, accurate maps are essential. For many regions topographic maps are available, and by means of topography, drainage, and culture, a precise location is possible. In recent years vertical aerial photographs have become increasingly important in geological field work. These photographs, made from directly above, are essentially maps. In some respects they are superior to topographic maps because they not only portray all natural and artificial features with great accuracy, but they reveal, too, many features such as trees, forests, open fields, and fences that are not generally indicated on topographic maps. However, they lack contours; moreover, in mountainous regions, the scale is not constant. In regions for which suitable maps or aerial photographs are not available, it may be necessary for the geologist to prepare his own base map, usually by plane table methods. A discussion of the technique of field methods is beyond the scope of the present book, but

[1] Goguel, J., *Traité de Tectonique*. Paris: Masson & Cie, 1952; especially p. 3.

this subject is adequately treated in the excellent books by Lahee,[2] and Greenly and Williams.[3]

Successful geological field work consists of the accumulation of significant facts. At each outcrop the geologist records whatever data are pertinent to his problem, and, ideally, he should never have to visit an outcrop a second time. This is especially true in areas that are difficult of access, but even in accessible regions the work should be so planned that a second visit to an outcrop is unnecessary.

Geologic mapping, when properly done, demands skill and judgment. Such mapping requires keen observation and a knowledge of what data are significant. As the field work progresses and the larger geological picture begins to unfold, experience and judgment are essential if the geologist is to evaluate properly the vast number of facts gathered from thousands of outcrops. Above all, the field geologist must use the method of "working multiple hypotheses"[4] to deduce the geological structure. While the field work progresses, he should conceive as many interpretations as are consistent with the known facts. He should then formulate tests for these interpretations,[5] checking them by data already obtained, or checking them in the future by new data. Many of these interpretations will be abandoned, new ones will develop, and those finally accepted may bear little resemblance to hypotheses considered early during the field work.

Nothing is more naïve than to believe that a field geologist should gather only "facts," the interpretation of which is to be made at a later date. Because of his numerous tentative interpretations, the field geologist will know how to evaluate the facts; these hypotheses, moreover, will lead him to critical outcrops that might otherwise never have been visited. On the other hand, the field geologist should never let his temporary hypotheses become ruling theories, thus making him incapable of seeing contradictory facts.

Although much structural information in the past has been gathered from direct observation, either on the surface of the earth, in open pits, or in mines, a progressively greater proportion of our data is gleaned from the depths of the earth by indirect means. The petroleum geologists, in particular, have obtained vast amounts of structural data from

[2] Lahee, F. H., *Field Geology*, 5th ed. New York: McGraw-Hill Book Company, Inc., 1952.

[3] Greenly, E., and H. Williams, *Methods in Geological Surveying*. New York: D. Van Nostrand Co., 1930.

[4] Chamberlin, T. C.. "The Method of Working Multiple Hypotheses," *Journal of Geology*, Vol. 5, pp. 837–848, 1897: also reprinted in K. F. Mather and S. L. Mason, *A Source Book in Geology,* pp. 604–612. New York: McGraw-Hill Book Company, Inc., 1939.

[5] Gilbert, G. K., "The Inculcation of Scientific Method, with an Illustration Drawn from Quaternary Geology of Utah," *American Journal of Science,* 3rd series, Vol. 31, pp. 284–299, 1886.

the study of drill holes and from geophysical data. In fact, a whole new field of the science, subsurface geology, has evolved during the last few decades.[6] Subsurface geology not only involves structural geology, but also paleontology, stratigraphy, sedimentation and geophysical methods.

Aerial photographs are not only of great value as base maps on which to plot geological data, as mentioned on p. 2, but in many areas the geological structure is strikingly shown. Such structural features as folds, joints, faults, and structures of plutonic rocks may be clearly observed. Moreover, under favorable circumstances quantitative data on the attitude of bedding may be obtained. In reconnaissance studies of little-known regions aerial photographs are indispensable, and even in regions that have been studied several times it is possible to observe previously unsuspected structural features. The use of aerial photographs in geological work is described in a number of papers and publications.[7]

A second objective of the structural geologist is to relate the structure to some chronology. One phase of this study is to determine the sequence in which the structural features developed. For example, he may find an anticline, a fault, and a dike. What are their relative ages? The anticline may be the oldest and the dike may be the youngest. It is also possible that the fault is the oldest and that the anticline is the youngest. There are also other possibilities. In some areas the sequence may be exceedingly complex. Nolan[8] has described an area in Utah where several successive stages of deformation are each characterized by folding and faulting.

The structural geologist is interested not only in the sequence of tectonic events in the area which he is studying, but he also wants to integrate them with the geological history of the whole earth. He wants to date his structure, that is, to determine the geological period in which it formed, or better yet, to determine in which part of the geological period it developed. In practice, detailed dating is often very difficult. In rocks younger than the beginning of the Cambrian period, fossils are of invaluable aid in correlating geological events.

A third objective of the structural geologist is to determine the physical processes that produced the observed structure.[9] What was the

[6] LeRoy, L. W., *Subsurface Geologic Methods,* 2nd ed. Golden, Colorado: Colorado School of Mines, 1156 pages, 1950.

[7] Smith, H. T. U., *Aerial Photographs and Their Applications,* New York: Appleton-Century-Crofts, Inc., 372 pp., 1943.

Smith, H. T. U., "Present Status of Photo Interpretation in Earth Science," *Photogrammetric Engineering,* Vol. 19, pp. 137–143, 1953.

Eardley, A. J., *Aerial Photographs: Their Use and Interpretation,* New York: Harper & Bros., 203 pp., 1942.

[8] Nolan, T. B., "The Gold Hill Mining District, Utah," *U. S. Geological Survey, Professional Paper 177,* 1935.

[9] Goguel, J., "Introduction à l'Étude Mécanique des Déformations de l'Écorce Terrestre," 2nd ed, *Mémoires pour la Carte Géologique Détaillée de la France,* Paris. 1948.

temperature and pressure at the time the structure formed, and what was the stress distribution? As Hafner[10] has pointed out, it is necessary to answer questions such as this before we try to deduce the ultimate causes. Without deducing the stress distribution at the time the structure formed, it is difficult to decide whether a given fold was the result of contraction of the earth, subcrustal convection currents, or the forceful injection of magma. Such studies involve a knowledge of dynamics. Unfortunately this approach has been woefully neglected in structural geology.

Experimental geology provides significant data for the understanding of tectonic processes. In many of these studies the physical properties of rocks have been investigated,[11] but usually it has not been possible to simulate natural conditions. However, a few experiments have been performed in which the laboratory conditions closely approximated those found in nature.[12]

In another type of experiment, attempts have been made to reproduce geological structures in small models, or to observe the structures that result from the application of known forces. A classic example is the formation of folds when layers of suitable material are slowly compressed by a moving piston (see also p. 227). But the significance of many of these experiments is questionable because in many cases the investigator repeatedly changed either the materials or the conditions of the experiment until he obtained the results he desired. It is possible, however, by the use of sound engineering principles, to construct small scale models that will simulate natural conditions.[13]

SCOPE OF THIS BOOK

Before it is possible to analyze the structure of entire mountain ranges, it is essential to have precise information on the many small separate areas that comprise the range. These small areas may cover 50 to 200 square miles, or they may be single mines or oil fields. This investigation of the structure of relatively local structure is the first and inevitable approach to the problem.[14]

Equally important, and perhaps in some ways more fascinating, is the

[10] Hafner, W., "Stress Distributions and Faulting," *Bulletin Geological Society of America*, Vol. 62, pp. 373–398, 1951.

[11] Birch, F., *et al.*, "Handbook of Physical Constants," *Geological Society of America, Special Papers, No. 36*, 1942.

[12] Griggs, D., "Experimental Flow of Rocks under Conditions Favoring Recrystallization," *Bulletin Geological Society of America*, Vol. 51, pp. 1001–1022, 1940.

Griggs, D., *et al.*, "Deformation of Yule Marble: Part IV, Effects at 150° C.," *Bulletin Geological Society of America*, Vol. 62, pp. 1385–1406, 1951.

[13] Hubbert, M. K., "Theory of Scale Models as Applied to the Study of Geologic Structures," *Bulletin Geological Society of America*, Vol. 48, pp. 1459–1520, 1937.

[14] Bucher, W. H., "Megatectonics and Geophysics," *Transactions American Geophysical Union*, Vol. 31, pp. 495–507, 1950.

synthesis or weaving together of the many facts obtained from local areas into a unified picture of the structure and tectonic history of the outer shell of the whole earth. Such studies are necessarily based in large part upon an intimate knowledge of the literature of structural geology because it is manifestly impossible for one man to investigate many areas in detail. But in order that he may more judiciously evaluate the reliability and importance of the published information, such an investigator must have made detailed studies of his own. One of the old classics in this field of synthesis is that by Eduard Suess, published in German and translated into French and English.[15] Excellent modern studies of this type are those by Bucher[16] and Umgrove.[17] Similar studies that are confined to North America have been made by Eardley and King.[18] The strength of the earth has been discussed by Daly.[19]

Only local structural units will be considered at any length in this book. Synthetic studies of world structure are, of course, important, but they are more advanced studies that cannot be understood until the local structures are fully comprehended. Moreover, to expand the text to include a study of world-wide structures would occupy far more space than is available in an elementary book on the subject. A discussion of the chronological sequence of structural events will not be emphasized in this book.

A study of geologic structures would be quite barren and fruitless if unaccompanied by a discussion of the forces involved. In the natural course of events, the structural geologist makes his observations first, then deduces the geological structure, and, finally, considers the nature of the causative forces. Normally, observation and description precede interpretation. It might seem logical, therefore, in a book such as this, to reserve a discussion of mechanics until the end. But it is far more satisfactory to treat each structural feature as a unit, describing it first and then considering the forces involved. It is essential, therefore, that a chapter on mechanical principles be given first in order that the origin of the various geological structures may be intelligently discussed.

[15] Suess, Eduard, *The Face of the Earth,* 5 Vols. Oxford: Clarendon Press, 1904–1924.

[16] Bucher, W. H., *The Deformation of the Earth's Crust.* Princeton: Princeton University Press, 1933.

[17] Umgrove, J. H. F., *The Pulse of the Earth,* 2nd ed. The Hague: Martinus Nijhoff, 1947. *Symphony of the Earth.* The Hague: Martinus Nijhoff, 1950.

[18] Eardley, A. J., *Structural Geology of North America.* New York: Harper & Bros., 1951.

King, P. B., *The Tectonics of Middle North America.* Princeton: Princeton University Press, 1951.

[19] Daly, R. A., *The Strength and Structure of the Earth.* New York: Prentice-Hall, Inc., 1940.

CHAPTER 2

Mechanical Principles

MATERIALS OF THE OUTER SHELL OF THE EARTH

Atoms

Matter is composed of atoms. Although different in size, all atoms are inconceivably small, and average 2×10^{-7} millimeter (0.0000002 mm.) in diameter. Some atoms are much heavier than others; the mass of uranium, one of the heaviest atoms, is about 237 times as great as that of hydrogen, the lightest. An atom of uranium weighs 392.98×10^{-24} gram; an atom of hydrogen weighs only 1.66×10^{-24} gram.

It was formerly believed that atoms were the smallest constituent particles of matter. Modern physical investigations reveal, however, that the atom is made of still smaller particles, such as protons, neutrons, electrons, and others. Although a detailed knowledge of atomic structure is essential to the geologist investigating radioactivity and the problem of the heat of the earth, the nature of the atom is not the direct concern of the structural geologist. For his purpose the atom is the smallest unit of significance. An elementary discussion of the nature of the atom may be found in Hecht;[1] a more advanced discussion is in Blatt and Weiskopf.[2]

Gases, Liquids, and Solids

At and near the surface of the earth, the atoms combine to form gases, liquids, and solids. Many substances are found in all three of these states. At sea level, water is a liquid between 0 and 100 degrees Centigrade, but above 100 degrees it becomes a gas, and below 0 degrees it becomes a solid. At exactly 0 degrees ice and water can exist together in equilibrium, and similarly at exactly 100 degrees water and steam are in equilibrium.

In a *gas* the atoms are in rapid motion, move independently of each other, and have no orderly arrangement. The forces of mutual attraction are less than the forces of movement. Gases have high mobility.

[1] Hecht, Selig, *Explaining the Atom*. New York: Viking Press, 1947.
[2] Blatt, John M., and Victor F. Weiskopf, *Theoretical Nuclear Physics*. New York: John Wiley & Sons, Inc., 1952.

In a *liquid* the atomic forces are strong enough to keep the atoms together, but there is either no orderly arrangement or only limited orderly arrangement. A liquid is fairly mobile.

Solids are characterized by "stiffness" or "rigidity." There are two kinds of solids: the crystalline solid and the noncrystalline solid.

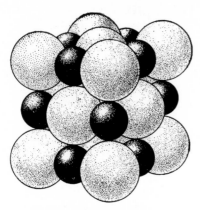

Fig. 1. Atomic structure of common salt. The large spheres represent chlorine atoms; the small spheres represent sodium atoms. (From R. W. G. Wyckoff's *Structure of Crystals,* 2nd ed. The Chemical Catalog Co., 1931.)

In the *crystalline solid* the atoms have an orderly arrangement. Common salt, for example, is composed of sodium and chlorine, always in the ratio of one to one. The relation of the atoms to each other is such as to form a cube (Fig. 1), and salt crystals occur as cubes or as some related form. Quartz is another example of a crystalline solid. For every atom of silicon there are two atoms of oxygen; the atoms are associated in such a way as to form an hexagonal pattern.

In the *noncrystalline solids*, there is no orderly arrangement of the atoms. The *vitreous solids*, or *glasses*, are liquids that have cooled so rapidly that the atoms have been unable to organize themselves into a systematic pattern. Technically these vitreous solids are supercooled liquids, and by some they are classified as liquids rather than solids. Window glass is a common example of a vitreous solid. Obsidian, a volcanic glass, is a well-known natural example. *Amorphous* solids do not have a definite arrangement of the atoms. They have not formed from the cooling of a liquid, however, and cannot properly be considered vitreous solids. Many organic substances and some minerals such as opal are amorphous.

The outer shell of the earth consists predominantly of solids, but gases and liquids are also present; their importance varies with time and space. Groundwater and active volcanoes attest to the importance of liquids at the present time, and the igneous rocks of intrusive bodies indicate the abundance of liquids in the past. Gases, present in the outer shell of the earth, are strikingly manifested in regions where petroleum is found; vast quantities of gas are sometimes expelled by active volcanoes. Never, however, does the gas occupy great underground chambers. The natural gas associated with petroleum occupies small pore spaces and fractures in solid rock, and the gas of volcanoes effervesces from magma.

In this section of the book we are concerned primarily with solids.

Gases and liquids are important only if their presence in pore spaces modifies the behavior of the solids.

The outer shell of the earth consists of sedimentary, igneous, and metamorphic rocks. The structural geologist, however, is interested primarily in the mechanical properties of the rocks with which he deals rather than in their origin. Is the rock well-consolidated or not? A poorly cemented sandstone will be weaker than a well-cemented one, and quartzite will have greater strength than lava full of gas bubbles. Is the rock massive or not? Thin-bedded strata are weaker than thick-bedded formations. A thick, massive limestone will be stronger than a series of thin lava flows, although in laboratory tests of individual specimens, the lava may be the stronger of the two. A thick, massive sandstone can be stronger than a highly fractured granite. Is the composition such that the fractures may be readily healed? Specimens of quartzite may be stronger than a limestone. But fractures in quartzite heal less readily than those in limestone.

FORCE

Force and Acceleration

Force is an explicitly definable vector quantity that changes or tends to produce a change in the motion of a body. The locomotive of a train exerts the force that moves the cars. Force is defined by its magnitude and direction; hence it may be expressed by an arrow, the length of which is proportional to the magnitude of the force, and the direction of which indicates the direction in which the force is acting.

An *unbalanced force* is one that causes a change in the motion of a body. The *acceleration* is the rate of change of velocity. If a train starts from rest and acquires a velocity of 20 miles per hour at the end of 10 minutes, the acceleration is two miles per hour per minute. A body dropped from a high building is subjected to an unbalanced force because of the gravitational pull of the earth, and the body accelerates at the rate of approximately 32 feet per second per second.

Balanced forces exist where no change in motion occurs. If a train is moving at a constant velocity, the frictional resistance of the tracks and the air equals the force exerted by the locomotive. If a man pushes against a wall that he cannot move, the wall is exerting a force equal and opposite to that exerted by the man.

The unit of force in the centimeter-gram-second system, commonly referred to as the c.g.s. system, is the *dyne;* the dyne is that force which, acting upon a mass of one gram, causes an acceleration of one centimeter per second per second.

Most problems confronting the structural geologist may be analyzed by assuming balanced forces because the velocity of rock bodies is so small that acceleration is negligible. Along faults, however, the motion causing earthquakes may be so rapid that acceleration is important.

Composition and Resolution of Forces

Force may be represented by a *vector*, that is, a line oriented in the direction in which the force is operating and proportional in length to the intensity of the force. Two or more forces may act in different directions at a point, as in Fig. 2, where *OX* (8 pounds) and *OY* (12 pounds) act at *O*. The same result would be produced by the force *OZ* (14¼ pounds) acting in the direction indicated; *OZ* is the resultant of *OX* and *OY*. A *resultant* is the single force that produces the same result as two or more forces, and it may be represented by the diagonal of a parallelogram con-

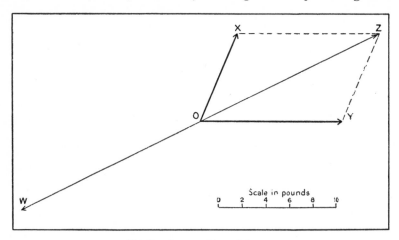

Fig. 2. Composition of forces.

structed on two arrows that represent the two forces. The *equilibrant* is the force necessary to balance two or more forces. In Fig. 2, *OW* is the force necessary to balance *OX* and *OY*; it is equal to the resultant of the two forces, but acts in the opposite direction. The process of finding the resultant of two or more forces is called the *composition of forces*.

Conversely, the effect of a single force may be considered in terms of two or more forces that would produce the same result. Thus, in Fig. 3A, *OY* and *OZ* would produce the same result as *OX*; in Fig. 3B, *OW* and *OV* would produce the same result as *OX*; in Fig. 3C, *OT* and *OU* would produce the same result as *OX*. A single force may thus be resolved into two *components*, acting in defined directions, by constructing a parallelogram the diagonal of which represents the given force, and the sides of which have the directions of the components. The process of finding the components of a single force is called the *resolution of forces*.

In Fig. 3D the force *OP* (12 pounds) impinges on the line *LM*, and it is necessary to find the value of the component parallel to *LM*. This component *OQ* has a value of about 11 pounds, as can be determined from the scale in the figure. *OR*, which is the component perpendicular to *LM*, has a value of about 5 pounds.

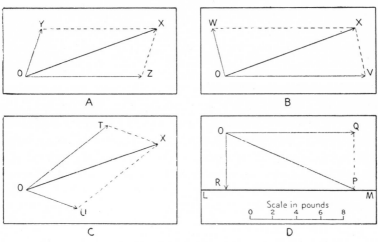

Fig. 3. Resolution of forces.

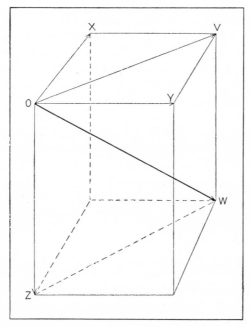

Fig. 4. Resolution of forces in three dimensions

The preceding discussion of the composition and resolution of forces has been confined to two dimensions, but geology is concerned with three dimensions. In Fig. 4 an inclined force OW lies in the vertical plane $OZVW$. This force may be resolved into two components, one of which, OZ, is vertical; the other, OV, lies in the horizontal plane $OXVY$. The OV may in turn be resolved into OX and OY, which lie in the horizontal plane and at right angles to each other. Moreover, any force, regardless of its value and its angle of inclination, may be similarly resolved into three components parallel to the X, Y, and Z axes of Fig. 4.

Lithostatic or Confining Pressure

The pressure on a small body immersed in a liquid is described as *hydrostatic pressure*. For example, at a depth of a mile in the ocean, the pressure is equal to the weight of a column of salt water one mile high. The pressure is 337,900 pounds per square foot, or 2,346 pounds per square inch. Every square inch of the surface of a small sphere at this depth would be under a pressure of 2,346 pounds per square inch. Such an undirected, all-sided pressure is called hydrostatic pressure.

Rocks in the lithosphere, because of the weight of whatever rocks lie above them, are subjected to a similar but not identical kind of pressure. The weight of a column of rock one mile high will be several times that of an equally high column of water, because rocks have a higher specific gravity. The weight of a column of granite one mile high and one inch square would be 6,178 pounds. A small imaginary sphere at a depth of one mile in the granite would be subjected to an all-sided pressure that would simulate hydrostatic pressure. This type of pressure may be called *lithostatic pressure*,[3] but in experimental work this equal, all-sided pressure on solids is called the *confining pressure*.

Obviously, the lithostatic pressure increases with depth in the earth and reaches tremendous values in the interior. It is equal to the weight of the overlying column of rocks, but near the surface this is only approximately true.

An increase in confining or lithostatic pressure causes a decrease in the volume of rocks but an increase in the density. A decrease in confining pressure causes an increase in volume but a decrease in density.

Differential Forces

In many instances the forces acting on a body are not equal on all sides. A body is said to be under *tension* when it is subjected to external forces that tend to pull it apart. Tension may be represented, as in Fig.

---

[3] Kennedy, G. C., " 'Pneumatolysis' and the Liquid Inclusion Method of Geologic Thermometry," *Economic Geology*, Vol. 45, pp. 533–547, 1950; especially p. 542.

5A, by two arrows that are on the same straight line and are directed away from each other; the arrows represent the forces, whereas the rectangle represents the body or part of a body upon which the forces act. The rectangle may be omitted.

A body is said to be under *compression* when it is subjected to external forces that tend to compress it. Compression may be represented, as in Fig. 5B, by two arrows that are on the same straight line and are

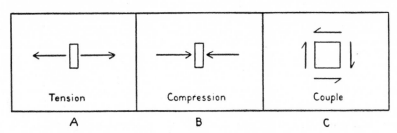

Fig. 5. Arrows representing tension, compression, and a couple.

directed toward each other; the arrows represent the forces, whereas the rectangle represents the body or part of the body acted upon. The rectangle may be omitted.

A *couple* consists of two equal forces that act in opposite directions in the same plane, but not along the same line. In Fig. 5C a couple is represented by the upper and lower arrows, which are not on the same straight line and which are directed away from each other. To prevent rotation and preserve equilibrium a second couple is necessary, as shown by the vertical arrows. The rectangle, which represents the body or part of the body acted upon, may be omitted.

Torsion results from twisting. If the two ends of a rod are turned in opposite directions, the rod is subjected to torsion (Fig. 6A). A plate undergoes torsion, as in Fig. 6B, if two diagonally opposite corners are

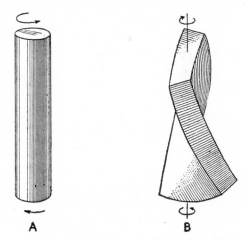

Fig. 6. Torsion. A rod (*A*) or plate (*B*) is subjected to torsion when the ends are twisted in opposite directions.

subjected to forces acting in one direction while the other two corners are subjected to forces acting in the opposite direction.

STRESS

Concept of Stress

Imagine a vertical column of material. Along any imaginary horizontal plane within this column the material above the plane, because of its weight, pushes downward on the material below the plane. Similarly, the part of the column below the plane pushes upward with an equal force on the material above the plane. The mutual action and reaction along a surface constitutes a stress.

Moreover, along any imaginary plane within the column there are similar actions and reactions. The imaginary plane may be horizontal, vertical, or inclined at any angle. The force, due to the weight of that part of the column that lies above the plane, acts in a vertical direction. This force would be directed normally to a horizontal plane. Along an inclined plane, however, the vertically directed force would be resolved into a normal component and a tangential component. If Fig. 3D were turned so that *OP* were vertical, *LM* would represent the inclined plane, *OR* the normal component, and *OQ* the tangential component.

The normal component is a *compressive stress* if it tends to push together the material on opposite sides of the plane. The normal component is a *tensile stress* if it tends to pull apart the material on opposite sides of the plane. The tangential component is generally called a *shearing stress* or *shear*.

In this book, in accordance with common geological practice, a compressive stress will be considered positive, and a tensile stress will be considered negative. In engineering and physics the opposite convention is often followed.

The *stress-difference* at any point in a body is the algebraic difference between the greatest stress and the least stress at that point. This concept is more fully developed in Chapter 10.

Physicists measure stress as the force per unit area; it is stated in pounds per square inch, tons per square foot, kilograms per square centimeter, or similar convenient units. Engineers prefer to use *unit stress* for the force per unit area.

Many geologists use stress as synonymous with external force. This usage is unnecessary and is hardly to be commended because it causes misunderstandings between geologists on the one hand and physicists, engineers, and mathematicians on the other. It is desirable to distinguish between the external force that is applied to a body and the resulting internal actions and reactions that constitute the stress.

Calculation of Stress

There is no direct way to measure the stresses in a body, but they may be calculated if the external forces are known. If a body is compressed or stretched, the stress is referred to a plane perpendicular to the direction in which the external forces are acting. Thus if a vertical square column 10 inches on a side supports a load of 5,000 pounds, every horizontal plane in the column is subjected to a compressive force of 5,000 pounds if we neglect the weight of the column itself. Each square inch on these horizontal planes supports a load of 50 pounds per square inch. The *compressive stress* is said to be 50 pounds per square inch. If a vertical rod with a cross-sectional area of 10 square inches carries a weight of 5,000 pounds at its lower end, every horizontal plane in the rod is subjected to a pull of 500 pounds per square inch. The *tensile stress* is said to be 500 pounds per square inch.

STRAIN

Definition

Strain is the deformation caused by stress; strain may be *dilation,* which is a change in volume, or *distortion,* which is a change in form, or both.

When there is a change in the confining pressure, an isotropic body —that is, a body whose mechanical properties are uniform in all directions—will change in volume, but not in shape. With increasing confining pressure, the volume of the body decreases and the dilation is negative. With decreasing confining pressure, the volume of the body increases and the dilation is positive. Granite has a higher *compressibility* than gabbro and diabase; that is, for unit increase in confining pressure, a granite undergoes a greater decrease in volume than do gabbro and diabase. Under low confining pressure, a unit increase in confining pressure causes a greater decrease in volume than under higher confining pressures.

Under directed forces distortion occurs. For example, a steel rod 10 inches long with a cross section of one square inch is subjected to tension. A pull of 20,000 pounds stretches the rod 0.007 inch. The stress is 20,000 pounds per square inch and the strain is 0.0007 inch per inch.

Three Stages of Deformation

If a body is subjected to directed forces, it usually passes through three stages of deformation. At first, the deformation is *elastic;* that is, if the stress is withdrawn, the body returns to its original shape and size. There is always a limiting stress, called the *elastic limit;* if this is exceeded, the body does not return to its original shape. Below the elastic limit, the deformation obeys *Hooke's law,* which states that strain is proportional to stress.

If the stress exceeds the elastic limit, the deformation is *plastic;* that is, the specimen only partially returns to its original shape even if the stress is removed. Steel rods under tension, for example, begin to get thinner or *"neck"* in the middle, and, even after the stress is released, the constriction remains in the rod.

When there is a continued increase in the stress, one or more fractures develop, and the specimen eventually fails by *rupture*. The arrangement and form of the fractures depend upon several factors which are fully discussed in Chapter 6.

Brittle substances are those that rupture before any plastic deformation takes place. *Ductile substances* are those that have a large interval between the elastic limit and rupture. After the elastic limit has been exceeded, ductile substances undergo a long interval of plastic deformation, and in some instances they may never rupture.

STRESS-STRAIN DIAGRAMS

In engineering practice the relation existing between stress and strain is commonly expressed in a graph known as the *stress-strain diagram* (Fig. 7). The stress is commonly plotted on the ordinate (vertical axis), the strain on the abscissa (horizontal axis). Curve *A* of Fig. 7 is a graph

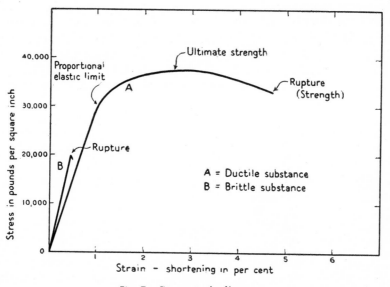

Fig. 7. Stress-strain diagrams.

of material under compression. The compressive stress is shown in pounds per square inch. With increasing stress, the specimen becomes shorter, and the strain is plotted in terms of the percentage of shortening of the specimen. Under a stress of 10,000 lb./in.², the specimen has shortened only a fraction of 1 per cent;[4] at 20,000 lb./in.², the shortening is 0.7 per cent. When the stress is 30,000 lb./in.², the specimen has been shortened 1 per cent of its original length. The shortening increases as the stress is increased and, just before rupture occurs, the specimen is 4.5 per cent shorter than it was originally. The point at which the curve departs from a straight line is known as the *proportional elastic limit;* it is usually essentially the same as the elastic limit (p. 15). The proportional elastic limit is 30,000 lb./in.², and the shortening at this point is one per cent.

Curve *B* of Fig. 7 is a graph of a brittle substance. The elastic limit is 20,000 lb./in.²; there is no plastic deformation before rupture takes place.

Strength, sometimes referred to as *rupture strength,* may be defined as the force per unit area necessary to cause rupture at room temperature and atmospheric pressure in short-time experiments. Under such conditions most rocks are brittle substances and, consequently, little or no plastic deformation precedes rupture.

Table 1 gives the strength for some common rocks. Data are more complete for some than for others, and such a table is merely indicative of the magnitude of the values. The values are in separate columns for compressive, tensile, and shearing strengths. Some granites, for example, can stand a compressive stress of only 370 kg./cm.² before rupturing;[5] other granites, however, can stand a compressive stress of 3,790 kg./cm.².

Table 1[6]

Rupture Strength of Rocks

(In kilograms per square centimeter)

Rock	Compressive		Tensile	Shearing
	Average	*Range*	*Range*	*Range*
Granite	1480	370–3790	30–50	150–300
Syenite	1960	1000–3440	—	—
Diorite	1960	960–2600	—	—
Gabbro	1800	460–4700	—	—
Felsite	2450	2000–2900	—	—
Basalt	2750	2000–3500	—	—
Sandstone	740	110–2520	10–30	50–150
Limestone	960	60–3600	30–60	100–200
Slate	1480	600–3130	250	150–250
Quartzite	2020	260–3200	—	—
Marble	1020	310–2620	30–90	100–300
Gneiss	1560	810–3270	—	—
Serpentine	1230	630–1230	60–110	180–340

[4] lb./in.² means "pounds per square inch."
[5] kg./cm.² means kilograms per square centimeter.
[6] Compiled from: *International Critical Tables,* Vol. 2, pp. 47–49. New York: McGraw-Hill Book Company, 1927; Birch, Francis, J. F. Schairer, and H. C. Spicer, "Handbook of Physical Constants," *Geological Society of America, Special Paper No. 36,* 1942, p. 111.

In tension, however, granite ruptures if the stress exceeds a value of 30 to 50 kg./cm.². In other words, granite is 33 times stronger under compression than it is under tension. Under shearing stress granite has a strength of 150 to 300 kg./cm.². Under compression, basalt is the strongest of all the rocks listed in the table.

In ductile materials, as shown in curve *A* (Fig. 7), the stress at the time of rupture may be considerably less than the maximum stress that the material has supported. The *ultimate strength* is the highest stress on the stress-strain curve.

Fundamental strength is defined on p. 24.

FACTORS CONTROLLING BEHAVIOR OF MATERIALS

Confining Pressure

The engineer is primarily interested in the physical properties of materials under atmospheric pressure and surface temperatures. Consequently, most of the available experimental data are distinctly limited in their application to geology. Factors that are important to the structural geologist are confining pressure, temperature, time, and solutions.

Griggs, Robertson, Balsley[7] and others have performed a number of experiments showing the effect of confining pressure on the properties of rocks. In one type of experiment small solid cylinders of rock, $\frac{1}{2}$ inch in diameter and $\frac{1}{4}$ to $1\frac{1}{4}$ inches long, are used. The confining pressure—in this case a hydrostatic pressure—is obtained through the medium of a fluid. An additional stress, compressive or tensile, is applied on the ends of the cylinder.

Figure 8, based on recent work by Robertson,[8] illustrates the behavior of Solenhofen limestone under such conditions. The compressive stress on the ends of the cylinder is given on the ordinate in kilograms per square centimeter. The percentage of shortening of the cylinder is given on the abscissa. Seven separate experiments are shown at confining pressures of 1, 300, 700, 1,000, 2,000, 3,000, and 4,000 kilograms per square centimeter. Separate curves are given for the behavior at each of these confining pressures. Below a compressive stress of 3,700 kg./cm.² the curves run together and appear as one. One experiment was run in air so that the confining pressure was equal to 1 kg./cm.², that is, 14.7 pounds per

[7] Griggs, David T., "Deformation of Rocks under High Confining Pressures," *Journal of Geology*, Vol. 44, pp. 541–577, 1936.

Griggs, David, *et al.*, "Deformation of Yule Marble: Part I," *Bulletin Geological Society of America*, Vol. 62, pp. 853–862, 1951.

Robertson, Eugene, "An Experimental Study of Flow and Fracture in Rocks," Doctoral thesis, Harvard University, 1952.

Balsley, J. R., "Deformation of Marble under Tension at High Pressures," *Transactions American Geophysical Union*, part 2, pp. 519–525, 1941.

[8] Robertson, *op. cit.*

square inch, or 1 atmosphere. This specimen behaved elastically up to a compressive stress of 2,800 kg./cm.², when it failed by rupture. The specimens tested under confining pressures of 300 and 700 kg./cm.² deformed elastically, went through a short stage of plastic deformation— that portion of the lines that is bending—and then failed by rupture. The specimens tested under confining pressures of 1,000 or more kg./cm.² began to deform plastically at a compressive stress of about 4,000 kg./cm.² and continued to deform plastically. The specimen tested under a confining pressure of 2,000 kg./cm.² had shortened 30 per cent when

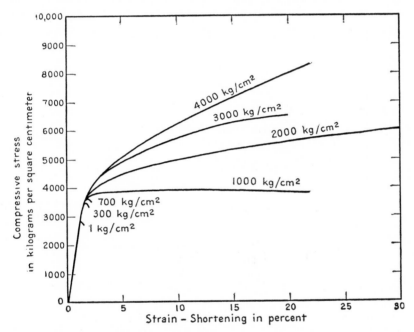

Fig. 8.   Effect of confining pressure on behavior of Solenhofen limestone under compression. (After E. Robertson.)

the test was terminated. The curves representing the tests at a confining pressure of 1,000, 2,000, 3,000, and 4,000 kg./cm.² end, not because of failure by rupture, but because the tests were not carried any further.

It is also readily apparent that the strength increases with the confining pressure. Whereas the specimen tested at a confining pressure of 1 kg./cm.² fails by rupture at a compressive stress of 2,800 kg./cm.² and the specimen tested at a confining pressure of 1,000 kg./cm.² cannot support a compressive stress greater than 3,900 kg./cm.², the specimen tested at a confining pressure of 4,000 kg./cm.² can support a compressive stress in excess of 8,000 kg./cm.².

Such experiments indicate that rocks exhibiting very little plastic deformation near the surface of the earth may be very plastic under high confining pressure. Thus under a confining pressure of 1,000 kg./cm.² or greater, Solenhofen limestone will deform plastically. This means that at a depth of 2.5 miles Solenhofen limestone will deform plastically if sufficient compressive stress is applied; as will be shown later, this figure may be still less because of other factors.

Different rocks, of course, behave differently. Fig. 9 shows the stress-strain diagram for several rocks and one mineral. The results are not strictly comparable because, as the figure shows, the confining pressure was not the same in all experiments, ranging from 300 to 500 kg./cm.².

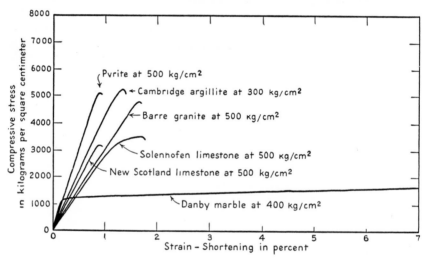

Fig. 9.   Effect of confining pressure on behavior of various rocks and pyrite under compression. (After E. Robertson.)

Pyrite, Cambridge argillite, and Barre granite are relatively brittle rocks, which behave elastically up to a compressive stress of over 4,500 kg./cm.². Above the elastic limit there is a small zone of plastic deformation, and then rupture takes place. New Scotland limestone was elastic up to a compressive stress of about 3,000 kg./cm.², deformed plastically for a short interval, and then ruptured at 3,200 kg./cm.². Solenhofen limestone shows a still larger range of plastic deformation. Danby marble is much weaker. It deforms elastically up to a compressive stress of 1,000 kg./cm.² and then deforms plastically. Although the curve scale ends at 7 per cent, Robertson's original data show that the specimen shortened 14 per cent before the test was ended.

Similar tests have been run on rocks under tension. As before, a confining pressure is exerted by a fluid, but the ends of the cylinders are pulled apart to produce tension.[9] Figure 10 shows five tests on a marble,

[9] Balsley, *op. cit.*

at confining pressures of **2,830, 4,500, 6,000, 8,000,** and **10,000** atmospheres (essentially the same as kg./cm.²). All the specimens went through a stage of elastic deformation, but the elastic limit ranges from **1,800** kg./cm.² to **3,300** kg./cm.², depending upon the confining pressure. Moreover, the ultimate strength increases, from a minimum of **2,400** kg./cm.² to **5,500** kg./cm.², again depending upon the confining pressure.

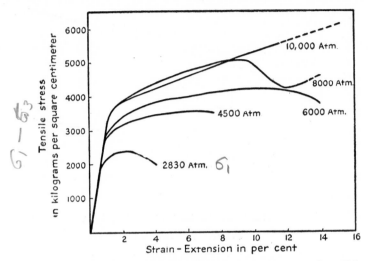

Fig. 10. Effect of confining pressure on behavior of marble under tension. (After J. Balsley.)

Temperature

Changes in temperature modify the strength of rocks. Hot steel, for example, undergoes plastic deformation much more readily than does cold steel. Figure 11 shows two tests run on Yule marble.[10] Conditions were identical except for temperature; the axes of the cylinders were perpendicular to the foliation, the confining pressure was **10,000** atmospheres, and the deformation was produced by compressive stress. The uppermost curve is that obtained at room temperatures, whereas the intermediate curve is that obtained at a temperature of 150° C. At room temperature the elastic limit is at a compressive stress of about **2,000** kg./cm.², at 150° C. the elastic limit is at about **1,000** kg./cm.². Moreover, to produce a given strain far less stress is necessary when the specimen is hot than when it is cold. For example, to produce a strain of 10 per cent at 150° C. the compressive stress is **3,000** kg./cm.², but at room temperature the stress necessary to produce a similar deformation is **4,500** kg./cm.².

It is apparent that plastic deformation is far less common near the

[10] Griggs, D. T., *et al.*. "Deformation of Yule Marble: Part IV, Effects at 150° C.,"*Bulletin Geological Society of America,* Vol. 62, pp **1385–1406, 1951.**

surface of the earth, where the confining pressure and the temperature are low, than it is at greater depths, where higher temperatures and greater confining pressure increase the possibility of plastic deformation.

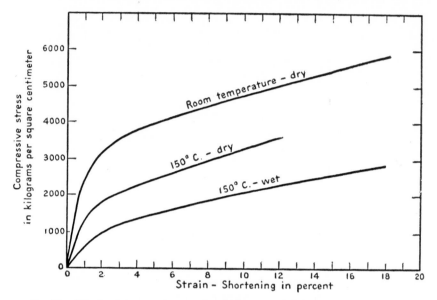

Fig. 11. Effect of temperature and solutions on deformation of marble. Yule marble, confining pressure of 10,000 atmospheres, cylindrical specimen cut perpendicular to foliation. (After D. T. Griggs *et al.*)

Time: Fatigue and Creep

Stresses that can be applied a few times without causing failure may, if repeated many times, cause rupture. This subject has been studied particularly in regard to metals. For example, a stress of 35,000 lb./in.^{2} repeated 100,000 times may not cause rupture; if, however, the same stress is repeated a million times, rupture occurs. If enough experiments are performed, a curve may be prepared, with the stress plotted on the ordinate, and the number of cycles of stress necessary to cause fracture plotted on the abscissa (Fig. 12). The curve becomes horizontal toward the right. The *endurance limit,* which is also known as the *fatigue limit,* is defined as the limiting stress below which the specimen can withstand hundreds of millions of repetitions of stress without fracture. In Fig. 12 the endurance limit is 30,000 lb./in.^{2}.

The endurance limit for many metals is approximately half that of the strength of the metal. For example, wrought iron, with a tensile strength of 46,900 lb./in.^{2}, has an endurance limit of 23,000 lb./in.^{2}; nickel steel, with a tensile strength of 111,800 lb./in.^{2}, has an endurance limit of 67,000 lb./in.^{2}.

Even more important to geology are those stresses, small though they may be, that act continuously for many years. *Creep* refers to slow deformation under small stresses acting over long periods of time; ordinarily the term is restricted to deformation resulting from stresses below

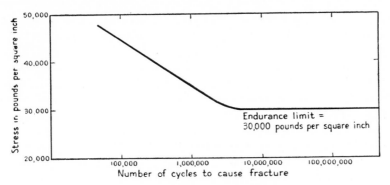

Fig. 12. Fatigue curve for a metal.

the elastic limit.[11] But the term is also used to refer to plastic deformation under any long-continued stress, even though the stress exceeds the elastic limit.

Solenhofen limestone under atmospheric pressure and at room temperature has a strength of 2,560 kg./cm.² In a long-time experiment, Solenhofen limestone subjected to a compressive stress of 1,400 kg./cm.² —half the value of the strength—deforms rapidly at first, then more slowly (Fig. 13). At the end of one day, it has been shortened about 0.006 per cent; after 10 days about 0.011 per cent; after 100 days about 0.016 per cent; and after 400 days a little more than 0.019 per cent.

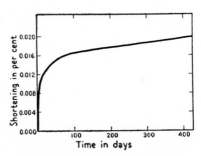

Fig. 13. Creep curve for Solenhofen limestone under a stress of 1,400 kg./cm.² (After D. T. Griggs.)

Creep is the combined effect of an elastic strain and a permanent strain.[12] The specimen recovers from that portion of the deformation that is caused by the elastic strain. The portion of the deformation that is the result of the permanent strain is, of course, unrecoverable. The relative importance of these two types of strain depends on many variables, but few precise data are available for rocks.

[11] Griggs, David T., "Creep of Rocks," *Journal of Geology*, Vol. 47, pp. 225–251, 1939.
[12] Nadai, A., *Theory of Flow and Fracture of Solids*. New York: McGraw-Hill Book Company, Inc., 1950. 572 pp., especially pp. 24–26.

The structural geologist is especially concerned with the time factor. He wants to know what stresses will cause failure if they operate over a long period of time. The *fundamental strength* of any material is defined as the stress which that material is able to withstand, regardless of time, under given physical conditions—temperature, pressure, solutions—without rupturing or deforming continuously. The fundamental strength, which is always less than the strength and the ultimate strength, is much more significant to the geologist. Unfortunately, at the present time we have few data on the value of the fundamental strength of rocks.

Time is also important in another respect. The amount of plastic deformation before rupture is less if the stress is applied slowly than it is if the stress is applied rapidly. Moreover, the stress necessary to cause rupture is less if the stress is applied slowly. We may cite as specific examples experiments on Solenhofen limestone. In one experiment the confining pressure was 10,000 atmospheres, and a little more than an hour elapsed before the maximum compressive stress was attained. When the stress reached 185,000 lb./in.^{2}, the specimen had shortened 30.3 per cent, but rupture had not occurred. In another experiment in which the confining pressure was the same (10,000 atmospheres), but in which 22 hours had elapsed before the maximum stress was attained, the specimen ruptured under a compressive stress of 96,000 lb./in.^{2}

Solutions

Geologists have for many years realized that much rock deformation takes place while solutions capable of reacting chemically with the rock are present in the pore spaces. This is notably true of metamorphic rocks, in which extensive or complete recrystallization occurs. The solutions dissolve old minerals and precipitate new ones. When rocks are deformed under conditions favoring recrystallization, the mechanical properties of rocks are greatly modified.

Experimental data corroborate these deductions, as shown in Fig. 14 from Griggs.[13] Creep experiments were performed on alabaster (a variety of gypsum). In all cases the compressive stress was 205 kg./cm.^{2} (less than half the normal elastic limit of 480 kg./cm.^{2}), and the temperature 24° C. The lowest curve represents the deformation of a dry specimen. Within a few days the specimen had shortened about 0.03 per cent, but there was no further detectable deformation even after 40 days. A specimen deformed under such conditions that water had access to the alabaster (intermediate curve) had shortened 1 per cent at the end of 30 days and 1.75 per cent by the end of 36 days, when the load was released.

---

[13] Griggs, David T., "Experimental Flow of Rocks under Conditions Favoring Recrystallization," *Bulletin Geological Society of America,* Vol. 51, pp. 1001–1022, 1940.

Griggs, David T., *et al.,* "Deformation of Yule Marble: Part IV, Effects at 150° C.," *Bulletin Geological Society of America,* Vol. 62, pp. 1385–1406, 1951.

A specimen deformed with access of dilute hydrochloric acid had deformed more than 2 per cent before rupturing at the end of 20 days. Whereas the strength of the dry alabaster under room temperature and a confining pressure of 1 atmosphere is 480 kg./cm.², and the ultimate strength is 520 kg./cm.², the fundamental strength under similar conditions, but with the specimen free to react with water, is estimated to be only 92 kg./cm.². In this particular case, therefore, the fundamental strength is less than 20 per cent of the strength and the ultimate strength.

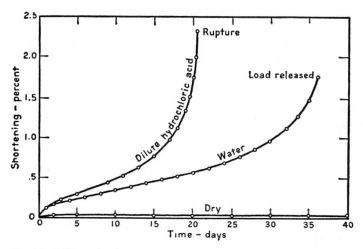

Fig. 14. Effect of solutions on deformation of alabaster. (After D. T. Griggs.)

The lowest curve in Fig. 11 shows the effect of water on the strength of Yule marble. At a temperature of 150° C. the elastic limit and strength of the wet specimen is much less than the strength of the dry specimen at the same temperature.

Anisotropy and Inhomogeneity

Most of the tests described in the preceding sections were made on isotropic materials, that is, rocks whose mechanical properties were uniform in all directions. Rocks that show bedding, banding, or foliation are not isotropic. The strength of such rocks would depend upon the orientation of the applied forces to the planar structures of the rock. This point is well illustrated in Fig. 15. The rock was Yule marble, confining pressure was 10,000 kg./cm.², and the tests were run at room temperature. All the specimens show great plastic deformation. The solid lines represent experiments under compression; in this case the stress is compressive and the strain is shortening parallel to the axis of the cylinder. Under compression the cylinder perpendicular to the foliation is stronger than the cylinder parallel to the foliation. The broken lines represent tests under tension; in this case the stress is tensile and the strain is lengthening parallel to the cylinders. Under tension the cylinder parallel to the foliation is much stronger than the cylinder perpendicular to the foliation.

In attempting to analyze the mechanics of rock deformation in the earth by the application of mathematical formulae, it is necessary to assume that the part of the crust being studied is homogeneous; that is, that it is all granite or limestone or some other rock. Actually, of course, the crust as a whole is exceedingly heterogeneous. This fact at once intro-

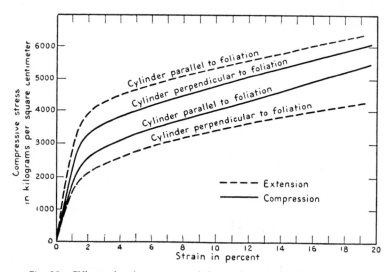

Fig. 15. Effect of anisotropy on deformation of marble. Yule marble at confining pressure of 10,000 kg./cm.² and room temperature. (After D. T. Griggs *et al.*)

duces many difficulties into any mechanical analyses. Thus although it is now becoming possible, as will be shown in later sections of this book, to apply mathematics and engineering principles to rock deformation, the heterogeneity of the crust in many cases prevents rigorous analysis.

Summary

It is clear that the mechanical properties of rocks are profoundly modified by confining pressure, temperature, the time factor, and the presence of reacting solutions. The combined effect of these factors is so great that it is impossible in the present state of our knowledge to treat rock deformation in a quantitative way. Increase in confining pressure increases the elastic limit and the ultimate strength. Increase in the temperature weakens the rocks. After long continued stress the rocks become much weaker. The fundamental strength is of more interest to the structural geologist than is the strength or ultimate strength. Reacting solutions lower the strength, the ultimate strength, and the fundamental strength of rocks.

MECHANICS OF PLASTIC DEFORMATION

Problem

The plastic deformation of solids[14] is a subject of utmost importance to structural geology. How can solid rocks change their shape without the appearance of any visible fractures? Just what happens within the rocks to permit such a change in form? The processes may be classified into intergranular movements, intragranular movements, and recrystallization.

Intergranular Movements

Intergranular movements involve displacements between individual grains. Intrusive igneous rocks are usually composed of such minerals as quartz, feldspar, mica, and hornblende. Sandstones consist of rounded grains, usually quartz, cemented together. Limestones are composed of small interlocking crystals of calcite. If such rocks are subjected to stress, the individual crystals and grains may move independently. All the displacements, because they are between grains, may be described as intergranular. The individual grains maintain their shape and size. The deformation of such a body might be compared to the change in shape undergone by a moving mass of B-B shot. Each grain can move and rotate relative to its neighbors.

In the plastic deformation of metals, such intergranular movements seem to be of subordinate importance. In rocks, particularly those of granitoid character, in which the crystals tend to interlock, more or less *granulation* takes place first; that is, the larger crystals are broken into smaller spherical grains that may rotate relative to each other.

Intragranular Movements

Intragranular movements are very important in the plastic deformation of metals. Displacements take place entirely within the individual crystals, and slipping takes place along *glide planes*. Some minerals have no glide planes. In others there is one glide plane—that is, one plane parallel to which there are a vast number of additional planes along

[14] Bridgman, P. W., *Studies in Large Plastic Flow and Fracture.* New York: McGraw-Hill Book Company, Inc., 362 pp., 1952.
   Nadai, A., *op. cit.*

PLATE II. *Horizontal Strata. Grand Canyon of the Colorado, Arizona, from Point Sublime.* (Infrared photo by Union Pacific Railroad.)

PLATE III. *Folded Rocks. In upper left-hand corner strata dip to the left. In the center and lower right-hand corner the zigzag ridges are resistant beds in plunging folds. Africa, lat. N. 30° 35′, long. W. 02° 10′.* (Photo by United States Air Force.)

which gliding can take place. In still other minerals there are several glide planes—that is, several planes, parallel to each of which there are a vast number of additional planes. The atomic structure controls the position and number of glide planes. Hence the glide planes are related to the symmetry of the mineral. Gliding is of two types, translation-gliding and twin-gliding.

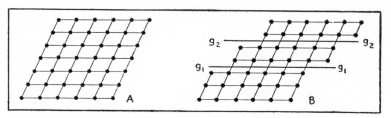

Fig. 16.   Translation-gliding. *A*. Arrangement of atoms before gliding. *B*. Arrangement of atoms after gliding along planes g_1g_1 and g_2g_2.

Translation-gliding is illustrated very diagrammatically by Fig. 16. The centers of the atoms are represented by dots, and the glide planes by heavy horizontal lines labeled g_1g_1 and g_2g_2. Diagram *A* shows the distribution of atoms before gliding takes place. The crystal lattice—that is, the spacing of the atoms relative to one another—is such as to give a characteristic pattern. Diagram *B* shows the arrangement of the atoms after gliding. Layers of atoms have slid to the right one interatomic distance relative to the layers beneath. The shape of the figure as a whole

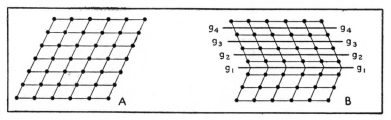

Fig. 17.   Twin-gliding. *A*. Arrangement of atoms before gliding. *B*. Arrangement of atoms after gliding on glide planes g_1g_1, g_2g_2, g_3g_3, and g_4g_4.

has been changed. The lattice, however, is unchanged; the same diamond-shaped pattern is maintained as before. The distance between planes of gliding differs with the substance. In gold the distance is 0.00045 millimeter, in zinc 0.00080 millimeter.

In *twin-gliding* the layers of atoms slide a fraction of an interatomic distance relative to the adjacent layers (Fig. 17). Figure 17A shows the distribution of the atoms prior to deformation and Fig. 17B shows the distribution of the atoms after deformation. In this way the lattice of the displaced part of the crystal is symmetrically altered with respect to the lower, undisplaced part. In the terminology of mineralogy, the displaced part bears a twinned relation to the undisplaced part.

The sheets of atoms cannot slip along the glide planes in any direction. There are a limited number of lines parallel to which the movement can take place, and these lines are known as the *glide directions*. The number and position of the glide planes and the glide direction depend upon the mineral. Aluminum, for example, has four glide planes and three glide directions; altogether, therefore, there are twelve possible movements in this mineral.

A rock is an aggregate of minerals. Because the individual grains comprising the rock can be permanently deformed through gliding, the shape of the entire body of rock can be changed.

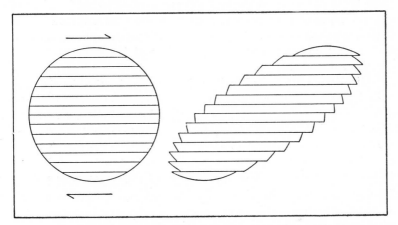

Fig. 18. Circle changed into ellipse by movement along glide planes.

Figure 18 illustrates in a two-dimensional model the deformation of a circle into an ellipse by gliding. One set of horizontal glide planes is present, and along these each successively higher sheet has moved toward the right. In the diagram the resulting ellipse is characterized by jagged edges, but in minerals the glide planes are so close that such irregularities are not detectable.

Recrystallization

Recrystallization is another mechanism aiding plastic deformation. Rocks can crystallize without any change in shape, as is shown by limestone altered to marble near igneous intrusions. The number of crystals per unit volume decreases, but the size of the individual crystals increases.

Under conditions of differential pressure, however, solution and recrystallization may proceed in such a way that the rock is shortened in one direction and lengthened in another. The process may be explained by the *Riecke principle*.[15] According to this principle the solutions in the pore spaces of the rocks dissolve that portion of the crystal under greatest stress. At the same time there is precipitation on that portion of the crystal subjected to the least stress. In this way the grain changes shape. If all the crystals in a body of rock are similarly affected, the mass as a whole changes shape.

It is obvious from observations in the field that plastic deformation and recrystallization have often been simultaneous, and we must accept the principle that recrystallization greatly facilitates plastic deformation.

DEFORMATION IN THE OUTER SHELL OF THE EARTH

The rocks in the outer shell of the earth are affected by all three of the major types of deformation: elastic, plastic, and rupture.

Tidal stresses and the passage of earthquake waves cause elastic strain; but since no permanent effect is recorded, it cannot be observed by the structural geologist.

Plastic deformation is involved in folding, in the development of certain kinds of cleavage, and in mass changes in the shape of rock bodies. Horizontal strata are permanently deformed by folding; although folding involves the sliding of beds past one another, each stratum undergoes plastic deformation. The origin of cleavage is a controversial subject, but that variety known as flow cleavage is generally considered to be the result of plastic deformation. As will be manifested later, solid rocks may flow from the limbs of folds and may concentrate near the axes. Even large bodies of solid granite, if subjected to sufficient stress, may change shape through plastic deformation. Rock salt, under the influence of gravity or tectonic forces, may move as a plastic body to form salt domes.

Rupture is involved in the formation of joints, faults, and some varieties of cleavage. In some instances the walls visibly slide past each other to produce faults, but if there is no obvious differential movement, the fractures are called joints or cleavage.

Although it might seem most logical to consider the results of plastic deformation first, and to follow this by a consideration of the results of rupture, such a treatment is not feasible because some types of cleavage are plastic in origin and others are due to rupture. It seems better, therefore, to utilize a geological classification and consider folds, joints, faults, and cleavage in that sequence. The subsequent chapters are therefore organized accordingly.

[15] Turner, F. J., and J. Verhoogen, *Igneous and Metamorphic Petrology*, pp. 394–395. New York: McGraw-Hill Book Company, Inc., 1951.

Ramberg, Hans, *The Origin of Metamorphic and Metasomatic Rocks*, p. 110. Chicago: University of Chicago Press, 1952.

CHAPTER 3

Description of Folds

INTRODUCTION

Folds are undulations or waves in the rocks of the earth. They **are** best displayed by stratified formations such as sedimentary and volcanic rocks, or their metamorphosed equivalents. But any layered or foliated rock, such as banded gabbro or granite gneiss, may display folds.

Some folds are a few miles across; the width of others is to be measured in feet or inches—or even in fractions of an inch. Folds of continental proportions are hundreds of miles wide.

ATTITUDE OF BEDS

The *strike* of a bed is its trend measured on a horizontal surface. More precisely, strike may be defined as the direction of a line formed by the intersection of the bedding and a horizontal plane. In Fig. 19A the strike is north; the upper part of the figure is a block diagram, the lower part a map or plan.

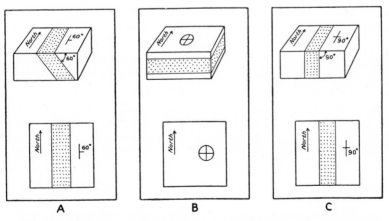

Fig. 19. Dip-strike symbols used for inclined, horizontal, and vertical strata. Block diagram above, map below. *A.* Inclined strata. *B.* Horizontal strata. *C.* Vertical strata, the position of the 90 may be used to indicate the top side of the bed. (See page 70.)

The *dip* of a stratum is the angle between the bedding and a horizontal plane; it is measured in a vertical plane that strikes at right angles to the strike of the bedding. In Fig. 19A the dip is 60 degrees to the east.

A special *dip-strike symbol* is employed on geological maps to show the attitude of beds (Plates III and IV). It is shaped somewhat like the capital letter *T*, but the relative lengths of the two parts are reversed (Fig. 19A). The longer line is parallel to the strike of the bedding, whereas the shorter line points in the direction of the dip, and a figure gives the value of the dip. For horizontal strata (Plate II), a special symbol ⊕ may be used (Fig. 19B). For vertical strata (Plate V) a long line gives the strike, and a short cross-bar extends on either side of the long line (Fig. 19C). Although most geological maps use symbols similar to these to give dip and strike of the bedding, the system is not standardized, and it is necessary to look at the legend accompanying the map in order to ascertain the meaning of the symbols employed.

PARTS OF A FOLD

The *axial plane* or *axial surface* of a fold is the plane or surface that divides the fold as symmetrically as possible. In a two-dimensional diagram, the axial plane is represented by a line.

In some folds the axial plane is vertical (Fig. 20A, B, and C), in others it is inclined (Fig. 20D and F), and in still others it is horizontal (Fig. 20E). Although, in many folds, the axial surface is a relatively smooth plane, it may be curved. The attitude of the axial plane is defined by its strike and dip, just as the attitude of a bed is defined. In Fig. 20, north is toward the upper left-hand corner. In Fig. 20A, B, and C, the axial plane strikes north and has a vertical dip. In Fig. 20D, the strike is north, the dip 45 degrees to the west. In Fig. 20F, the axial plane strikes north and dips 60 degrees to the west; in Fig. 20E, the axial plane is horizontal. If the axial plane is curved, the dip or strike—or both— may differ from place to place, as in the case of a curved bedding plane.

An *axis* of a fold is the intersection of the axial surface with any bed. Such an intersection is a line, and in Fig. 20 it is lettered *aa′*. Actually, of course, there is an axis for every bed, and every fold has countless axes. Inasmuch as these axes are generally parallel, one axis is sufficient to define the attitude of the fold. In some folds the axes of the fold are horizontal (Fig. 20A, D, E); in others, the axes are inclined (Fig. 20B, F); and in still others, the axes are vertical (Fig. 20C).

The sides of a fold are called the *limbs* or *flanks*. Terms used in the past, but now obsolete, were *legs, shanks, branches,* and *slopes*. A limb extends from the axial plane in one fold to the axial plane in the next. For example, in Fig. 21A, *a′b* is the limb of a fold. It may be considered

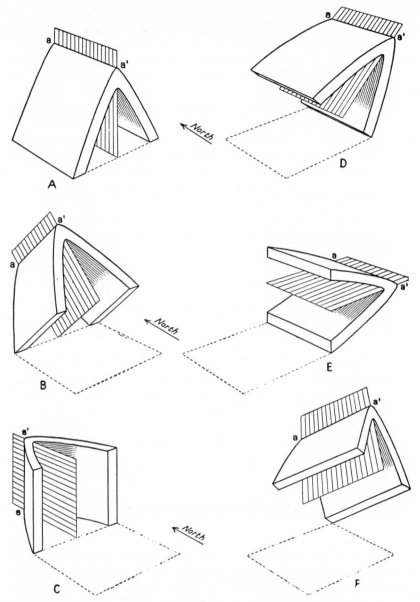

Fig. 20. A few of the different attitudes assumed by axial planes and axes of folds. The axial plane is shaded in each diagram; *aa'* is axis of fold.

either the east limb of the upfold or the west limb of the adjacent down-fold. In other words, every limb is mutually shared by two adjacent folds.

Although in many instances the axis is at the highest part of the fold, as in Fig. 21A, this is not necessarily the case. In Fig. 21B, for example, *a* and *a'* are axes, or, to be more precise, the intersection of axes with the plane of the paper; c and c' are the highest points on the folds. The *crest* is a line along the highest part of the fold, or, more precisely, the line connecting the highest points on the same bed in an infinite number of cross sections. There is a separate crest for each bed. The plane or surface formed by all the crests is called the *crestal plane* (cc' of Fig. 21B).

In many phases of geology, the distinction between the crest and axis is not important, either because the two correspond or, if there is a difference, because the distinction is of academic interest only. The same is true of the distinction between crestal plane and axial plane. In the

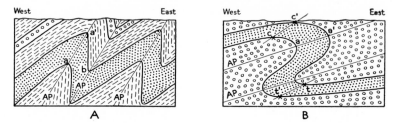

Fig. 21. Parts of a fold. AP = axial plane; $a'b$ = limb of a fold; c = crest on one bed, c' = crest on another bed, cc' = crestal plane; t = trough on one bed, t' = trough on another bed, tt' = trough plane.

accumulation of gas and petroleum, however, the difference is significant. The trapping of such materials is controlled by the crest and crestal plane rather than by the axis and axial plane. In American oil fields, however, the crestal plane and axial plane are usually identical.

The *trough* is the line occupying the lowest part of the fold, or, more precisely, the line connecting the lowest parts on the same bed in an infinite number of cross sections. In Fig. 21B, t and t' are troughs. The plane connecting such lines may be called the *trough plane*.

NOMENCLATURE OF FOLDS

During the last one hundred years, a rather elaborate terminology has been evolved to describe the geometrical aspect of folds. Many of the terms refer to the appearance of folds in vertical cross sections perpendicular to the strike of the axial planes of the folds. Other terms refer to the attitude of the axes. The nomenclature based on the appearance of folds in cross sections may be considered first. As is to be expected, these terms refer primarily to the attitude of the axial plane and the attitude of the limbs.

An *anticline* is a fold that is convex upward or, in more complicated folds, is inferred to have had such an attitude at some stage in its development (Plates VII and VIII). The word is from the Greek; it means "opposite inclined." It refers to the fact that, in the simplest anticlines, the two limbs dip away from each other (Fig. 22A). In some anticlines, however, the two limbs dip in the same direction (Fig. 22B), or are horizontal (Fig. 22C). Still other anticlines have attained such a compli-

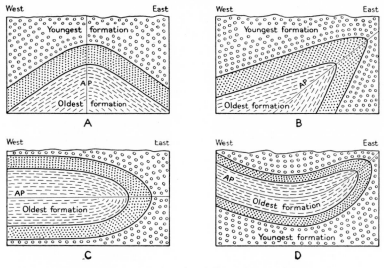

Fig. 22. Some varieties of anticlines. AP = axial plane.

cated form (Fig. 22D) that no simple definition can be given. An anticline may also be defined as a fold with older rocks toward the center of curvature. This is correct, unless the structural history has been unusually complex.

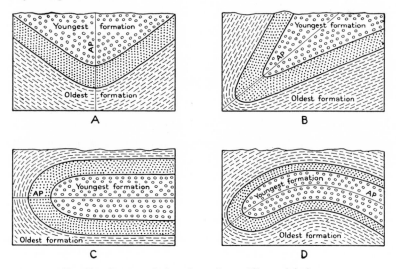

Fig. 23. Some varieties of synclines. AP = axial planes.

PLATE IV. *Inclined Strata Forming Hogbacks. Cretaceous strata, southwestern Colorado, a few miles east of Durango.* (Photo by Soil Conservation Service, United States Department of Agriculture.)

PLATE V. *Vertical Strata. Middle Cretaceous limestones, Huasteca Canyon, near Monterrey, Mexico.*
(Photo by M. P. Billings.)

A *syncline* is a fold that is concave upward, or, in more complicated folds, is inferred to have had such an attitude at some stage in its development (Plate VI). The word is from the Greek, meaning "together inclined," and refers to the fact that in the simplest synclines, the two limbs dip toward each other (Fig. 23A). But the limbs may dip in the same direction, be horizontal, or be complexly folded (Fig. 23B, C, and D). A syncline is generally a fold with younger rocks toward the center of curvature.

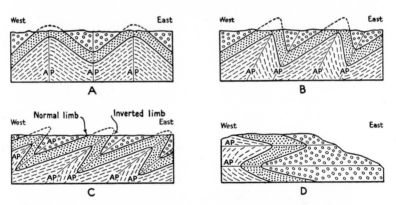

Fig. 24. Some varieties of folds. AP = axial plane. *A.* Symmetrical folds. *B.* Asymmetrical folds. *C.* Overturned folds (overfolds). *D.* Recumbent folds.

Another set of terms refers to the attitude of the axial plane. A *symmetrical fold* is one in which the axial plane is essentially vertical. In other words, the two limbs have the same angle of dip (Fig. 24A).

In the *asymmetrical fold* the axial plane is inclined; the two limbs dip in opposite directions but at different angles (Fig. 24B).

In the *overturned fold* or *overfold* the axial plane is inclined, and both limbs dip in the same direction, usually at different angles (Fig.

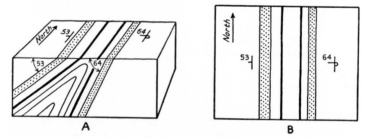

Fig. 25. Dip-strike symbol for overturned strata. *A.* Block diagram. *B.* Map. The dip-strike symbol with **53** beside it indicates beds that dip 53 degrees to the west (left) and are not overturned. The dip-strike symbol with **64** beside it indicates beds that dip 64 degrees to the west (left), but are overturned.

24C). The *overturned, inverted,* or *reversed limb* is the one that has been rotated through more than ninety degrees to attain its present attitude. A special dip-strike symbol is commonly used on modern maps to indicate overturned strata (Fig. 25). The *normal limb* is the one that is right-side-up.

A *recumbent fold* is one in which the axial plane is essentially horizontal (Fig. 24D). Large-scale folds of this type are rare in North America, but they are common in the Alps.[1] Consequently, a rather elaborate terminology has been evolved by European geologists to describe such folds (Fig. 26). The strata in the inverted limb are usually much thinner than the corresponding beds in the normal limb. The *arch-bend* is the curved part of the fold between the normal and inverted limbs. Many of the recumbent folds in the Alps have Paleozoic crystal-

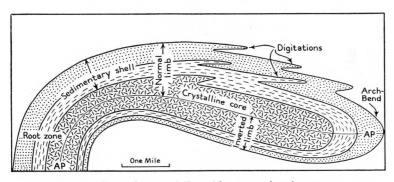

Fig. 26. Recumbent anticline with names of various parts.

line rocks in the center and Mesozoic sedimentary rocks in the outer covering. Thus there is a distinct core of crystalline rocks within a shell of sedimentary rocks. Even in a recumbent fold composed entirely of one kind of rock, the terms *core* and *shell* may be used to refer, respectively, to the inner and outer parts of the fold. Many recumbent folds have subsidiary recumbent anticlines attached to them; these subsidiary folds may be called *digitations* because they look like great fingers extending from a hand. All recumbent folds, if satisfactory exposures are available, may be traced back to the *root* or *root-zone*—that is, to the place on the surface of the earth from which they arise; in other words, recumbent folds may be traced to the place where the axial plane becomes much steeper.

An *isoclinal fold,* from the Greek meaning "equally inclined," refers to folds in which the two limbs dip at equal angles in the same direction (Fig. 27). A vertical or symmetrical isoclinal fold (Fig. 27A) is one in which the axial plane is vertical (Plate X); an inclined or overturned

---

[1] Collet, L. W., *The Structure of the Alps,* 2nd ed. London: Edward Arnold and Co.. 1935.

isoclinal fold is one in which the axial plane is inclined. A recumbent isoclinal fold is one in which the axial plane is horizontal. Many recumbent folds are isoclinal.

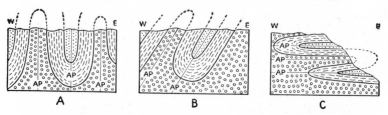

Fig. 27. Isoclinal folds. $AP = $ Axial planes. *A*. Vertical isoclinal folds. *B*. Inclined isoclinal folds. *C*. Recumbent isoclinal folds.

Although most folds are relatively well-rounded at the anticlinal and synclinal axes, some are sharp and angular. Such folds are called *chevron folds* (Fig. 28A).

A *fan fold* is one in which both limbs are overturned (Fig. 28B). In the anticlinal fan fold, the two limbs dip toward each other; in the synclinal fan fold, the two limbs dip away from each other. Fan folds are not as common as was formerly supposed; fifty years ago they were thought to be abundant in the Alps.

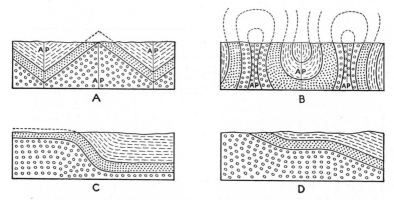

Fig. 28. Some varieties of folds. $AP = $ Axial planes. *A*. Chevron fold. *B*. Fan fold. *C*. Monocline. *D*. Structural terrace.

In plateau areas, where the bedding is relatively flat, the strata may locally assume a steeper dip (Fig. 28C). Such a fold is a *monocline*. The beds in a monocline may dip at angles ranging from a few degrees to ninety degrees, and the elevation of the same bed on opposite sides of the monocline may differ by hundreds or even thousands of feet.

In areas where dipping strata locally assume a horizontal attitude, a *structural terrace* is formed (Fig. 28D). This usage should not be con-

PLATE VI. *Anticlines and Synclines. Purgatory Wash, west side of Virgin River, between St. George and Hurricane, Utah.* (Photo by National Park Service.)

PLATE VII.   *Asymmetrical Anticline with Gentle Plunge. Upper Cretaceous limestone in fold. Overlain unconformably by gently dipping volcanic rocks of Tertiary age, which appear in upper lefthand corner. Looking southeast along the west side of the Andes near Yura. Arequipa quadrangle, southern Peru. (Photo by W. F. Jenks.)*

fused with that of the physiographer, who employs the term to refer to terraces that are structurally controlled.

The term *homocline*, from the Greek meaning "one inclination," may be applied to strata that dip in one direction at a uniform angle. Although many homoclines are, if large areas are considered, limbs of folds, the term is useful to refer to the structure within the limits of a small area.

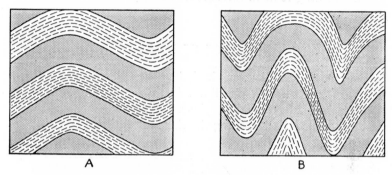

Fig. 29. Open and closed folds. *A*. Open folds. *B*. Closed folds.

A *closed* or *tight fold* is one in which the deformation has been sufficiently intense to cause flowage of the more mobile beds so that these beds thicken and thin (Fig. 29B). Conversely, an *open fold* is one in which this flowage has not taken place (Fig. 29A). Although the more extreme cases of these two types may be readily distinguished from each other, there are intermediate examples that are difficult to classify.

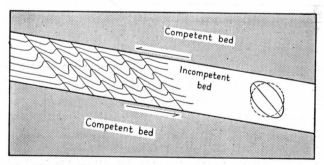

Fig. 30. Drag folds resulting from shearing of beds past each other.

Drag folds form when a competent ("strong") bed slides past an incompetent ("weak") bed (Fig. 30). Such minor folds may form on the limbs of larger folds because of the slipping of beds past each other, or they may develop beneath overthrust blocks (Chapter 11). The axial planes of the drag folds are not perpendicular to the bedding of the competent strata, but are inclined at an angle. Under a couple, of the type illustrated in Fig. 30, an imaginary circle in the incompetent bed would be deformed into an ellipse. The traces of the axial planes of the folds are parallel to the long axis of this ellipse. The acute angles between the axial planes and the main bedding plane point in the direction of the differential movement.

The use of drag folds in solving structural problems will be discussed on pp. 78–83.

PLUNGE OF FOLDS

In the preceding section, emphasis has been placed upon the appearance of folds in cross sections. But folds, like any geological structure, must be considered in three dimensions. The attitude of the axis is of the greatest importance in describing the third dimension.

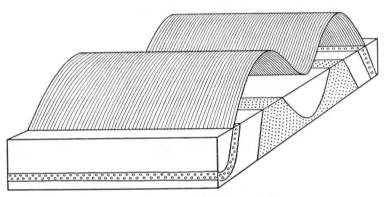

Fig. 31. Nonplunging folds.

In some folds the axis is horizontal (Fig. 20A, D, and E); in other folds the axis is inclined (Fig. 20B, C, and F). The attitude of the axis of a fold is defined by two measurements: the *strike of its horizontal projection* and the *plunge*. It must be remembered that an axis is a line, such as FD in Fig. 32. Of all the possible vertical planes in the figure, only one, $ADFG$, contains the line FD. The intersection of this plane with the horizontal plane $ABCD$ is the line AD. The line AD is the horizontal projection of FD. In Fig. 32 the line AD strikes northwest, and this is therefore the strike of the horizontal projection of FD. The plunge of FD is the angle P, which is the angle between AD and FD measured in the vertical plane $ADFG$.

Although the larger plunging folds cannot be directly observed, they are easily recognized from their outcrop pattern. Figure 31 is a block diagram of a fold that does not plunge. On the map, the beds on the op-

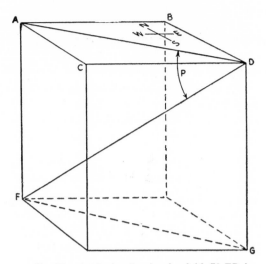

Fig. 32. Attitude of axis of a fold. If *FD* is the axis, *AD* is the strike of the horizontal projection of the axis; the angle of plunge is *P*.

posite limbs strike parallel to each other; they do not converge. Figure 33 is a geological map of a nonplunging syncline. Figure 34 is a block diagram of plunging folds and shows that on the map the beds converge; the formations have a zigzag pattern. Figures 35 and 36 are geological maps of plunging folds; the beds on the opposite limbs strike toward each other

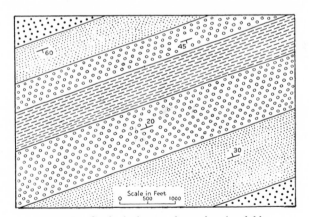

Fig. 33. Geological map of nonplunging fold.

and the formations converge. Figure 35 shows a plunging anticline; Figure 36 shows a plunging syncline. The place on the map where a bed shows the maximum curvature is known as the *nose* of the fold; there is a nose for each stratum. The *axial trace* of a fold connects the points where, on the map, each bed shows the maximum curvature (Figs. 35

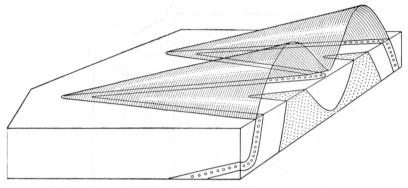

Fig. 34. Plunging folds. Plunge is about 10 degrees to the left. One bed is shown by open circles; the part of this bed that has been removed by erosion is shown by lining.

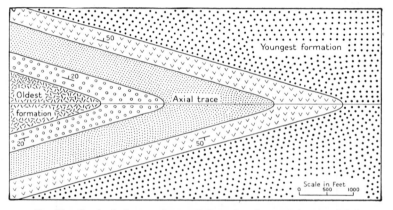

Fig. 35. Geological map of an anticline plunging east (to the right).

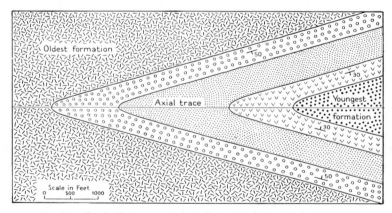

Fig. 36. Geological map of a syncline plunging east (to the right).

and 36). On most published geological maps this is called the axis, but this term is preferably used in a different sense, as defined on p. 34. For symmetrical folds or nonplunging folds, the axial trace and the horizontal projection of the axis coincide, but this is not true if the axial plane is inclined and the fold plunges. Plunging folds are shown in Plate IX.

In the preceding paragraphs it has been tacitly assumed that the plunge is constant. In most instances, however, the value of the plunge changes along the strike, and the direction of plunge may even be re-

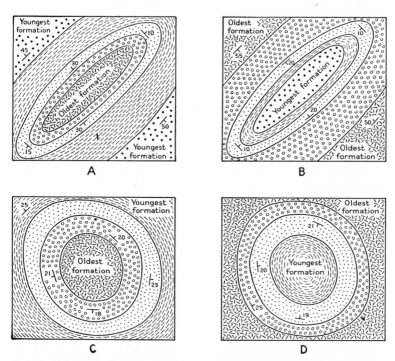

Fig. 37. Maps of plunging folds. *A.* Doubly plunging anticline. *B.* Doubly plunging syncline. *C.* Dome. *D.* Basin.

versed. Figure 37A is a geological map of a symmetrical anticline, the axial trace of which trends northeast. In the northeast corner of the map, the fold plunges 10 degrees to the northeast, and the strata converge northeastward. Toward the southwest, the value of the plunge decreases, and in the center of the map it is zero because the strata on opposite limbs are parallel in strike. In the southwest corner, the anticline plunges 15 degrees to the southwest. Figure 37B shows a syncline that plunges southwest at the northeast corner of the map, and northeast at the southwest corner.

A *doubly plunging fold* is one that reverses its direction of plunge within the limits of the area under discussion. Most folds, if followed far enough, are doubly plunging.

A *dome* is an anticlinal uplift that has no distinct trend (Fig. 37C). A *basin* is a synclinal depression that has no distinct trend (Fig. 37D).

The angle of plunge is commonly not great, but in some regions, particularly those composed of metamorphic rocks, the angle of plunge may approach 90 degrees. In some localities the folds may even have inverted plunges.

An excellent discussion of the effect of plunge on the map pattern and cross sections is contained in a paper by Mackin.[2] The use of plunge in the construction of cross sections of folds has been described by Stockwell.[3]

REFOLDING

Unusually complex map patterns result when folds are refolded. Figure 38A and B are diagrams to illustrate folded recumbent folds. Figure 38A shows two recumbent folds, the anticlinal cores of which are labeled *a* and *b*. In Fig. 38B the recumbent folds have themselves been folded into anticline *F* and an adjacent syncline; the axial planes of these later folds dip 40° S.

Figure 38A and B can be rotated 90 degrees to illustrate vertical

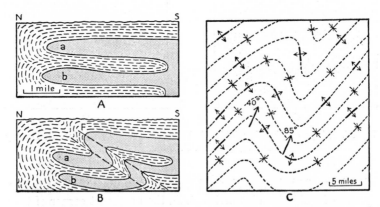

Fig. 38. Refolding. *A*. Recumbent folds. *B*. Recumbent folds have been refolded. *C*. Gordon Lake area, North West Territories, Canada. Older isoclinal folds shown as follows: anticlinal axes are heavy lines away from which small arrows point; synclinal axes are light lines toward which small arrows point. Large arrows show plunge of large younger folds. (After J. F. Henderson.)

[2] Mackin, J. Hoover, "The Down-Structure Method of Viewing Geologic Maps," *Journal of Geology*, Vol. 58, pp. 55–72, 1950.

[3] Stockwell, C. H., "The Use of Plunge in the Construction of Cross-Sections of Folds," *Proceedings Geological Association of Canada*, Vol. 3, pp. 97–121, 1950.

PLATE VIII. *Anticline. Middle Cretaceous strata in Lebanon Mountains, northeast of Beirut, Syria.* (Photo by K. F. Mather.)

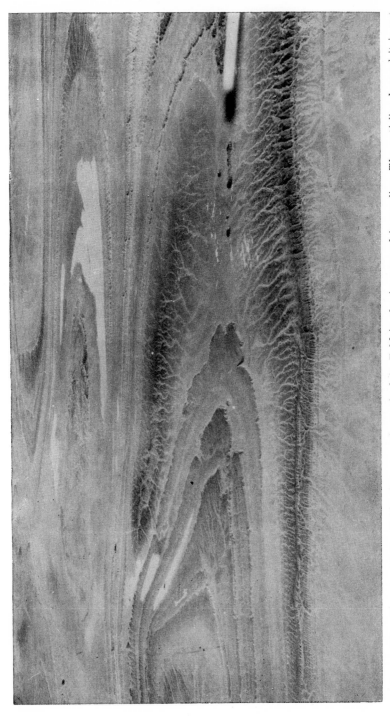

PLATE IX. *Plunging Folds. Folds plunge gently to the left. Fold in the foreground is syncline. The anticline beyond it is not conspicuous. In the middle and far distance are an anticline and a syncline; the syncline is concave to the left and the anticline is convex to the left. Africa, lat. N. 25° 25', long. E. 01° 35'. (Photo by United States Air Force.)*

isoclinal folds that are later refolded. Such structures have been described from eastern Vermont.[4]

Figure 38C is greatly simplified from a map of the Gordon Lake area in North West Territories, Canada.[5] The strata were first thrown into gently to moderately plunging vertical isoclinal folds. The folded sediments were then refolded into large folds, the axes of which trend north-northeast and are about ten miles apart. One of these folds plunges 85° N., the other 40° N.

FOLD SYSTEMS

The preceding discussion has been concerned primarily with single folds. Folds, however, are seldom found alone, but commonly belong to a system composed of many folds. In some regions the axial traces ("axes") of the folds are parallel and straight; whereas in other regions the axial traces are parallel and curved. Most characteristically, however, they are neither parallel nor straight.

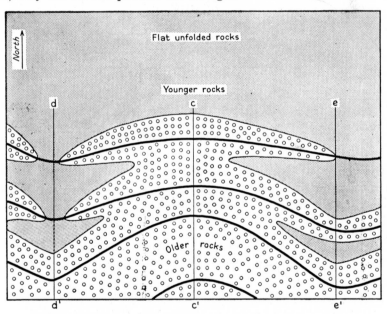

Fig. 39. Convergence and divergence of axial traces of folds. The axial traces (axes) are shown as heavy black lines. These lines diverge from one another on either side of *cc'*, and converge toward *cc'* if approached from *dd'* or *ee'*.

[4] White, Walter S., and M. P. Billings, "Geology of the Woodsville Quadrangle, Vermont-New Hampshire," *Bulletin Geological Society of America,* Vol. 62, pp. 647–696, 1951.

[5] Henderson, J. F., "Structure and Metamorphism of Early Pre-Cambrian Rocks between Gordon and Great Slave Lakes, North West Territories," *American Journal of Science,* Vol. 241, pp. 430–446, 1943.

Figure 39 is a geological map of an area in which the axial traces are curved. Along the line *cc′* they are convex toward the north, and they diverge toward the east and west.

In some localities individual folds do not extend any great distance, but overlap one another, *en échelon*, as is shown in Fig. 40.

In a *salient* the axial traces of the folds are convex toward the outer edge of the folded belt. The lines labeled *cc′* in Figs. 39 and 41 are located on a salient. In a *recess* the axial traces are concave toward the outer edge of the folded belt. In Figs. 39 and 41, the lines *dd′* and *ee′* are located on recesses.

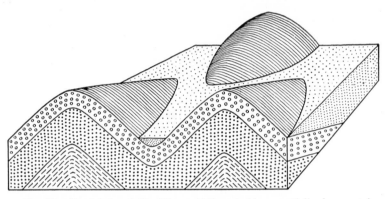

Fig. 40. *En échelon* folds. The anticlines hold up anticlinal mountains rising above a flat plain. The axial trace of the fold in the background is *en échelon* relative to the folds in the foreground.

Over large parts of a folded belt the axial planes of many of the folds dip in the same direction. In the Valley and Ridge Province of the Appalachian Highlands, for example, the axial planes dip toward the southeast. Most of the thrust faults, as well as the cleavage, dip in the same direction in this region.

In many areas all the folds plunge in the same direction. In Fig. 41, the folds between *cc′* and *ee′* plunge toward the east. East of *ee′* the folds plunge to the west. West of *cc′*, but east of *dd′*, the folds plunge to the west. West of *dd′* the folds plunge to the east. The line *cc′* represents a culmination; *dd′* and *ee′* represent depressions. *Culminations* and *depressions* trend essentially at right angles to the trend of the folds; the folds plunge away from culminations toward depressions. The concept of culminations and depressions has proved of great importance in understanding the structure of the Alps.

Many folds have minor folds on their flanks. In western New Hampshire, for example, the distance between the crests of major anticlines is several miles. Superimposed on these major folds are subsidiary folds, the axes of which are thousands of feet apart. On these subsidiary folds are lesser folds, the axes of which are hundreds of feet apart. On these lesser folds are minor folds, which may be observed in single outcrops; the distance between the crests of the minor folds is measured in feet. On the limbs of the minor folds are small crenulations, less than an inch apart. Microscopic study shows still smaller folds, too minute for the unaided eye to detect.

A major anticline that is composed of many smaller folds is called an *anticlinorium*. An anticlinorium must be a large fold, of the magnitude of a mountain or a mountain range; that is, it must be at least several miles across. A *synclinorium* is a large syncline that is composed of many smaller folds.

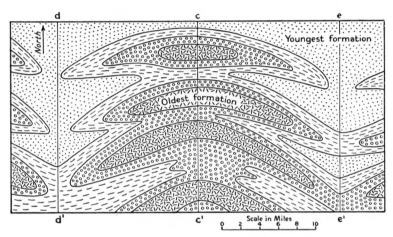

Fig. 41. Culmination and depression. The line *cc'* is a culmination, away from which the folds plunge; *dd'* and *ee'* are depressions, toward which the folds plunge.

Two terms that are frequently misused are *geosyncline* and *geanticline*. *Geosyncline* literally means an "earth syncline." The term should not be used, however, for every large syncline. A *geosyncline* is a large basin in which many thousands of feet of sediments accumulate.[6] Although the sediments deposited in the Appalachian geosyncline during the Paleozoic Era were 40,000 feet thick in places, the water was never very deep. In fact, many of the sediments were deposited above sea level on the surface of deltas. The floor of the basin sank while the sediments accumulated. European geologists believe that the Alpine geosyncline, on the other hand, was at times very deep. Recent studies show that a modern geosyncline exists along the coast of the Gulf of Mexico; the Cenozoic sediments here are many tens of thousands of feet thick.[7]

[6] Kay, Marshall, "North American Geosynclines," *Memoir 48, Geological Society of America,* 1951.

[7] Murray, Grover E., *et al.,* "Sedimentary Volumes in Coastal Plain of United States and Mexico," *Bulletin Geological Society of America,* Vol. 63, pp. 1157–1228, 1952.

A *geanticline,* the counterpart of a geosyncline, is an area from which the sediments are derived.

BEHAVIOR OF FOLDS WITH DEPTH

What happens to folds at depth? Do they continue downward indefinitely, or do they gradually or suddenly disappear? Most structure sections show the folds as continuing downward without change, but this is merely a convention because, without precise information, little else can be done.

A theoretical approach sheds some light on the problem. Figure 42A illustrates *similar folding.* The line *a* is taken as the form of the fold

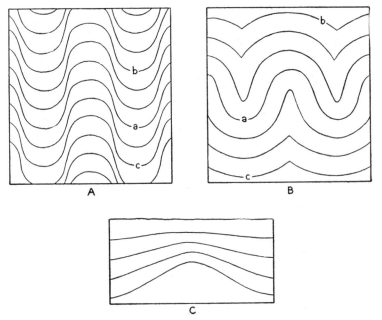

Fig. 42.   Types of folding. *A.* Similar folding. *B.* Parallel folding. *C.* Supratenuous folding.

shown by one bedding plane. The other lines have been drawn on the assumption that they have the same form as the line *a.* In this way the form of the fold is propagated indefinitely upward and downward. Moreover, the lines *b* and *c* have the same length as *a.* In this type of folding every bed is thinner on the limbs and thicker near the axes. To produce folds of this type there is considerable plastic movement of material away from the limbs and toward the axes. In natural folds the stronger or more competent beds preserve a relatively uniform thickness, but the

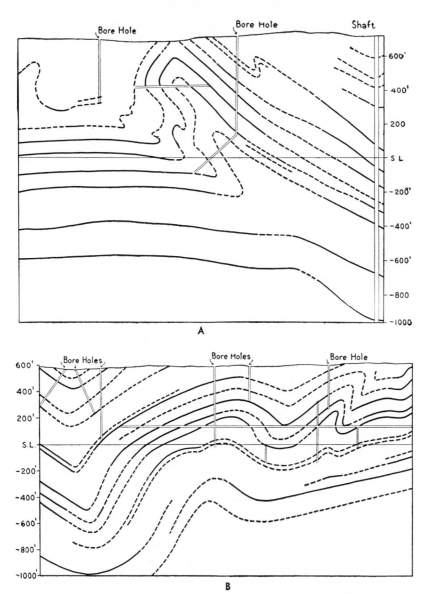

Fig. 43. Cross sections of disharmonic folds in the Northern Anthracite Basin of Pennsylvania. Solid lines: beds of coal that have been mined out. Broken lines: beds of coal based on drill records. (After N. H. Darton.)

weaker, less competent beds adjust themselves by flowage and drag folding.

Figure 42B illustrates *parallel folding (concentric folding)*.[8] The line *a* is taken as the form of the fold shown by one bedding plane. The rest of the figure has been constructed on the assumption that the thickness of the beds has not changed during the folding. It is apparent that, under such conditions, the form of the fold must change upward and downward. The anticlines become sharper with depth, but broader and more open upward. Conversely, the synclines become broader with depth, but sharper upward. The folds die out downward and upward. In regions of gentle folding, where the dips do not exceed 10 or 20 degrees, the folding may well approach the parallel type. In Fig. 42B, the lines *b* and *c* are shorter than *a*, but in the original basin of deposition, they must have had the same length as *a*.

Where unusually good data are available, it is clear that most folding is *disharmonic;* that is, the form of the fold is not uniform throughout the stratigraphic column. Figure 43 shows structure sections in the Northern Anthracite Basin of Pennsylvania, based on data obtained from mines and drill holes.[9] In Fig. 43A a symmetrical anticline between two bore holes passes downward into an overturned anticline at 400 feet above sea level. At 400 feet below sea level the fold has disappeared. Similar changes are illustrated by Fig. 43B. Disharmonic folding is well displayed on some of the great cliffs in the Alps. Figure 44 is one exam-

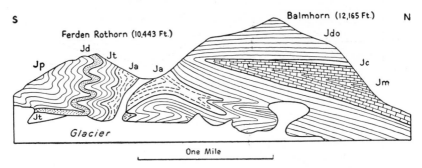

Fig. 44. Folds in the Ferden Rothorn and Balmhorn, Switzerland. Sketched by author from the Hockenhorn. The cliff on the east slope of the Balmhorn is about 4,000 feet high; that on the east face of the Ferden Rothorn is about 1,600 feet high. *Jp* = Pliensbachian limestone; *Jd* = Domerian quartzite; *Jt* = Toarcian formation; *Ja* = Aalenian shale; *Jdo* = Dogger shale; *Jc* = Callovian shale; *Jm* = Malm limestone.

[8] Mertie, J. B. Jr., "Delineation of Parallel Folds and Measurement of Stratigraphic Dimensions," *Bulletin Geological Society of America*, Vol. 58, pp. 779–802, 1947.
[9] Darton, N. H., "Some Structural Features of the Northern Anthracite Coal Basin, Pennsylvania," *U. S. Geological Survey Professional Paper 193*, pp. 69–81, 1940.

ple, but inasmuch as the folds are recumbent, the change of form takes place in the horizontal direction rather than with depth. The formation labeled *Jd* shows four recumbent synclines approximately equal to each other in size; the bottom (south) of formation *Ja* shows folds of very different form.

Piercing or *diapir folds* are anticlines in which a mobile core has been able to break through the more brittle overlying rocks. Such folds have been described in Romania and France, where mobile salt beds have penetrated the overlying rocks.[10]

PLATE X. *Vertical Isoclinal Syncline. About 3 miles west of Cerro de Pasco, Peru. Strata are of Tertiary age.* (Photo by W. F. Jenks.)

Supratenuous folds develop if folding and sedimentation are contemporaneous. In Fig. 42C, the strata are thinnest on the crest of the anticline and are thickest in the trough of the syncline. The beds are thinnest on top of the anticline because it was rising during sedimentation; conversely, the beds are thickest in the syncline because it was sinking during sedimentation.

A sheet of sedimentary rocks may break loose from the underlying for-

---

[10] Mrazec, M. L., "Les plis diapirs et le diapirisme en général," *Comptes rendus, Institut géologique de Roumanie,* Vol. 6, pp. 226–272, 1927.

Dupouy-Camet, Jacques, "Triassic Diapiric Salt Structures, Southwestern Aquitaine Basin, France," *Bulletin American Association Petroleum Geologists,* Vol. 37, pp. 2348–2388, 1953.

mations and fold independently. This is called a *décollement*, that is, a shearing-off. In the Jura Mountains, as is shown by Fig. 45, the Mesozoic and Tertiary strata are thrown into a series of anticlines and synclines that do not affect the underlying Paleozoic crystalline rocks. The weak shales and salt beds near the base of the Mesozoic served as a lubricant over which the higher stratigraphic units slid.

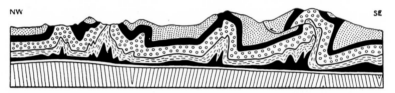

Fig. 45. *Décollement* of the Jura Mountains. The lowest formation, with nearly vertical structure, consists of Paleozoic crystalline rocks. Directly above these is a thin bed of flat-lying Triassic quartzite, left blank. The lower, solid black formation, which is very incompetent, consists of anhydrite, shale, and salt. The higher beds are Triassic, Jurassic, Cretaceous, and Tertiary sedimentary rocks. (After A. Buxtorf.)

CALCULATING THE DEPTH OF FOLDING

The depth of folding can be calculated under certain conditions.[11] In Fig. 46A it is assumed that the vertical rectangle dl is changed into the rectangle $b(d + h)$, with no change in area. Then:

$$dl = b(d + h)$$

With certain modifications, the same concept may be extended to folded belts. It is assumed that there is no lengthening or shortening parallel to

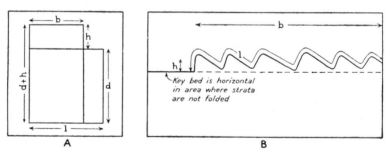

Fig. 46. Method of calculating depth of folding. $b =$ present breadth of folded belt; $h =$ average uplift due to folding; $l =$ original breadth of folded belt; $d =$ depth of folding. *A.* Square deformed into a rectangle, no change in area. *B.* Folded strata. (After R. T. Chamberlin.)

[11] Chamberlin, R. T., "The Appalachian Folds of Central Pennsylvania," *Journal of Geology,* Vol. 18, pp. 228–251, 1910; see also Rodgers, John, "Evolution of Thought on Structure of Middle and Southern Appalachians," *Bulletin American Association of Petroleum Geologists,* Vol. 33, pp. 1643–1654, 1949.

the axes of the folds and that the rocks do not change in volume. The term b is the present breadth of the folded area; the l, which is the original width before folding, is measured along some convenient bed in the folded belt. The term h is the amount of uplift due to folding.

In Fig. 46B the heavy black line represents a single bed. At the left end of the section it is flat and has not been affected by the folding. In the folded area it has been uplifted from the position of the broken line to the position shown by the heavy solid line. The average uplift h can be determined in several ways. The simplest is to measure the actual uplift at stated intervals—such as at every millimeter in the figure shown —and to compute the average. All the factors in the equation given above, except d, are known. For convenience in computation, the equation can be rewritten:

$$d = \frac{bh}{l - b}$$

The answer d gives the depth of folding measured from the key bed where it is horizontal.

Several assumptions are made in applying this method. One assumption is that there is a sharp break between the folded rocks and the unfolded rocks below; in other words, a *décollement* is assumed. If the folds gradually disappear downward, the calculations would be incorrect, and the depth of folding would be greater than the calculations indicate. Secondly, the method assumes that the base of the strata is not depressed by the folding. There are reasons for believing, however, that in many folded belts the basement is down-folded by horizontal compression. If this is so, the method employed for determining h gives too low a value, and the depth of the folded zone would be much greater than the calculated value.

Bucher[12] has calculated the depth of folding in the Jura Mountains. In this case the method is applicable because a relatively thin column of sedimentary rock is separated from a crystalline basement by a *décollement*. The calculated depth is comparable to that deduced by the Europeans by other means.

[12] Bucher, W. H., *Deformation of the Earth's Crust,* pp. 155–156. Princeton: Princeton University Press, 1933.

CHAPTER 4

Field Study and Representation of Folds

RECOGNITION OF FOLDS

Direct Observation

Folds may be recognized in many ways. The easiest and most satisfactory method is to observe the fold, but this can be done in comparatively few regions. Folds may be readily seen on some of the great cliffs

SE   NW

Scale in Feet
0   50   100

Fig. 47. Folds in highway cut one mile south of Alexandria, Pennsylvania. Strata belong to the Wills Creek formation, which is of upper Silurian age. The bed represented by solid black is a red calcareous shale.

in the Alps (Fig. 44). Folds are exposed in some parts of the Appalachian Mountains in large highway cuts (Fig. 47), railroad cuts, or in natural exposures (Fig. 48). Folds may be observed also in the Rocky Mountains

Fig. 48. Anticline one-quarter mile east of Roundtop, Maryland. View looking across Potomac River from West Virginia. Strata belong to upper Silurian Bloomsburg formation.

and in other parts of the North American Cordillera, as well as in many other places in the world. Far more commonly, however, folds must be deduced from other data, and detailed studies show that most visible folds, even in such places as the Alps, are minor features associated with much larger folds.

Wherever small folds are observed in single outcrops, it is desirable to record their attitude. To do this one must measure the attitude of the axes and the attitude of the axial planes.

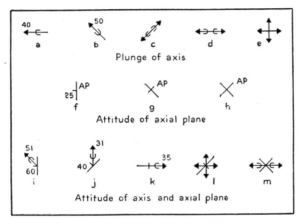

Fig. 49. Symbols to represent attitude of folds. *a.* Axis if anticline plunges 40° W. *b.* Axis if syncline plunges 50° NW. *c.* Axis if anticline is horizontal and strikes NE. *d.* Axis if syncline is horizontal and strikes E. *e.* Vertical axis. *f.* Axial plane strikes N., dips 25° W. *g.* Vertical axial plane strikes NW. *h.* Horizontal axial plane. *i.* Axis of anticline plunges 51° NW., axial plane strikes N. and dips 60° W. *j.* Axis of syncline plunges 31° N., axial plane strikes NE., dips 40° NW. *k.* Axis of syncline plunges 35° E., vertical axial plane strikes E. *l.* Axis vertical, axial plane is vertical and strikes NE. *m.* Axis of syncline is horizontal and strikes E., axial plane horizontal.

The attitude of the axis of a fold may be readily measured if it is possible to look down on the fold. One edge of the compass is held in such a way as to cover the axis of the fold. In this way the strike of the horizontal projection of the axis is obtained (see also Fig. 32). The plunge is measured by means of the clinometer attached to the compass. The attitude of the axis can then be recorded by an arrow. The symbols given in the upper row of Fig. 49 for the attitude of fold axes are based on those recommended by the U. S. Geological Survey. Figure 49a means that the axis of the fold plunges west at an angle of 40 degrees; the semicircle convex toward the arrowhead means the fold is an anticline. Figure 49b means that the axis of the fold plunges northwest at an angle of 50 degrees; the semicircle concave toward the arrowhead means that the fold is a syncline. Figure 49c means that the axis of an anticline strikes northeast-southwest and is horizontal. Figure 49d indicates the axis of a syncline that strikes east-west and is horizontal. No symbol is given by the U. S. Geological Survey for vertical axes; the symbol in Fig. 49e is herewith proposed.

A notebook or sheet of paper may be held parallel to the axial plane of a fold in order to measure its attitude. A second person measures the strike and dip of the notebook, just as the attitude of a bedding plane is measured. An experienced field geologist can measure the attitude of the axial plane without the help of a second person. The map symbols used by the U. S. Geological Survey contain none for the attitude of the axial plane. It is obvious from Fig. 20, however, that it is not sufficient to record the attitude of the axis only. For example, the axes of the folds shown in Fig. 20A, D, and E have identical attitudes. But the axial planes dip from zero to vertical. To show the differences between these three folds, it is necessary that the attitude of the axial plane be shown. Symbols similar to those for bedding may be used, except that the letters *AP* are placed beside the symbol. Figure 49f indicates an axial plane striking north and dipping 25° W. Figure 49g represents a vertical axial plane striking northwest. Figure 49h is a horizontal axial plane.

Normally, of course, the symbols for axial plane and axis will be combined to form the symbols shown in the lowest row of Fig. 49. Figure 49i indicates an anticline plunging 51° NNW., with the axial plane striking north and dipping 60° W. It is not necessary to add the letters *AP* because the symbol for the axis shows that the entire symbol refers to a fold. Figure 49j is a syncline plunging 31° N., with the axial plane striking northeast and dipping 40° NW. Figure 49k is a fold plunging 35° E. and a vertical axial plane striking east. Figure 49l is a vertically plunging fold, the vertical axial plane of which strikes northeast. Figure 49m is the symbol for a syncline with a horizontal axial plane and a horizontal axis that strikes east-west.

In order to visualize the three dimensional attitude of folds, take a sheet of paper and bend it back on itself to make an isoclinal fold. The crease is the axis of the fold, and the plane of the paper not only represents the two limbs of the fold, but the axial plane as well. The fold may then be held in any position desired to show the distinction between the attitude of the axial plane and the attitude of the axis.

In a larger fold that cannot be observed in a single outcrop or in a series of closely adjacent outcrops, the attitude of the axial plane and the axis cannot be measured directly. Nevertheless the same principles apply, and the geologist should always think of folds in three dimensions. Methods of calculating the attitude of the axis and axial plane are discussed on pages 459–463.

Plotting Attitude of Beds

The most common way to recognize folds that are larger than an outcrop is to plot on a map the strike and dip of beds. In Fig. 50A, the dips indicate an asymmetric anticline, the axial plane of which strikes north and dips to the west. In Fig. 50B, the symbols indicate a symmetrical syncline that plunges south at an angle of 14 degrees.

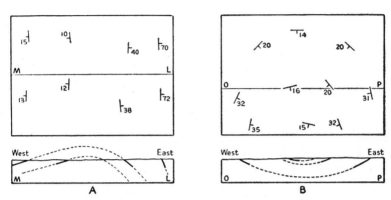

Fig. 50. Fold shown by dip-strike symbols. Maps are above, structure sections are below. *A*. Asymmetric, nonplunging anticline. *B*. Symmetrical syncline plunging south.

The applicability of this method depends upon the complexity of the structure and the number of exposures. If the structure is simple, a few exposures may suffice. On the other hand, if the structure is complex, many exposures are necessary. In regions of extremely complex structure, this method may fail—even though exposures are reasonably good—unless other significant data are available. The use of sedimentary features in connection with this method are discussed on pp. 70–78.

Map Pattern

The pattern shown by the different units that can be mapped may be very useful in deducing the structure. Figure 51A represents the geological map of a region where the actual outcrops might constitute 25 per cent of the area. In practically all of the exposures, the strata strike northeast and dip steeply to the northwest. A traverse across the region from *M* to *N* suggests that there are five stratigraphic units: two sandstones, two conglomerates, and one slate. The map shows, however, that the two sandstones at opposite ends of *MN* belong to the same formation. Moreover, the map reveals that there is only one conglomerate. The pattern is that of a plunging fold—either an anticline that plunges southwest, or a syncline that plunges to the northeast. Without some additional data, a solution would not be possible. At some such place as locality *1*, the nose of the fold might be exposed. By following the base of the conglomerate, one might be able to ascertain that it plunges to the northeast. If this were so, the sandstone would be the oldest formation, and the slate would be the youngest formation. Primary features (pp. 70–78) might solve the problem. If cross-bedding in the conglomerate at locality *2* shows the top to be to the southeast, the fold is a syncline plunging northeast. Fossils might give the answer to the problem; if fossils in the slate are younger than those in the sandstone, the fold is a syncline plunging northeast.

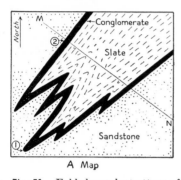
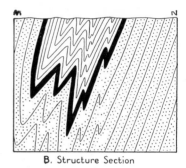

A Map   B. Structure Section

Fig. 51. Fold shown by pattern of formations on a map. *A.* Geological map.
B. Inferred structure section.

A cross section along the line *MN* of Fig. 51A is given in Fig. 51B. The section must satisfy the condition that the beds dip steeply to the northwest. Moreover, although no direct evidence for subsidiary folds may be obtained along the line *MN*, it is obvious from the map that such folds must exist, and, assuming harmonic folding, the number and location of these folds can be predicted from the map. Every anticline shown by the map must also appear in the structure section. The depth of each anticlinal crest and synclinal trough depends upon the value of the plunge. In this case the plunge is about 60 degrees to the north-northeast.

Topography

Topography is often useful in the study of folds. In heavily forested or deeply weathered regions, it may be possible to trace key units for long distances by means of the topography. A resistant formation will stand up in ridges, an easily eroded bed will be followed by valleys, and a limestone may be traced by karst topography. In reconnaissance studies, particularly by airplane, the topography may give important clues to the geological structure.

Figure 52 is a topographic map of an area in which ridges rise more than 1,500 feet above sea level. The ridges are heavily wooded, and exposures are scanty. But a good section is exposed at the water gap where the Red River cuts through the ridge. At this locality, hard quartzites dipping 45 degrees to the north are right-side-up. Apparently this same quartzite holds up Pine Mountain throughout its extent. The zigzag pattern of the ridge indicates that the strata are folded.

The observations at the water gap reveal that this portion of the ridge is on the south limb of a syncline. The axis of the syncline must lie at Lookout Point, where the ridge makes a sharp bend. In plan, the ridge is concave toward the northeast; the syncline, therefore, plunges to the northeast because the pattern of a plunging syncline is concave in the direction of plunge (Fig. 36, p. 48).

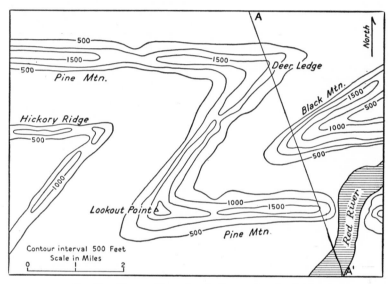

Fig. 52. Zigzag ridges that indicate plunging folds.

Another fold axis must be located at Deer Ledge. This is an anticlinal axis, and it must plunge to the northeast because the pattern of the plunging anticline is convex in the direction of plunge.

It follows that Black Mountain is held up by some resistant formation stratigraphically higher than the quartzite on Pine Mountain. Hickory Ridge is held up by a formation stratigraphically lower than the quartzite on Pine Mountain. The inferred structure is shown in Fig. 53.

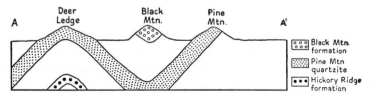

Fig. 53. Cross section along line *AA'* of Fig. 52.

The value of the dips at Deer Ledge and Black Mountain are necessarily schematic unless actually observed in the field.

The careful field geologist would consider such an interpretation suggestive, and he would feel compelled to visit as many outcrops as his time permitted.

The illustration given on p. 67 manifests how topography may be utilized to extrapolate from observations made at a single locality—in this case the water gap through Pine Mountain.

The attitude of beds may be determined quantitatively from the relation of bedding to contours. If the contact between two formations is rigorously parallel to the contours, the strata are horizontal (Fig. 54A).

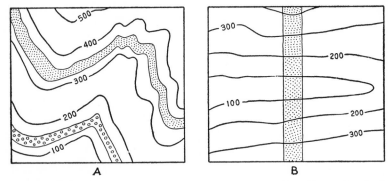

Fig. 54. Relation of outcrop pattern to topography. Every hundred foot topographic contour is shown; special beds are shown by dots and circles. *A.* Horizontal beds. *B.* Vertical beds.

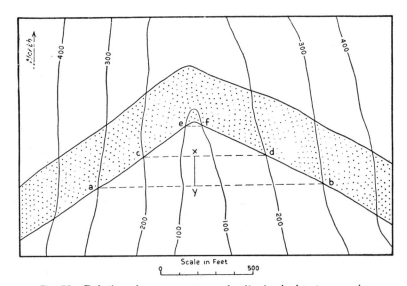

Scale in Feet

Fig. 55. Relation of outcrop pattern of a dipping bed to topography.

If, regardless of the topography, a contact maintains a uniform strike, the strata are vertical (Fig. 54B). Dipping strata have an outcrop pattern that is partially controlled by the contours. The strike and dip of the beds may be calculated, as is shown by Fig. 55. The southern boundary of the stippled bed crosses the 300-foot contour at a and b on opposite sides of the valley. Inasmuch as those two points are at the same altitude, the line ab is horizontal; moreover, ab lies in the plane of the bedding. It is apparent, therefore, that ab gives the strike of the bedding; in this instance it is east-west. Similarly, the lines cd and ef are parallel to the strike. The dip may be readily determined. The line xy is perpendicular to ab and cd, and it is 160 feet long; that is, the bed drops 100 feet vertically in 160 feet horizontally. The dip is found by the equation

$$\tan \delta = \tfrac{100}{160}$$

and

$$\delta = 32°$$

The reliability of this method depends upon the accuracy of the topographic map and upon the precision of the geological mapping.

The interpretation of topography in areas for which no geological information is available may be hazardous. Cuestas indicate gently dipping formations, whereas hogbacks indicate steeply dipping formations. The strata dip in the same direction as the gentler slopes of such ridges. A concentric series of ridges, with steep inner slopes, but with gentle outer slopes, indicate a domical structure.

Drilling

Where exposures are rare or absent, the structure may be deduced from drilling. If some bed is sufficiently distinctive, either because of lithology or because of fossil content, its altitude in various drill holes can be recorded and the structure determined. If drill cores are obtained, the angle of dip of the bedding can be determined.[1] The more complex the structure, the greater should be the number of drill holes per unit area. This method is expensive, however, and has been used only where the possibility of financial return has justified the cost. A thorough discussion of the use of drill records is given by LeRoy.[2]

Mining

Mining operations give the most complete information concerning geological structure. Coal mining, especially, furnishes valuable data because individual beds are followed for long distances. The Northern Anthracite Basin of Pennsylvania is unusually well known, and Darton

[1] Lahee, F. H., *Field Geology,* 5th ed. Cf. especially pp. 581–584. New York: McGraw-Hill Book Company, Inc., 1952.

[2] LeRoy, L. W., *Subsurface Geologic Methods,* 2nd ed. Golden, Colorado: Colorado School of Mines, 1950.

has recently published an invaluable series of structure sections of this region.[3] Two of these sections are reproduced in Fig. 43. It is obvious that this method can be used only where there is economic incentive, and ordinarily the structural geologist must rely on other, less precise, methods.

Two extensive treatments of the type of structural data obtained from mining have been edited by Newhouse[4] and Wilson.[5]

Geophysical Methods

During the last few decades, under the impetus of the exploration for petroleum and metals, various geophysical methods have been utilized in order to determine geological structure. The principal methods may be classified as *gravimetric, magnetic, seismic,* and *electrical.* These methods will be discussed in Chapter 23.

DETERMINATION OF TOP OF BEDS BY PRIMARY FEATURES

Nature of the Problem

In overturned folds and in recumbent folds the strata on one limb are overturned. Obviously, it would greatly facilitate the solution of structural problems if methods were available to determine whether the beds are right-side-up or overturned. Where the folds are exposed on the face of a great cliff, the whole structure may be clearly observed, and special methods are unnecessary. In some instances, even in regions of low relief, the exposures may be sufficiently continuous to show a progressive change from beds that are right-side-up to those that are overturned. Figure 56A illustrates such a case. At *a* the beds are in normal position, but toward the east they become progressively steeper and are vertical at *b*; still farther east, as at *c*, they dip to the west and must be overturned. In many areas, however, exposures are not sufficiently numerous to show the gradual change. In Fig. 56B for example, the beds at *d* and *e* dip toward each other, and at first it might be supposed that the structure is a simple syncline. If, however, the strata at *e* are overturned, such an interpretation is impossible, and the structure would be that shown in Fig. 56C.

[3] Darton, N. H., "Some Structural Features of the Northern Anthracite Coal Basin, Pennsylvania," *U. S. Geological Survey Professional Paper 193,* pp. 69–81, 1940.

[4] Newhouse, W. H., *et al., Ore Deposits as Related to Structural Features.* Princeton: Princeton University Press, 280 pages, 1942.

[5] Wilson, M. E., *et al., Structural Geology of Canadian Ore Deposits.* Montreal: Canadian Institute of Mining and Metallurgy, 948 pages, 1948.

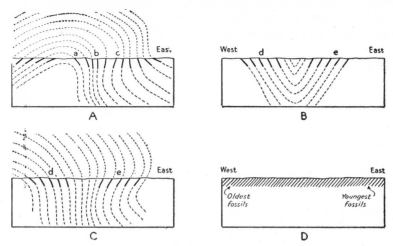

Fig. 56. Importance of determining top and bottom of beds. *A.* The gradual change from beds that are right-side-up at *a* through vertical beds at *b* to overturned beds at *c* may be observed. *B.* Beds at *d* and *e* dip toward each other, suggesting a syncline. *C.* If beds at *e* are overturned, the structure cannot be a simple syncline such as shown in diagram *B. D.* Beds dip west; fossils indicate that the strata are overturned.

Paleontological Methods

Paleontological methods, of course, may be of great aid in indicating whether beds are right-side-up or not. In Fig. 56D the beds dip **48** degrees to the west. If the youngest fossils are at the east end of the section, it is apparent that the strata are overturned.

Use of Primary Features

In many localities, however, fossils are either absent, or, if present, they are not sufficiently diagnostic to be used in distinguishing top from bottom. Other means must be employed. The most reliable information is furnished by features developed during the deposition of sediments[6] or during the eruption of lavas; they are commonly called *primary structures,* or, more suitably, *primary features.*

Shrock[7] gives a very complete discussion of the use of primary features useful in determining top and bottom. In his book a very elaborate and detailed genetic classification is followed. In the ensuing pages a complete discussion is not attempted, but rather the emphasis is upon the principles involved and upon the most useful criteria.

[6] Twenhofel, W. H., *Principles of Sedimentation.* Cf. especially pp. 494–568. New York: McGraw-Hill Book Company, Inc., 1939.

[7] Shrock, Robert R., *Sequence in Layered Rocks: A study of features and structures useful for determining top and bottom or order of succession in bedded and tabular rock bodies.* New York: McGraw-Hill Book Company, Inc., 507 pages, 1948.

Those primary features that are most commonly used are ripple-marks, cross-bedding, graded bedding, and pillow structure in lavas. Less commonly employed are mud-cracks, local unconformities, channeling, rain-imprints, and attitude of fossils.

Ripple-Marks

Ripple-marks may be aqueous or eolian in origin; that is, ripple-marks may form on the bottom of a body of water or, by wind action, at the surface of the earth. The origin and formation of ripple-marks is a subject that cannot be fully discussed here, and only those phases of the subject that are significant to the structural geologist will be considered.

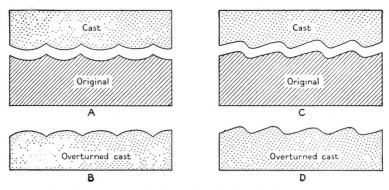

Fig. 57. Ripple-marks. *A*. Original oscillation ripple-marks and the cast. *B*. Overturned cast of oscillation ripple-marks. *C*. Original current ripple-marks and the cast. *D*. Overturned cast of current ripple-marks.

Oscillation ripples, as shown in Fig. 57A, are symmetrical, and they consist of broad troughs that are convex downward and of sharp crests that point upward. Ideally, oscillation ripples form in bodies of standing water. Whenever waves disturb the upper surface of the body of water, the individual water particles move in vertical orbits that are nearly circular. Although the wave form moves across the water, the individual particles do not. The motion of the particles is transmitted downward with decreasing intensity. The sand or mud on the bottom is affected by the same motion and is thrown into ripples.

Current ripples, as shown in Fig. 57C, are asymmetrical, and both the crest and trough are rounded. Such ripples develop when a current, either of water or of air, moves across sand or mud. In Fig. 57C, the current moved from left to right.

Forms transitional between oscillation ripples and current ripples are not uncommon; although these forms are asymmetrical, they have sharp crests that point upward. There are other forms of ripple-marks, but they do not concern the structural geologist.

Either the original ripple-mark itself or its cast may be preserved. In Fig. 57A, original oscillation ripple-marks are represented on the lower block; the upper block is the cast. Figure 57B shows the cast after it has been removed from the original and has been turned over. In Fig. 57C, original current ripple-marks are represented on the lower block; the upper block is the cast. Figure 57D shows the cast after it has been removed from the original and has been turned over.

Oscillation ripple-marks can readily be used to tell whether a bed is right-side-up or overturned. The sharp crest points toward the younger beds, whereas the rounded trough is convex toward the older beds. This is true whether the specimen is an original or a cast. In Fig. 58 the beds at outcrop *I* dip to the west at an angle of 30 degrees. At *a* the originals of ripple-marks are preserved; the crests point upward to the left, indicating that the beds are right-side-up. At *b* there is an overhanging cliff

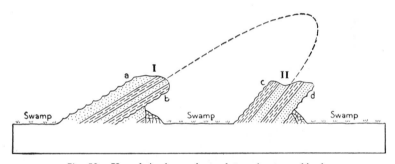

Fig. 58. Use of ripple-marks to determine top of beds.

on which the casts of ripple-marks are preserved; here, also, the crests point upward to the left, confirming the conclusion that the beds are right-side-up. At outcrop *II*, the beds dip 50 degrees to the west. On the sloping surface of the outcrop at *c*, the casts of ripple-marks are preserved; the crests point downward to the right, indicating that the beds are overturned. On the face of the overhanging cliff at *d*, the originals are preserved, and again the crests point downward to the right. The inferred structure is indicated by a broken line.

A brief consideration of Fig. 57 shows that current ripples cannot be used to determine top from bottom. An overturned current ripple has the same form as one that is right-side-up.

Cross-Bedding

Cross-bedding,[8] which is also known as *cross-stratification, cross-lamination,* or *false-bedding,* is illustrated by Fig. 59A. Whereas the true

---

[8] McKee, E. D. and G. W. Weir, "Terminology for Stratification and Cross-Stratification in Sedimentary Rocks," *Bulletin Geological Society of America,* Vol. 64, pp. 381–390, 1953.

bedding in this figure is horizontal, the cross-bedding is inclined at vary-ing angles. Cross-bedding develops wherever sand has dropped over the edge of a growing sand bar, over the front of a sand dune, or over the edge of a small delta. The upper extremity of each cross-bed is commonly inclined at a considerable angle to the true bedding, whereas the lower

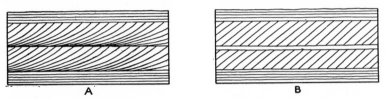

Fig. 59. Cross-bedding. *A.* Normal cross-bedding. *B.* Torrential cross-bed-ding.

extremity is essentially parallel to the true bedding. The cross-beds thus are sharply truncated above and are tangential to the true bedding below. The cross-beds in *torrential cross-bedding* are inclined to the true bed-ding at a considerable angle at both their upper and lower extremities (Fig. 59B).

The use of cross-bedding to distinguish the top from the bottom of beds is apparent from Fig. 59A. The cross-beds are tangential downward, but are truncated upward. Thus in Fig. 60A, the beds, which dip 45 de-grees to the left, are right-side-up. The top of the vertical beds in Fig. 60B is to the right. The beds in Fig. 60C, which dip 45 degrees to the

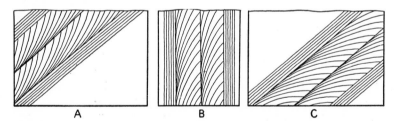

Fig. 60. Use of cross-bedding to determine attitude of beds. *A.* Beds are right-side-up. *B.* Top is to the right. *C.* Beds are overturned.

left, are overturned. In order to use cross-bedding properly, the tangen-tial portion must be observed; it is insufficient to observe that the cross-beds are sharply truncated. If the beds in Fig. 59B were folded to a ver-tical position, the cross-bedding could not be used to tell top and bottom.

Graded Bedding

In many instances the grains in a thin bed are progressively finer from bottom to top (Fig. 61A). This feature is known as *graded bedding.*[9] The

[9] Kuenen, P. H., "Significant Features of Graded Bedding," *Bulletin American Association Petroleum Geologists,* Vol. 37, pp. 1044–1066, 1953.

materials comprising a sediment are transported when the currents are swifter than usual. As the velocity subsides, the largest particles are dropped first, and then progressively finer particles are deposited. Although this generalization may seem correct, field experience proves that there are many exceptions, especially among such coarse sedimentary rocks as conglomerate. On the other hand, in the finer sedimentary rocks —notably shales and siltstones, where the individual beds are a fraction of an inch thick—the method is more reliable, but by no means infallible. Pyroclastic volcanic rocks (page 267) may show graded bedding.

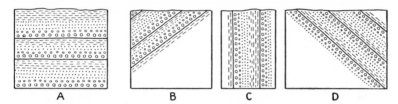

Fig. 61. Graded bedding. *A*. As deposited in horizontal beds; each bed gets finer toward the top. *B*. Dipping beds, right-side-up. *C*. Vertical beds, top toward the right. *D*. Dipping beds, overturned.

If this method is applied to the examples shown in Fig. 61, the beds in Fig. 61B are right-side-up; the tops of the beds in Fig. 61C are to the right; and the beds in Fig. 61D are overturned.

Local Unconformities, Channeling, and Related Features

During the accumulation of sediments, particularly those laid down by rivers, erosion may alternate with deposition. In Fig. 62A, for example, conglomerate occupies a channel in shale. After the original mud had

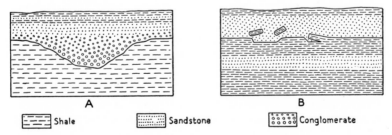

Fig. 62. Channeling and local unconformity. *A*. Channel cut into shale has been filled by conglomerate. *B*. Fragments of shale deposited in overlying sandstone.

been deposited, swiftly flowing streams in flood carved a channel. When the flood was subsiding, or at some later time, gravel was deposited in the channel. The base of the conglomerate truncates the bedding of the shale.

A related feature is illustrated by Fig. 62B where sandstone lies on top of shale. The currents that transported the sand ripped up pieces of mud, fragments of which are preserved as shale in the sandstone. Similarly, fragments of lava may be found in the sedimentary rocks directly above a lava flow.

Features that are the results of short intervals of erosion during a period of sedimentation are known as *local unconformities* (Fig. 62A).

In Fig. 63 the beds dip to the west. By following the contact of the

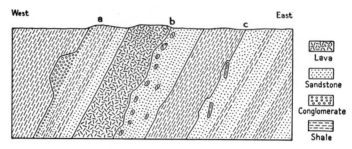

Fig. 63. Overturned beds. Shown by channeling, pebbles of lava in sandstone, and fragments of shale in sandstone.

conglomerate and shale at *a*, it becomes obvious that the conglomerate truncates the shale and fills a channel in it. Also, at *b*, the sandstone contains pebbles of the lava to the west, and the sandstone at *c* contains fragments of the shale directly west of it. All the evidence thus indicates that the beds are overturned.

Mud-Cracks

Mud-cracks, which are sometimes called *sun-cracks* or *shrinkage-cracks,* are polygonal in plan and taper downward. They characteristically form in mud and ooze that are exposed to the atmosphere and have dried out; under special conditions mud-cracks may form under water. Because of the loss in volume that accompanies desiccation, tensional stresses are set up, and ruptures develop. The sediments deposited on top of the mud-cracked layers fill in the cracks. The cast, therefore, shows a polygonal system of ridges, whereas the original shows a polygonal series of cracks.

Rain-Imprints, Pits, and Mounds

The surface of some fine-grained sedimentary rocks are pitted by small circular depressions a few millimeters across; a small rim, a fraction of a millimeter high, may surround the depressions in some cases. Some of these depressions are caused by raindrops falling on soft sediments. It has been suggested that some of these pits may have been made by hailstones. On the original, these imprints are depressions, but on the cast they are little mounds. In either case the hemispherical form, regardless of whether it is a depression or a mound, will be concave toward the top of the bed.

Some of the pits may be caused by rising gas. Moreover, in some areas, the surface of the beds is covered by both pits and mounds. Water rising through small tubes may deposit small particles to form the mounds. Gas, rising through the same or similar tubes, may blow out small crater-like depressions. It is apparent, therefore, that small mounds and depressions must be used with considerable care in deducing the top and bottom of beds.

Fossil Shells and Animal Tracks

Shells of such animals as brachiopods or pelycepods lying on a firm sea floor with their convex side downward are in a very unstable position. Every current tends to flip them over. But once they are lying concave downward, they are relatively stable. Hence under these conditions, the shells are convex upward.

An animal track is a depression. Consequently, regardless of whether it is an original or a cast, it will be convex toward the bottom of the bed.

Contemporaneous Deformation

If contemporaneous deformation is followed by subaqueous erosion, some of the small folds or thrusts may be truncated by the overlying bed (Fig. 204). No such truncation would occur on the underside of the deformed bed.

Pillow Structure

Some lavas, particularly those of basaltic composition, are characterized by pillow structure (Fig 64A). The individual pillows are roughly ellipsoidal, and they range from a foot to several feet in diameter. In flat lavas, the tops and bottoms of the pillows are generally convex upward.

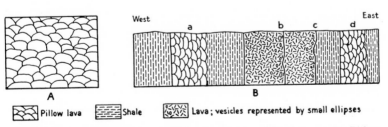

Fig. 64. Top of lava flows. *A*. Pillow structure, right-side-up. *B*. Pillow structure and vesicular structure show the top is to the right.

This method of distinguishing top from bottom has been used with particular success in the pre-Cambrian rocks of the Canadian Shield.[10]

Vesicular Tops of Lavas

Whereas the base of a lava flow is generally massive, the top tends to be vesicular—that is, full of gas bubbles. If the lava on one side of a contact is vesicular, whereas the lava on the other side is massive, the latter is likely to be younger than the former.

Fig. 64B illustrates the use of these methods in a series of beds that are vertical. The pillows in lava flows at *a* and *d* are convex toward the east. At *b*, vesicular lava lies to the west of the contact, whereas massive lava is to the east. The eastern contact of the lava at *c* is vesicular, but the western contact of this same flow is not. All observations show that the top is toward the east.

Field Methods

In those areas where primary features such as those described above are preserved, and where these primary features must be utilized in order to solve the structure, some systematic method of recording the data should be employed. Special symbols that are used for the different primary features indicate the direction of the top of beds.

DETERMINATION OF TOP OF BEDS BY DRAG FOLDS

Relation of Drag Folds to Axes of Major Folds

On p. 45 it has been shown that drag folds develop when beds slide past each other—especially if an incompetent stratum lies between two competent strata (Fig. 30).

Ordinarily, the upper beds slide away from the synclinal axes relative to the lower beds, as is shown by the arrows in Figs. 65 and 66. This fact is of the utmost importance in using drag folds to deduce the larger structures.

Ideally, the drag folds are systematically related to the major folds. Such cases are described first, but on page 83 it is pointed out why this is not always true. The drag folds in an incompetent bed between two competent beds assume the attitudes shown in Figs. 65 and 66. The acute angles between the axial planes of the drag folds and the main bedding planes point in the direction of differential movement.

[10] Wilson, M. E., "Structural Features of the Keewatin Volcanic Rocks of Western Quebec," *Bulletin Geological Society of America,* Vol. 53, pp. 53–70 (especially pp. 62–64), 1942.

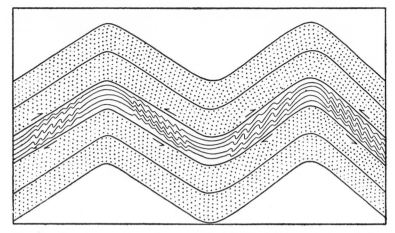

Fig. 65. Structure section of symmetrical folds showing relation of drag folds and direction of shearing.

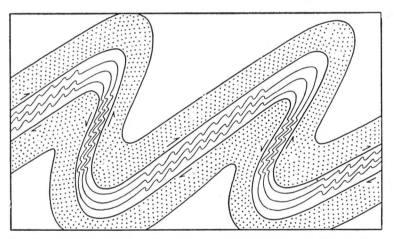

Fig. 66. Structure section of overturned folds showing relation of drag folds and direction of shearing.

Drag Folds in Cross Section

The use of drag folds in deducing the larger structures is illustrated by Figs. 67, 68, 69, and 70. At *a* in Fig. 67, the strata are vertical and the drag folds show that the beds slipped past each other in the manner indicated by the arrows. The synclinal axis must lie to the east. The beds at *b* dip to the west, and the drag folds show that the bed to the left moved upward relative to the bed to the right; the synclinal axis must lie to the west, and the strata are right-side-up. At *c* the beds also dip to the west, but the drag folds reveal that the beds to the right moved up-

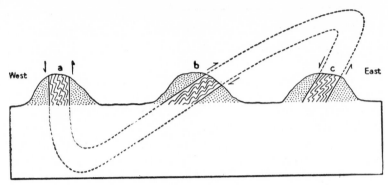

Fig. 67. Use of drag folds in determining major structure. Letters are referred to in text.

ward relative to the beds to the left. The synclinal axis must lie to the right. Assuming that the beds at *a, b,* and *c* are the same, the probable structure is indicated by the broken lines.

Drag Folds in Three Dimensions

So far we have considered drag folds only in vertical sections, and we have tacitly assumed that the axes of the major folds are horizontal.

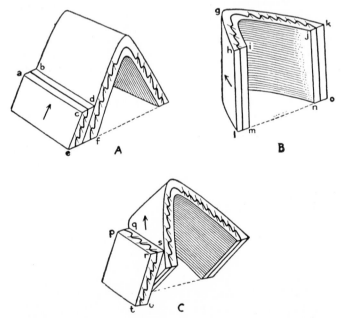

Fig. 68. Drag folds in three dimensions. The small blocks on the left side of diagrams *A* and *C* show the appearance of the drag folds on a map and on a vertical section that strikes perpendicular to the axial plane of the fold.

Under such circumstances, the beds would slide parallel to the direction of dip, as is shown by the arrow in Fig. 68A, and the axes of the drag folds would be horizontal. If, however, the major folds are plunging, there will be a component of the movement parallel to the strike of the beds. Figure 68C shows an anticline plunging 45 degrees away from the observer. The younger beds move upward relative to the older beds in the direction of the arrow—that is, at right angles to the axis of the fold. In such a case the axes of the drag folds will also plunge 45 degrees away from the observer. If the plunge of the major fold is vertical, the beds slide past one another horizontally (Fig. 68B). The axes of the drag folds will have a vertical plunge.

A major principle is suggested by these facts: drag folds plunge in harmony with the major folds, and the axes of the drag folds are parallel to those of the major folds.

Each of the three diagrams in Fig. 68 illustrates the appearance of the bedding on a horizontal surface and on a vertical section at right angles to the strike of the axial plane of the fold. In Fig. 68A the drag folds appear on the vertical plane *cdef*. These drag folds are not apparent on the horizontal plane *abcd*, where the trace of the bedding forms a straight line, because the fold does not plunge. In Fig. 68B the drag folds appear on the horizontal plane *ghijk*. In the vertical sections *hilm* and *jkno*, however, the trace of the bedding forms a straight line. In the most general case, illustrated by Fig. 68C, the drag folds appear on both the horizontal plane *pqrs* and on the vertical plane *rstu*.

Figure 69 is a map of folds that plunge to the north, a major syncline lying between two anticlines. The wavy lines show the pattern of the drag folds, and the arrows indicate the horizontal component of differential movement.

In utilizing drag folds to determine the top of beds, a vertical section

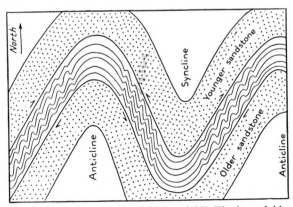

Fig. 69. Geological map of drag folds. The large folds, as well as the drag folds, plunge north. Horizontal component of shear is shown by arrows.

that strikes at right angles to the bedding is analyzed to ascertain in which direction the synclinal and anticlinal axes are located. The horizontal section is then studied in order to determine the direction of plunge.

Example of Use of Drag Folds

Figure 70 shows the drag folds in two different outcrops. In both instances the vertical face shows that the beds dip steeply to the east. In outcrop *a*, the drag folds reveal that the more easterly beds moved upward relative to the more westerly beds. In outcrop *b*, the more westerly beds moved upward relative to the more easterly beds. A synclinal axis

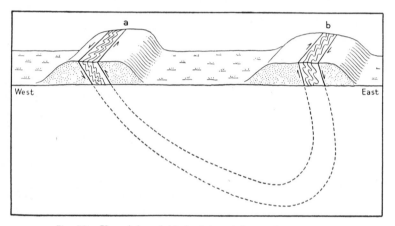

Fig. 70.   Use of drag folds in determining major structure.

must lie between the two outcrops. The top of outcrop *a* shows that the eastern bed moved north relative to the western bed; the major fold, therefore, must plunge north. Outcrop *b* corroborates this conclusion.

Even in those cases where only a flat exposure is available, the plunge of the drag folds may be observed directly if the surface of the outcrop is somewhat rough.

Minor Folds

In many regions all the strata have essentially the same competency. Drag folds, in the narrowest sense of the word, do not form. Nevertheless, large masses of rock move past one another, and the strata are thrown into *minor folds*. The minor folds usually bear the same relation to the major folds as do drag folds, and they are even called drag folds by many geologists.

Congruous and Incongruous Drag Folds

Hills[11] has emphasized the importance of distinguishing between *congruous* and *incongruous drag folds*. Congruous drag folds are those that are systematically related to the major structure in the manner described above. Incongruous drag folds are those that are not systematically related to the major structure, or, at least, not in the way indicated on the preceding pages. Generally there is no *a priori* way to distinguish incongruous drag folds from congruous drag folds. All possible methods must be used to solve the structure in order to reach a solution. But in many regions, once it has been established that the drags are congruous it is permissible to interpret more complex parts of the area in the light of this hypothesis.

Incongruous drag folds may be present for several reasons. (1) The minor folds may form later than the major structure under very different stress conditions.[12] (2) The minor folds may be the result of contemporaneous deformation, and thus distinctly older than the major structure. (3) During a single period of orogeny, partly because of inhomogeneities in the rocks and partly because they have been so tightly squeezed, the strata may shear past one another in directions other than that perpendicular to the fold axes. (4) Bain[13] has suggested that under special conditions very plastic rocks may flow toward the center of a syncline, just as in hot weather, tar on a highway flows away from the crown of the road. The resulting folds are the opposite of drag folds.

REPRESENTATION OF FOLDS

Photographs and Sketches

Folds may be represented in a variety of ways. Where direct observation is possible, as in cliffs or artificial cuts, photographs may be taken or sketches may be made. Articles describing the structure of the Alps are replete with significant sketches (Fig. 44), but even here the largest folds are too large to be included in a single view. Moreover, although great cliffs give the vertical aspect of the structure, they give only one horizontal dimension. In such ranges as the Appalachians, the Jura, and even the North American Cordillera, the larger structures cannot be photographed or sketched in the field.

[11] Hills, E. S., *Outlines of Structural Geology*, 3rd ed. London: Methuen and Co., Ltd., 182 pages, 1953, especially p. 98.

[12] White, W. S., and M. P. Billings, "Geology of the Woodsville Quadrangle, Vermont-New Hampshire," *Bulletin Geological Society of America*, Vol. 62, pp. 647–696, 1951.

[13] Bain, G. W., "Flowage Folding," *American Journal of Science*, 5th series, Vol. 22, pp. 503–530. 1931.

Maps

A good geological map may adequately represent the folds. Such maps vary greatly in elaboration. Some are simple black and white maps on which each formation is shown by a special pattern; in order to be useful, such maps must include dip and strike symbols, or, as described below, they must be accompanied by structure sections. Figure 71A is a simple geological map. If no other data are given, however, numerous interpretations of the structure are possible; four possible interpretations are given in the accompanying structure sections (Fig. 71B). If there is no topographic relief, the structure could be either a doubly plunging syncline (diagram *1*) or a doubly plunging anticline (diagram *2*). On the

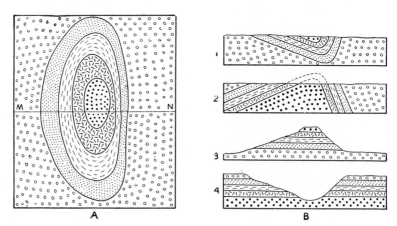

Fig. 71. Geological map with alternate interpretations of structure. *A*. Geological map. *B*. Alternate interpretations.

other hand, the pattern would also be consistent with a hill (diagram *3*) or with an enclosed depression in horizontal strata (diagram *4*). If such maps are accompanied by dip and strike symbols to show the attitude of the bedding, as in Fig. 50, there is no ambiguity.

The most satisfactory geological maps, however, are those which show not only topography, drainage, and culture, but which also indicate the geology by numerous colors and patterns. These maps may be accompanied by elaborate symbols to reveal the attitude of bedding and other structural features. But such maps are expensive to print. The geological folios and geological quadrangle maps of the U. S. Geological Survey are excellent examples of this type of map. The ease with which such maps may be interpreted depends upon the complexity of the geology and the skill of the reader.

Structure Sections

Structure sections, such as Fig. 72, are highly satisfactory means by which to represent geological structure. These structure sections purport to show the structure of folds as they would appear in imaginary vertical slices down into the earth. In themselves, however, such representations are inadequate because, although they show the vertical dimension, they can show only one horizontal dimension. The accuracy of such sections depends upon many factors. If the sections are based solely upon data obtained at the surface of the earth, they are at best only approximations, and their precision depends upon the complexity of the geology, the number of exposures, the care and skill of the field geologist, and the time available for the field work.

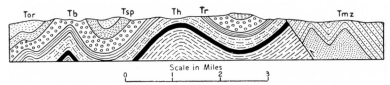

Fig. 72. Folds in the Coast Range of California. Formations are of Tertiary age. Tmz = Martinez formation; Th = Hombre sandstone; Tr = Rodeo shale; Tb = Briones sandstone; Tsp = San Pablo formation; Tor = Orinda formation. (Part of section CC', Concord quadrangle, San Francisco Folio, U. S. Geol. Survey; after A. C. Lawson.)

In many publications the folds are represented by a combination of the methods described above; a geological map is accompanied by a series of structure sections and pertinent photographs and sketches.

Structure Contours

Structure contours, an example of which is given in Fig. 73, provide the most precise way by which to represent folds in three dimensions. Such a map is read in the same way as a topographic contour map. The contours are based on a single horizon, such as the bottom or top of some particular bed. The position of the bed is given in reference to some datum plane, usually mean sea level. Inasmuch as the key horizon may go below sea level, negative contours are not uncommon. For a given contour interval, the dip is steepest where the contours are closest together. In Fig. 73 the contour interval is 25 feet, and every 100-foot contour is labeled. The structure shown is an asymmetric doubly plunging anticline, bounded on the southeast by a syncline that plunges to the northeast. The southeast limb of the anticline, where the contours are close together, is much steeper than the northwest limb, where the contours are far apart. The southwestward plunge of the southwestern end of the anticline is gentler than the northeastward plunge of the north-eastern end. If one knows the scale of the map, one can determine the dip at any place in feet per mile, and, if desirable, one can then readily convert it into degrees. On the northwestern limb of the anticline, the key bed drops from 200 feet to 100 feet in one mile. The dip on this limb is thus 100 feet per mile, or approximately one degree.

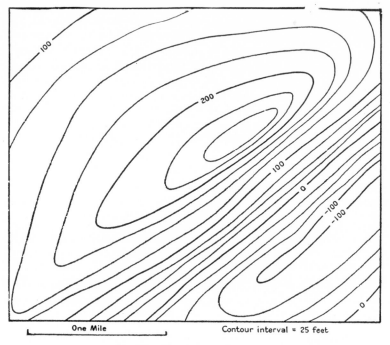

One Mile   Contour interval = 25 feet

Fig. 73. Structure contour map.

Structure contour maps are particularly useful in regions where the dips are low. Obviously where strata are overturned, such maps are diffi-cult to use, although broken lines or some other device could be used for overturned beds.

Block Diagrams

Folds may be shown by block diagrams, such as Figs. 31 and 34. Block diagrams are particularly useful to illustrate the general features of the structure and, especially, to indicate the relation between folds and topography (Fig. 74). Block diagrams cannot be used, however, to show the structure of an area precisely because, first, the scale is variable in different directions; again, only two sides of the block are available for structure sections; and, finally, the upper surface of the block is generally used to show topography.

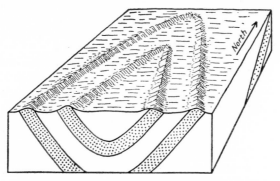

Fig. 74. Block diagram showing relation between geological structure and topography. The topography indicates that the syncline plunges south.

Models

Both the surface geology and topography may be shown on models made of wood, plaster, or some similar substance. The correlation between geology and topography is clearly portrayed, and these models are of great aid to a person not trained in reading geologic maps. The folds, however, can be shown only on the four sides of the model. Obviously this method is not very useful in distributing information to thousands of geologists all over the world.

For very special purposes, cross sections of the folds may be drawn on vertical sheets of glass that are mounted in their appropriate positions. A view of the folds in three dimensions is thus available. As in the case of the models, however, structural information cannot be readily published in this way.

CHAPTER 5

Mechanics of Folding

INTRODUCTION

In an analysis of folding we are confronted with two separate but related problems. One concerns the mechanics of folding, that is, the internal changes that take place in a mass of strata that is being folded and the stresses involved. The mechanics of folding is the subject of the present chapter. A second problem is the cause of the folding; is folding the result of horizontal compression, the intrusion of igneous rocks, or subcrustal convection currents? A consideration of this phase of the problem is reserved for Chapter 14.

In general, four principal types of folding may be recognized, but transitions are common. The four principal types are: (1) flexure folding; (2) flow folding; (3) shear folding; and (4) folding due to vertical movements.

FLEXURE FOLDING

Flexure folding, also known as *true folding*, may result from either compression or a couple. For purpose of analysis, the behavior of flat beds under a compressive force acting parallel to the bedding may be discussed

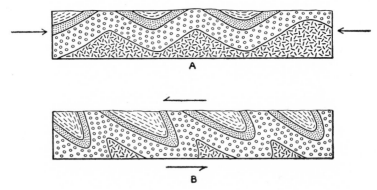

Fig. 75. Strata deformed by flexure folding. *A*. Folds resulting from simple compression. *B*. Folds developed by (1) a couple or (2) compression and a couple combined.

88

(Fig. 75A). The deformation of a single homogeneous bed should be considered first. If such a sheet is bent (Fig. 76A), the part on the convex side is subjected to tension, whereas the part on the concave side is subjected to compression. There is an intermediate *surface of no strain*. If the sheet is sufficiently ductile it will yield plastically (Fig. 76B). Minute adjustments between and within the grains permit this permanent change in shape (pp. 27–30). On the convex side it will lengthen and thin, but on the concave side it will shorten and thicken. If it is brittle,

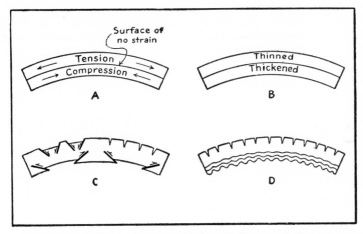

Fig. 76. Principles of flexure folding. *A*. Stresses in bent beam. *B*. Deformation entirely plastic. *C*. Deformation by rupture. *D*. Deformation by rupture and by crumpling.

it would yield by rupture (Fig. 76C). As shown in Chapter 10, tension fractures or small gravity faults might form on the convex side, whereas small thrust faults might form on the concave side. Under certain conditions the rocks on the concave side might be crumpled (Fig. 76D).

The unique feature of sedimentary rocks, however, is the presence of bedding planes. Usually, therefore, folding is analogous to the bending of a thick package of paper, and a very important factor is the sliding of beds past one another, as illustrated in Fig. 77. Each bed slips past the

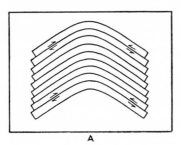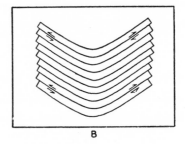

Fig. 77. Cross sections illustrating flexure folding. *A*. Anticline. *B*. Syncline

beds on either side of it. Of two adjacent beds, the upper one moves away from the synclinal axis relative to the lower bed (Fig. 77B). This principle is of great importance in interpreting certain types of drag folds (pp. 78–83) and some cleavage (p. 350). Some geologists[1] refer to the types of folding illustrated in Fig. 76 as flexure folding, and those illustrated in Fig. 77 as *flexural-slip folding*.

In the folding of sedimentary rocks, some formations are competent, whereas others are incompetent. Competency is a relative property. A *competent formation* is strong and can transmit the compressive force much farther than a weak, *incompetent formation*. Many factors determine whether or not a formation is competent. The crushing strength is one of these factors. If specimens from two different formations are tested in the laboratory, the one with the greater crushing strength will be the more competent in folding, provided, of course, that all other factors are equal.

Table 1, p. 17, gives the compressive strength of common rocks. Quartzite and marble are stronger than sandstone and limestone, and shale is the weakest of all.

The massiveness of the formation is an important factor. If, in two formations composed of the same kind of limestone, the beds of one formation are a foot thick, whereas in the other the beds are 100 feet thick, the thick-bedded formation will be the more competent.

The ability of fractures to heal may be an important factor. If a stratum fails by rupture, it is no longer competent to transmit a compressive force. A sandstone may be inherently stronger than an adjacent limestone. But once the sandstone has broken, the fracture may heal with difficulty, whereas the rupture in the limestone may heal relatively rapidly.

If the column of sedimentary rocks is composed of materials of greatly differing competency, the competent beds transmit the force, whereas the incompetent beds behave more or less passively; they are either lifted by the rising arch of competent rock or flow into potential cavities beneath the arch.

In summary, flexure folding involves the bending or buckling of the more competent layers under compressive force, the more passive behavior of the incompetent beds, and the sliding of beds past one another.

FLOW FOLDING

All transitions exist between flexure folding and flow folding. *Flow folding* or *incompetent folding*[2] is typical of regions where thick, com-

---

[1] Turner, F. J., "Mineralogical and Structural Evolution of the Metamorphic Rocks," *Memoir 30, Geological Society of America*, 342 pages, 1948; especially pp. 172–174.

[2] Fairbairn, H. W., *Structural Petrology of Deformed Rocks*. Cambridge, Mass.: Addison-Wesley Press, Inc., 344 pages, 1949.

petent beds are absent and where all the rocks are plastic, either because of inherent characteristics or because of high temperature or high confining pressure. Under such conditions, a single stratum cannot transmit the compressive force any great distance. The whole mass is forced to move under compression, but its behavior is analogous to that of a viscous liquid rather than that of a solid. The problem is one in hydromechanics. This type of deformation is characteristic of the central part of some orogenic belts, where thin-bedded shales and sandstones were rendered even more incompetent by high temperatures and moving solutions. If sufficiently small volumes of sedimentary rocks are considered, however, the folding is similar to flexure folding. The more competent beds may transmit forces for short distances, and the strata slide past one another as in flexure folding. In many respects flow folds do not differ in appearance from flexure folds, but minor folds are more abundant.

SHEAR FOLDING

Shear folding, also known as *slip folding,* results from minute displacements along closely spaced fractures. In Fig. 78A, original horizontal strata are broken into blocks by fractures that dip 60 degrees to the left. In Fig. 78B, blocks *1* and *11* remain undisturbed. Block *6* has moved upward the greatest amount; the blocks on either side of it have moved

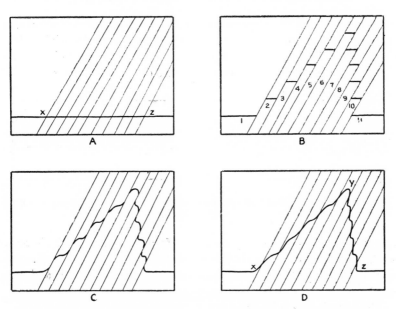

Fig. 78. Cross sections illustrating shear folding. Heavy black line, *xz,* is a bedding plane. Inclined light lines are fractures. *A.* Before displacement on fractures. *B.* After displacement. *C.* Because of friction, beds tend to parallel the fractures. *D.* Fold results if bed maintains continuity.

upward in amounts that decrease progressively. Each fracture is actually a fault. If, however, the fractures are only a fraction of an inch apart, and the beds, because of friction, tend to parallel the fractures, as is shown in Fig. 78C, the resulting structure is a major fold with many associated minor folds (Fig. 78D). In the simplest case, such shear folds should always be accompanied by visible fractures, usually cleavage. It is conceivable, however, that such fractures could be eliminated by later recrystallization of the rocks.

It is evident from Fig. 78 that in shear folding the beds are thinned, but are never thickened. Inasmuch as blocks *1* and *11* have not moved toward each other during the folding, the beds that originally had a length *xz* have been stretched so that they now have a length of *xyz*.

In the example cited, the beds were assumed to have been horizontal at the beginning of the deformation, and all of the folding is of the shear type. After earlier folds develop by some other mechanism, however, their form may be modified by shear folding. The presence of visible fractures with conspicuous, even though minute, offsets, is no proof that the folding was entirely of the shear type. Under conditions of extreme deformation, after an initial phase of flexure folding or flow folding, closely spaced fractures may develop and slippage may take place. In the experience of the author, most shear folds evolve in this way.

FOLDS RESULTING FROM VERTICAL MOVEMENTS

Differential vertical movements, unassociated with any fractures, may cause folds in the outer shell of the earth. A bed with an original length *ac* (Fig. 79A) is uplifted into a dome by vertical forces. Points *a* and *c* remain the same horizontal distance apart during the deformation and,

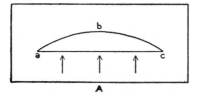 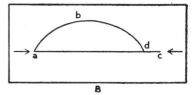

Fig. 79. Fold resulting from vertical movements. *A*. By doming. *B*. By flexure folding.

consequently, the beds are stretched to form the arc *abc*. This mechanism is different, of course, from flexure folding. In flexure folding, as is illustrated by Fig. 79B, the two ends move toward each other, and ideally there is no lengthening of the sedimentary bed; actually there may be some lengthening, but it is incidental to the process and is not essential.

CHAPTER 6

Failure by Rupture

INTRODUCTION

In Chapter 2 it has been shown that rocks first undergo elastic deformation, then plastic deformation. If deformation proceeds far enough, the rock eventually may fail by rupture—that is, by breaking. The stresses necessary to cause rupture are listed in Table 1 (page 17).

The most precise information about the relation between external forces and rupture comes, of course, from engineering practice, especially from controlled laboratory experiments.[1] Geologists have also performed numerous experiments in their laboratories. In other cases, where experiments are impossible, certain deductions from field geology seem justified. It is essential, however, to distinguish between observation and deduction.

All ruptures may be classified as *tension fractures* and *shear fractures*. *Tension fractures* result from stresses that tend to pull the specimen apart. When the specimen finally breaks, the two walls may move away from each other. *Shear fractures* result from stresses that tend to slide one part of the specimen past the adjacent part. When the specimen finally breaks, the two walls may slide past one another.

It is of the utmost importance to distinguish between the character of the external force and the type of fracture. Tension fractures may result not only from tension, but also from couples and even from compression; as will be shown later, however, a special name is given to tension fractures formed by compression. Shear fractures may develop not only under compression, but also from couples and from tension.

EXPERIMENTAL DATA

Tension

In the simplest type of tension, the opposite ends of a rod are pulled apart. After elastic and plastic deformation, the specimen fails by rup-

[1] Bridgman, P. W., *Studies in Large Plastic Flow and Fracture.* New York: McGraw-Hill Book Company, Inc., 362 pages, 1952.
Nadai, A., *Theory of Flow and Fracture of Solids.* New York: McGraw-Hill Book Company, Inc., 592 pages, 1950.

ture. The nature of the rupture depends upon the brittleness of the material. In brittle substances, such as wrought iron or a piece of blackboard chalk, a single tension fracture forms at right angles to the axis of the rod (Fig. 80A).

In more ductile substances, rupture may be preceded by *"necking"*; that is, the central part of the rod thins more than the ends (Fig. 80B). A conical fracture develops and, when failure ultimately occurs, a conical protuberance withdraws from a conical depression. In this case, the specimen has failed along shear fractures. In some material the rupture is a combination of a shear fracture and a tension fracture (Fig. 80C).

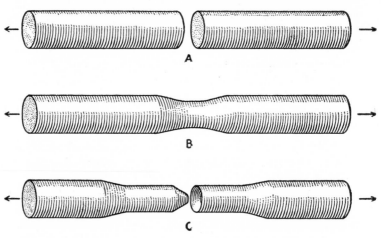

Fig. 80. Rod subjected to tension. *A*. Brittle material, with a tension fracture at right angles to the axis of the rod. *B*. Ductile material that has "necked," but not ruptured. *C*. Ductile material that has ruptured; the conical surface is a shear fracture; the blunt end of the cone is a tension fracture.

Consolidated rocks near the surface of the earth are brittle substances and, when they are subjected to tension, we should generally expect them to fail by the formation of tension cracks. In other words, fractures should form at right angles to the tensional forces.

Rocks have a much lower tensile strength than compressive strength, as is shown by Table 1. Sandstone, for example, has an average compressive strength of 740 kilograms per square centimeter, but the same rock possesses an average tensile strength of only 20 kilograms per square centimeter.

Compression

In the simplest type of compression, the test specimen, usually a cylinder or a square prism, is subjected to a compressive force at two opposite ends, and the sides are free to expand outward. In other experiments, a square prism is again compressed at the two ends, but it is confined on two opposite sides; the other two sides are free to move.

If the block is a square prism, unconfined on the sides, four sets of shear fractures develop. The four planes parallel to which the fractures form are illustrated in Fig. 81A by the planes *ABCD, EFG, HIJ*, and *KLMN*. Ordinarily, many fractures develop parallel to each of these four planes. As the compressive force is increased, the fractures increase in number and size, until, eventually, one fracture cuts all the way across

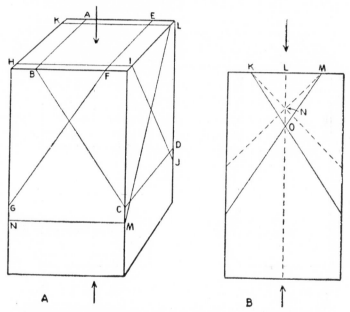

Fig. 81. Shear fractures due to compression. Arrows indicate compressive force. *A.* In a square prism subjected to simple compression, four sets of shear fractures develop; they are parallel to the planes *ABCD, EFG, HIJ*, and *KLMN. B. KN* and *MN* represent planes of maximum shearing stress deduced mathematically; *KO* and *MO* represent approximate position of shear fractures that form in experiments.

the specimen and the block collapses. Some sets may be much more extensively developed than others, especially if the specimen lacks homogeneity.

The angle that is bisected by the compressive force—angle *KOM* of Fig. 81B—is always less than 90 degrees, generally about 60 degrees. That is, the angle between the compressive force and the shear fractures is about 30 degrees.

If the square prism is confined on two opposite sides, two sets of fractures dip toward the unconfined sides of the specimen. If the front and back of the block shown in Fig. 81A were confined, only two sets of fractures, represented by *ABCD* and *EFG*, would form.

If the test specimen is cylindrical, the surfaces of rupture tend to assume a conical form; this is similar to the shear fractures that form in ductile materials under tension.

In many cases, however, specimens under compression fail along fractures parallel to the sides of the prism, especially if a lubricant is placed along the contact of the specimen and the piston exerting the

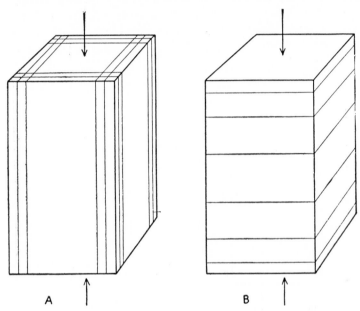

Fig. 82. Extension fractures and release fractures due to compression. Arrows indicate compressive force. *A.* Extension fractures; form parallel to sides of the prism. *B.* Release fractures; form parallel to top of prism. (After D. T. Griggs.)

compressive force (Fig. 82A). From one point of view these are tension fractures, on the principle that active compression in one direction sets up tensional forces at right angles. There are, however, theoretical objections to such an analysis, and ruptures of this type are preferably called *extension fractures*.[2]

Yet another type of fracture results indirectly from compression.[3] The specimen, while immersed in a fluid and under high confining pressure, is subjected to compression. After the load is released and the speci-

    [2] Bridgman, P. W., "Reflections on Rupture," *Journal of Applied Physics,* Vol. 9, pp. 517–528, 1938.
    [3] Griggs, D. T., "Deformation of Rocks under High Confining Pressures," *Journal of Geology,* Vol. 44, pp. 541–577, 1936.

men removed, there are numerous fractures at right angles to the axis of compression (Fig. 82B). Such fractures are, in a sense, tension fractures caused by expansion of the specimen upon the release of load, but because there is no active tension they may be called *release fractures*.

Couples

The relation of ruptures to couples is illustrated by Fig. 83. A sheet of rubber is placed across a square iron frame, with hinges at each of the four corners. The rubber is then coated by a thin layer of paraffin. If the frame is then sufficiently deformed by a couple, the paraffin is broken by numerous cracks. The first ruptures are vertical tension fractures (*t* of Fig. 83B) which strike parallel to the short diagonal of the parallelogram.

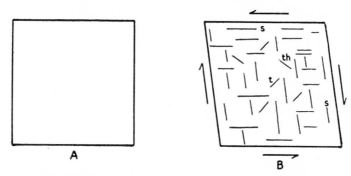

Fig. 83. Ruptures due to a couple. *A*. Square frame that is covered by a sheet of rubber, on which is a layer of paraffin. *B*. Fractures that develop because of a couple: *t* = tension fractures (perpendicular to plane of paper); *s* = shear fractures (perpendicular to plane of paper); *th* = thrust faults (inclined to plane of paper). (After W. J. Mead.)

This is not unexpected, for obviously the paraffin is being stretched parallel to the long diagonal of the parallelogram. After further deformation, vertical shear fractures (*s* of Fig. 83B) develop parallel to the sides of the wooden frame. These fractures are also not unexpected for they are analogous to the shear fractures that develop under compression. Their orientation, however, is controlled by the sides of the frame. Small thrust faults (*th* of Fig. 83B), which develop in the last step of the deformation, strike parallel to the long diagonal of the parallelogram.[4]

Torsion

If the two ends of a piece of blackboard chalk are pulled apart, a tension fracture forms at right angles to the long axis of the specimen, as in Fig. 80A. If the same material is twisted, a helical fracture develops,

[4] Mead, W. J., "Notes on the Mechanics of Geologic Structures," *Journal of Geology*, Vol. 28, pp. 505–523, 1920.

as is shown in Fig. 84A. Although chalk illustrates the difference between the ruptures produced by tension and torsion, the rock masses with which the structural geologist deals can scarcely be compared to rods. The twisting of sheet-like bodies, involving either a single bed, a formation, or the whole outer shell of the earth, is far more significant than the twisting of a rod.

The stresses developed in a twisted sheet can be resolved into the simpler stresses, tension or compression, and the ruptures obey the generalizations already set forth. Many years ago rather simple experiments

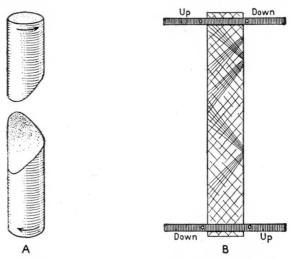

Fig. 84. Rupture due to torsion. *A.* Helical fracture due to twisting of a piece of blackboard chalk. *B.* Tension fractures on a piece of glass. Fractures that extend from upper left to lower right-hand corner are on upper side of sheet of glass; those that extend from upper right to lower left-hand corner are on under side of the sheet of glass.

were performed by twisting a sheet of glass. As shown in Fig. 84B, the upper right and lower left-hand corners were moved down, whereas the upper left and lower right-hand corners were moved up. Two sets of fractures developed.[5] On the upper surface the fractures were diagonal, and they extended from the upper left-hand corner to the lower right-hand corner. On the under side the fractures were also diagonal, but they extended from the upper right-hand corner to the lower left-hand corner.[6] A brief consideration explains why the glass fractures in this manner. If a sheet is bent, as in Fig. 76A, the upper part is subjected to tension, the

[5] Daubrée, A., *Études Synthétiques de Géologie Expérimentale*, pp. 306–314. Paris, 1879.
[6] Mead, W. J., *op. cit.*

a maximum on a plane perpendicular to the greatest principal stress axis and is at a minimum on a plane perpendicular to the least principal stress axis. We should intuitively expect, therefore, that the planes of fracture would lie somewhere between the planes of maximum shearing stress (SS' and $S''S'''$) and P. That is, the shear fractures will be parallel to the planes represented by FF' and $F''F'''$ in Fig. 85C. A rigorous mathematical proof of this is given in Anderson and Hubbert.

It is apparent that tension fractures cannot form perpendicular to P —at least while compression is still being applied—because the normal stress is at a maximum along this plane. Conversely, the normal stress n is at a minimum perpendicular to R; it is parallel to this plane that extension fractures are most likely to form under compression.

As will be shown in a later section, the stress ellipsoid may have any conceivable orientation within the crust of the earth. Consequently, shear fractures and tension fractures may have any conceivable attitude. It should also be emphasized that, even if the orientation of the stress ellipsoid can be deduced from the pattern shown by the fractures, the exact nature of the external forces can be determined only if additional data are available.

RELATION OF RUPTURE TO STRAIN

Strain Ellipsoid

In the preceding section the relation of rupture to stress has been analyzed. Another method of analysis is to relate the rupture to strain. This approach has been extensively used in geology, especially in North America.

A convenient way of visualizing deformation is to imagine the change in shape of an *imaginary* sphere in the rocks. For example, imagine a sphere in a cube of granite. If the granite were compressed from the top and bottom, the imaginary sphere would become deformed into an oblate spheroid, the short axis of which would be vertical. The most general solid resulting from the deformation of a sphere is an ellipsoid (Fig. 86A). This imaginary figure may be called the *strain ellipsoid* or the *deformation ellipsoid*. The largest axis of the ellipsoid may be called the *greatest strain axis* (Fig. 86A); the intermediate axis is the *intermediate strain axis,* and the shortest axis is the *least strain axis.*

Rupture and the Strain Ellipsoid

If tension fractures form, they are parallel to the plane that contains the least and intermediate strain axes (Fig. 86A); that is, tension fractures form at right angles to the greatest axis of the strain ellipsoid (Fig. 86B). If the attitude of the strain ellipsoid is known, the position of the

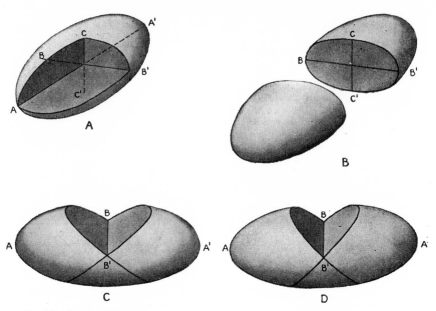

Fig. 86. Strain ellipsoid. *A. AA'* is the greatest strain axis, *BB'* is the intermediate strain axis, and *CC'* is the least strain axis. *B.* Tension fractures form perpendicular to the greatest strain axis. *C.* Every ellipsoid has two circular sections
that intersect at the intermediate axis *BB'*. Acute angle between circular sections is
bisected by *AA'*. *D.* Obtuse angle between shear fractures is bisected by *AA'*.

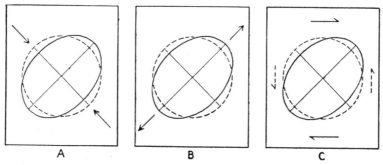

Fig. 87. Deformation of circle into an ellipse. *A.* Compression. *B.* Tension.
C. Couple.

tension fractures may be predicted. Conversely, if fractures can be identified as of tensional origin, the greatest axis of the strain ellipsoid is
readily determined; the plane containing the least and intermediate axes
is also defined, but the position of these axes within this plane can be
determined only if additional data are available.

Most sections through ellipsoids are ellipses (Fig. 86A). Two of
the sections, however, are circles. These *circular sections* pass through the
intermediate axis *BB'* (Fig. 86C). For a long time it was assumed in the

American geological literature that shear fractures formed parallel to these two circular sections. A consideration of Fig. 88 shows, however, that this is not true. In this two dimensional representation, the intermediate axis is perpendicular to the page. The planes SS' and $S''S'''$ are the traces of the circular sections. The angle between them and CC' is always greater than 45°. If this particular ellipse were the result of compression parallel to CC', we know from experimental evidence (page 95) that shear fractures would form parallel to FF' and $F''F'''$; that is, the angle between shear fractures and CC' is approximately 30°. (See also Fig. 86D.)

We may utilize this concept as follows. If two sets of shear fractures are present and are the product of the same deformation, the line formed

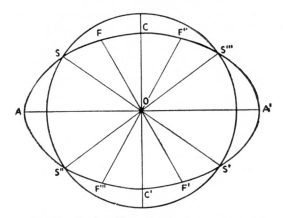

Fig. 88. Strain ellipse. AA' is the greatest strain axis. CC' is the least strain axis. SS' and $S''S'''$ are the traces of the circular sections of the ellipsoid. FF' and $F''F'''$ are the traces of the planes parallel to which shear fractures form.

by their intersection is parallel to the intermediate axis of the strain ellipsoid. Moreover, the least strain axis CC' bisects the *acute* angle between the shear fractures.

A point of fundamental importance is that the strain gives us no direct evidence of the external forces that caused the deformation. An ellipsoid may be formed from a sphere by simple compression, by tension, or by a couple. This fact is illustrated in two dimensions by Fig. 87, where the intermediate axis is perpendicular to the page. The three ellipses are identical. The ellipse in Fig. 87A, however, is the result of compression; that in Fig. 87B is the result of tension; and that in Fig. 87C is the result of a couple, as is shown by the solid arrows. The dotted arrows would give the same result. Thus even though the field geologist may accurately describe the strain, he cannot directly deduce the external forces without some additional evidence.

A simple example may serve to illustrate the use of the concept of the strain ellipsoid in relation to ruptures. Figure 89A is a cross section through a fault—that is, a fracture along which the blocks on opposite sides have been displaced relative to each other. Scratches on the surface of the fault indicate that the movement was parallel to the dip of the fault. The problem is to decide whether the eastern block moved up or down relative to the western block—that is, which arrows, those at a or those at b, represent the movement?

On the east side of the fault are short, open tension fractures, arranged *en échelon* as shown in Fig. 89A. The long axis of the strain ellipse AA' is therefore vertical, as is shown in Fig. 89B, and the ellipse is oriented as shown. If the couple along the fault acted as shown by the

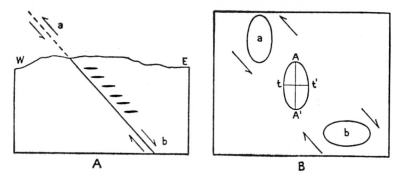

Fig. 89. Use of strain ellipse in a structural problem. A. Cross section; heavy diagonal line is a fault; problem is to decide whether movement has been of type represented by arrows at a or by arrows at b. Small gashes are open tension cracks. B. The tension cracks of Fig. 89A are represented by tt'; therefore the greatest strain axis lies in direction AA', which is the long axis of the strain ellipse. The movement represented by the arrows at a would give such an orientation of the strain ellipse; the movement represented by the arrows at b would not.

arrows at b, the long axis of the ellipse would be horizontal. If the couple acted as shown by the arrows at a, the long axis of the ellipse would be vertical. Inasmuch as the latter corresponds to the orientation deduced from the tension cracks, it is concluded that the east wall moved up relative to the west wall. This problem has been analyzed by omitting the third dimension, but in this case the intermediate axis of the strain ellipsoid is perpendicular to the plane of the paper and may be neglected.

Other examples of the use of the strain ellipsoid are cited in later sections of this book.

The concept of the strain ellipsoid is used extensively in the literature on structural geology. It has been used particularly in attempts to relate ruptures to strain and to external forces; the student should be familiar with the methods employed. On the other hand, many geologists feel that little is to be gained by analyzing field problems in this way. In general, however, the concept of the strain ellipsoid is exceedingly useful if it is employed with discrimination. It is helpful in visualizing in three dimensions the change in shape that masses of rock may undergo. Moreover, it is clear that tension fractures form at right angles to the greatest strain axis. Shear fractures pass through the intermediate strain axis and make an angle of about 30 degrees with the least strain axis.

RUPTURE IN ROCKS

Failure by rupture is expressed in the rocks of the outer shell of the earth by joints, faults, and some kinds of cleavage. The next few chapters are devoted, therefore, to these subjects. Many ruptures are now occupied by veins or dikes. Although the origin of the ruptures is the concern of the structural geologist, the nature of the material that fills them is the concern of the economic geologist or the petrologist.

CHAPTER 7

Joints

GENERAL FEATURES

Rocks are characteristically broken by smooth fractures known as joints (Plates XI, XII, and XIII). *Joints* may be defined as divisional planes or surfaces that divide rocks, and along which there has been no visible movement parallel to the plane or surface. Although most joints are planes, some are curved surfaces. There has been no visible movement parallel to the surface of the joint; otherwise it would be classified as a fault. Movement at right angles to the surface of the joint may take place, however, and produce an open fracture.

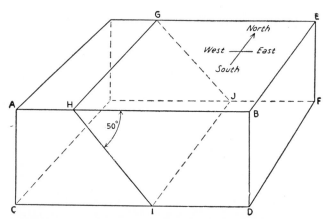

Fig. 90. Attitude of joints. Plane *ABCD* represents a vertical joint that strikes east-west; plane *BDEF* represents a vertical joint that strikes north-south; plane *GHIJ* represents a joint that strikes north-south and dips 50 degrees east.

Joints may have any attitude; some joints are vertical, others are horizontal, and many are inclined at various angles. The strike and dip of joints are measured in the same way as in bedding. The strike is the direction of a horizontal line on the surface of the joint; the dip, measured in a vertical plane at right angles to the strike of the joint, is the angle between a horizontal plane and the joint. In Fig. 90 the geographic directions are shown. The front of the block (plane *ABCD*) is a joint that strikes east and has a vertical dip. The right-hand side of the block (plane *BEDF*) is a joint that strikes north and has a vertical dip. The plane *GHIJ* is a joint that strikes north and dips 50 degrees east.

The symbols used by the U. S. Geological Survey are shown in Fig. 91.

Joints differ greatly in size. Some are only a few feet long, but observations in quarries show that others may be followed for hundreds of feet along the strike and for similar distances down the dip. Joints that are hundreds and even thousands of feet in length and in height may be observed in mountainous regions.

Fig. 91. Map symbols for joints. *A.* Strike and dip of inclined joint. *B.* Strike of vertical joint. *C.* Horizontal joint.

Joints never occur alone. The interval between them may be hundreds of feet or only a few inches. As will be shown on p. 339, if the interval is a fraction of an inch, the term fracture cleavage is applied.

The term joint is said to have originated in the British coal fields because the miners thought that the rocks were "joined" along the fractures, just as bricks are put together in a wall.

Joints may be classified either geometrically or genetically. A geometrical classification is strictly descriptive and comparatively easy to apply, but does not indicate the origin of the joints. A genetic classification is more significant, but, as will be seen, is not readily applied in many cases.[1]

GEOMETRICAL CLASSIFICATION

In a geometrical classification, the joints may be classified on the basis of their attitude relative to the bedding or some similar structure in the beds that they cut. *Strike joints* are those that strike parallel or essentially parallel to the strike of the bedding of a sedimentary rock, the schistosity of a schist, or the gneissic structure of a gneiss. In Fig. 92, in which the bedding is shown in solid black, *BDEF* and *MNO* are strike joints. *Dip joints* are those that strike parallel or essentially parallel to the direction in which the bedding, schistosity, or gneissic structure dips. In Fig. 92, *ABCD* and *GHI* are dip joints. *Oblique* or *diagonal* joints are those striking in a direction that lies between the strike and direction of

[1] For especially good papers dealing with joints see the following:

Bucher, W. H., "The Mechanical Interpretation of Joints," *Journal of Geology,* Vol. 28, pp. 707–730, 1920; Vol. 29, pp. 1–28, 1921.

Sheldon, Pearl, "Some Observations and Experiments on Joint Planes," *Journal of Geology,* Vol. 20, pp. 53–79, 164–190, 1912.

Swanson, C. O., "Notes on Stress, Strain, and Joints," *Journal of Geology,* Vol. 35, pp. 193–223, 1927.

dip of the associated rocks. In Fig. 92, *PQR* and *STU* are oblique joints. *Bedding joints* are parallel to the bedding of the associated sedimentary rocks. In Fig. 92, *JKL* is a bedding joint.

Characteristically a large number of joints are parallel. A *joint set* consists of a group of more or less parallel joints. A *joint system* consists of two or more joint sets or of any group of joints with a characteristic pattern.

Joints may be classified according to their strike. It is thus possible to speak of the north-south set, the northeast set, or the east-west set. In

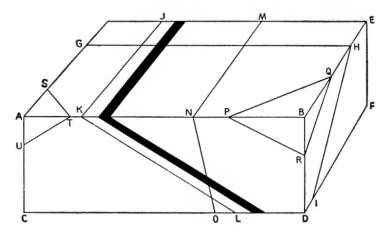

Fig. 92. Geometrical classification of joints. Heavy black band is bedding. *ABCD* and *GHI* are dip joints; *BDEF* and *MNO* are strike joints. *JKL* is a bedding joint. *PQR* and *STU* are diagonal joints.

some regions there may be several north-south sets; one set may be vertical, a second set may dip 40 degrees east, and a third set may dip 60 degrees west.

In order to ascertain the number of sets present, the joints can be plotted on a map. Figure 93 shows at a glance that in the Adirondack Mountains of New York there are two prominent sets of joints that are essentially vertical, and that one set strikes northeast, the other northwest.[2]

Various types of diagrams may be used to portray the attitude of the joints in an area. A precise way of representing joints is to plot the poles of perpendiculars to the joints. All the joints are imagined to be at the center of a sphere. A line drawn perpendicular to each joint will pierce the sphere at two points, called the poles. In Fig. 94 the poles of a hori-

[2] Balk, Robert, "Structural Geology of the Adirondack Anorthosite," *Mineralogische und Petrographische Mitteilungen,* Leipzig, Vol. 41, pp. 308-433, 1931. For a more accessible excellent example of a map of joints see Lowe, K. E., "Storm King Granite at Bear Mountain, New York," *Bulletin, Geological Society of America,* Vol. 61, pp. 137-190. 1950; especially Pl. 4 and Fig. 7.

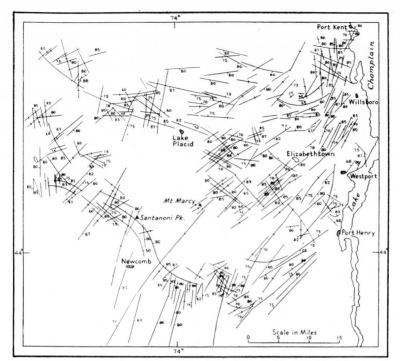

Fig. 93. Joint map of part of the Adirondack Mountains of New York. Generalized from detailed maps; data for many joints are combined into one dip-strike symbol. Length of lines is intended to show relative importance of different groups of joints, but does not mean that one can be followed for that distance. (After R. Balk.)

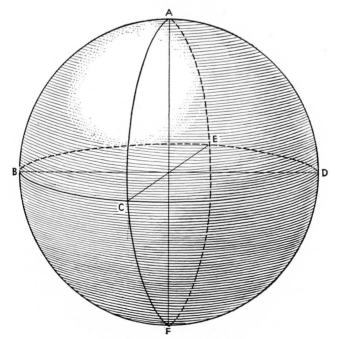

Fig. 94. Sphere with all joints passing through center. *ABFD,* *ACFE,* and *BCDE* are joints.

109

zontal joint *BCDE* are at *A* and *F*. The poles of a vertical joint *ABFD*, parallel to the page, lie at *C* and *E*. The poles of a vertical joint *ACFE*, perpendicular to the page, are at *D* and *B*. It is obvious that, for plotting data, one need use only the top or bottom half of the sphere because the poles on one hemisphere are the mirror image of those on the other. Moreover, it is far more convenient to project the surface of the hemisphere on to the plane of the paper. Figure 95 is an example of a projection in which the lower hemisphere was used. Point *1* represents a horizontal joint; point *2* represents a vertical joint that strikes north; point *3*

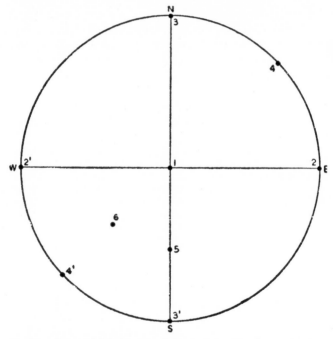

Fig. 95. Poles of joints plotted in a circle. Numbers represent different joints. (See text.)

represents a vertical joint that strikes east; and point *4* represents a vertical joint that strikes northwest. Point *5* represents a joint striking east and dipping 45 degrees north. Point *6* represents a joint striking northwest and dipping 45 degrees northeast. All vertical joints, of course, can be represented by two points, and points *2'*, *3'*, and *4'*, respectively, represent the same joints as *2*, *3*, and *4*. But only one point should be plotted for each vertical joint, or the reader may derive a wrong impression of their abundance. Which of the two possible points is to be plotted is an arbitrary matter.

The exact distance that a point lies from the center of the circle depends upon the size of the projection circle, the dip of the joint, and the type of projection used. The stereographic projection, as used in mineralogy, could be employed. More useful, however, is the *equal area projection*, which is also used in structural petrology (Chapter 22). The scale for a projection circle with a radius of 10 centimeters is shown in Fig. 96.

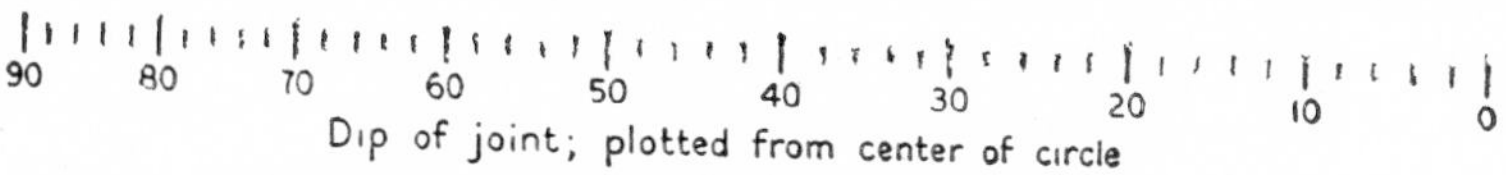

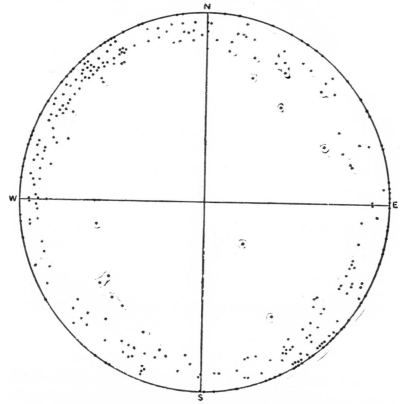

Fig. 96. Scale used to plot poles of joints. To be used on a circle with a radius of 10 centimeters; based on equal area projection.

It is customary in structural geology to make the plot on the lower hemisphere. To plot the projection of the pole of a particular joint, one draws a line from the center of the circle at right angles to the strike of the joint and opposite to the direction of dip. Using the scale in Fig. 96, one plots the dip outward from the center of the circle, which has a radius of 10 centimeters.

Fig. 97. Point diagram of 311 joints in Adirondack Mountains shown in Fig. 93. Plotted on lower hemisphere.

Figure 97, which is a plot of the poles of the joints in the Adirondack
Mountains shown in Fig. 93, is known as a *point diagram*. Points on the
circumference of the circle indicate vertical dips; such points could be
placed at either end of a diameter and have been distributed arbitrarily
in order to equalize the number of points on the circumference in opposite quadrants. This plot shows that practically all of the joints dip
steeply, for the points are at or near the circumference of the circle.
Moreover, the greater concentration of points in the northwest and southeast quadrants indicates that the majority of the joints strike in a general
northeasterly direction. This fact is also apparent from the map, Fig. 93.

From the point diagram a *contour diagram* may be prepared, such as
that shown in Fig. 98. The solid black area, labeled "11–12%," means
that 11 to 12 per cent of all the points shown in the point diagram (Fig.
97) lie within an area equal to one per cent of the total area of the dia-

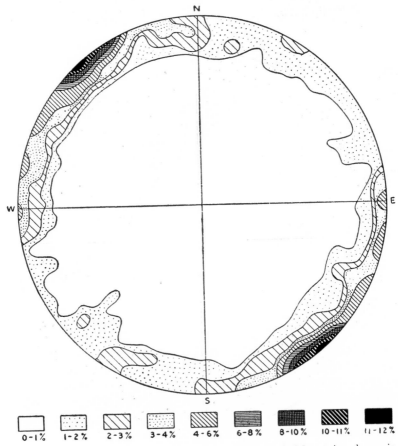

Fig. 98. Contour diagram of 311 joints in Adirondack Mountains shown in
Fig. 93. Plotted on lower hemisphere.

gram. That is, if a small circle, covering an area equal to one per cent of the area of the large circle, were placed over this solid black area, it would contain 11 to 12 per cent of the points. The high percentages on the circumference in the northwest and southeast quadrants indicate that the majority of the joints strike northeast and that they are essentially vertical.

The preparation of such a contour diagram from a point diagram is illustrated by Fig. 99. A piece of tracing paper is placed over the point diagram. The center counter, *CC* of Fig. 99, consists of a circular hole

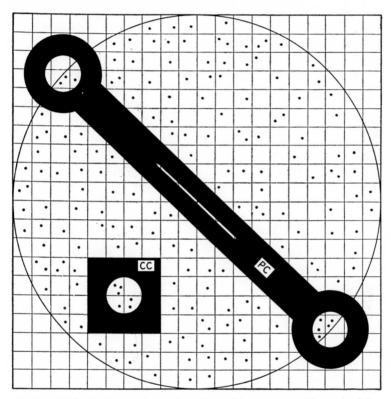

Fig. 99. Method of counting points in making contour diagram. *CC* = center counter; *PC* = peripheral counter.

in the center of a piece of paper, cardboard, celluloid, or any satisfactory material. The area of this circle is equal to one per cent of the area of the large circle; if the large circle has a radius of 10 centimeters, the small circle has a radius of 1 centimeter. Two hundred points are plotted on Fig. 99. (Some of the 200 points are covered by the counters.) Six of these points lie within the center counter; six points are 3 per cent of the total number of points in the large circle, and the figure *3* is written in the center of the center counter. The center counter is moved **over** the whole diagram, and the percentage of points at each place is recorded. In order that the sampling may be systematic, a grid system is placed on the point diagram—or beneath it if the point diagram is on tracing paper—and the center counter is moved from left to right one centimeter at a time. After a traverse from left to right has been completed, the counter is moved down one centimeter, and a second traverse is run. It should be noted that a single point in the point diagram may lie within the center counter several times in its successive positions. The point is counted each time.

For points closer to the circumference than a distance equal to the diameter of the center counter—one centimeter if the large circle is 10 centimeters—a special technique is required. The peripheral counter (*PC* of Fig. 99) is used for such points; it is made of paper, cardboard, celluloid, or any satisfactory material. Half of each of the two circles at either end extends beyond the circumference of the large circle. The points in each circle are added together. In Fig. 99 they total *8*, which is 4 per cent of the total *200*. The figure *4* is then entered on the diagram in the center of *both* circles at the ends of the peripheral counter.

After the diagram has been covered with percentage figures, contours are drawn in the same manner by which topographic contours are prepared from points of known altitude.

There are various modifications of the technique outlined above, and for more complete discussion the reader is referred to additional publications.[3]

Representing the attitude of joints by point diagrams and contour diagrams is by far the most satisfactory method yet devised. Once a geologist has learned to read such diagrams, they are very serviceable. The same type of diagram may be used for faults, veins, and dikes. These diagrams are superior to maps because, although any systematic strike can be readily discerned on the map, one must read each dip figure in order to determine the attitude. These diagrams are useful only if the joint pattern is relatively homogeneous over the whole area being studied. They do not distinguish between joints in different parts of the area. The diagram for a group of vertical joints radiating from a common center would consist of points distributed more or less evenly around the circumference of the diagram. Vertical joints that strike in various directions, but are haphazardly distributed throughout the area, would give a diagram that is similar to or identical with that given by radiating joints.

Any method of recording joints on maps or diagrams introduces a quantitative problem. The strike and dip of the joint can be expressed

[3] Knopf, E. B., and E. Ingerson, "Structural Petrology," *Memoir 6, Geological Society of America*, pp. 245–251, 1938.

Fairbairn, H. W., *Structural Petrology of Deformed Rocks*, 2nd ed. 344 pages, Cambridge, Mass.: Addison-Wesley Press, Inc., 1949; especially pp. 275–291

quantitatively, but curving joints present a problem. Ordinarily, the average attitude is recorded. The joints may differ greatly in size, and it may be necessary to adopt some arbitrary system (such as using a heavy line for a "big" joint, a medium weight line for an "intermediate" joint, and a light line for a "little" joint) in order to indicate the magnitude of a joint. What is "big," "intermediate," or "little" is strictly relative, depending upon the local geology. Unless a very large scale map is employed, it may be impossible to plot all the joints on a map, and one symbol may have to represent 5 to 10 joints in those parts of the area where joints are abundant. If so, the weight of the line might indicate the number of joints represented by the symbol.

GENETIC CLASSIFICATION

In many instances it is difficult to ascertain the origin of joints. It is not always possible to distinguish *tension joints,* which form perpendicularly to forces tending to pull the rock apart, from *shear joints,* which are due to forces tending to slide one part of the rock past an adjacent part. Even if this can be done, and the attitude of the stress axes and strain axes can be established, it may be impossible to deduce with satisfaction the character of the external forces.

Tension joints due to a decrease in volume are one of the easiest types

PLATE XI. *Columnar Jointing. Devil's Post Pile National Monument, California.* (Photo by United States Forest Service.)

of joints to recognize. The columnar jointing in basalt is of this origin (Plate XI); this is also the origin of mud-cracks and joints in loess. An ideal example is a cooling horizontal sheet of basalt, either a flow or a sill. The basalt solidifies at about 1,000° C., and during subsequent cooling it contracts. The resulting tensional forces act primarily in the horizontal plane and are equal in all directions within this plane. When rupture eventually takes place, three vertical fractures, making angles of 120 degrees with each other, radiate out from numerous centers (Fig.

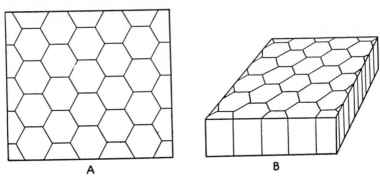

A   B

Fig. 100. Hexagonal fractures in a sheet. The tension results from loss of volume either because of cooling of lava or desiccation of mud. *A.* Upper surface of sheet. *B.* Block diagram of sheet.

100). If the centers are evenly distributed, the fractures bound vertical hexagonal columns. Actually, of course, the perfection of the hexagonal columns differs greatly, depending on many factors. In many instances the fractures are so irregularly distributed that the hexagonal form is unrecognizable.

Theoretically, of course, the cooling of a horizontal sheet of solid basalt is a three-dimensional problem. Because of gravity, however, tension does not necessarily develop in the vertical direction because the top of the basalt gradually lowers to take care of shrinkage in this direction. In the horizontal plane, however, the sheet cannot shrink in size, and the tensional forces develop. Even in the vertical direction, however, tension is set up, and the hexagonal columns may be broken by horizontal cross fractures. In places, the cross fractures assume a "cup and socket" form similar to the conical fractures found experimentally in ductile materials.

For simplicity of discussion it has been assumed that the sheet of basalt is horizontal. An analogous situation is found, however, if the sheet of basalt is vertical, as in a dike (p. 307). In this case the axes of the hexagonal columns are horizontal. The basalt is frozen to its walls, and, despite gravity, the shrinking sheet cannot move as a unit. The tensional forces that develop are equal in all directions in the vertical plane.

Mud-cracks form because of forces similar to those in the cooling sheet of solid basalt. In this case, however, the shrinkage is due to the loss of water during desiccation of the wet mud.

Tension fractures due to a couple are represented by some of the crevasses in glaciers and by feather joints. Figure 101A is a diagrammatic map of vertical crevasses that are diagonal to the contact between a glacier and the rock walls; the direction in which the ice flows is shown

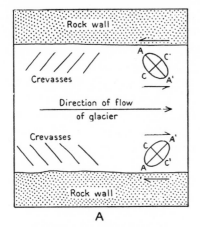 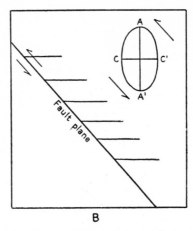

Fig. 101. Tension fractures. *A.* Crevasses along side of glacier. Couples caused by friction are shown by smaller arrows. Ellipses represent orientation of strain ellipsoid. *B.* Cross section to show feather joints, which are represented by horizontal lines to right of fault plane. Arrows near fault show relative movement along it. Orientation of ellipse resulting from this movement shown in upper right-hand corner. (After E. Cloos.)

by the large arrow. The friction with the walls sets up couples, which are indicated by the smaller arrows. The intermediate axis of the strain ellipsoid is perpendicular to the surface of the ice, and the greatest and least axes are respectively *AA'* and *CC'*. The tension cracks develop at right angles to the greatest strain axis *AA'*.

Feather joints are tension fractures related to faulting. Figure 101B is a vertical section of a fault on which the right-hand block has moved up relative to the left-hand block, as shown by the arrows along the fault. The intermediate axis of the strain ellipsoid is perpendicular to the plane of the paper, and *AA'* and *CC'* are oriented as shown in the figure. Tension joints which form perpendicularly to *AA'* may be confined to one side of the fault if the rocks on that side have a lower tensile strength than the rocks on the other side.

Joints perpendicular to the axes of folds are common in orogenic belts (Fig. 102, plane *ABCD*). Such joints may be *extension joints*, resulting from slight elongation parallel to the axes of the folds. They would be analogous to the ruptures that form parallel to the sides of specimens under compression (Fig. 82A).

Joints parallel to the axial planes of folds (Fig. 102, plane *EFGH*) may be *release joints,* similar to those that form at right angles to the

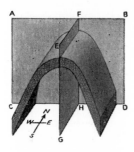

axis of compression when the load is released (Fig. 82B). Other joints with this attitude may be due to tension on the convex side of a bent stratum (Fig. 76).

Shear joints are difficult to recognize. If a joint is slickensided (p. 149), the opposite walls have obviously slipped past one another. But this is not proof that the fracture originated under shearing stress. The stress may have been tensional, and the sliding of walls past each other could be a later phenomenon. It is often supposed

Fig. 102. Fold with vertical dip joint and vertical strike joint. *ABCD* = vertical dip joint. *EFGH* = vertical strike joint.

that tension fractures break around the pebbles of conglomerates and that only shear fractures cut indiscriminately across pebbles and matrix. Although this may be true for loosely consoli-

dated conglomerates, apparently it is not a reliable criterion in well-cemented conglomerates.

Two sets of joints that intersect at a high angle to form a conjugate system are often considered shear fractures, especially if they are symmetrically disposed about the strain axes. Figure 103A is a block diagram of an area in which horizontal fold axes trend north-south. There are two sets of vertical joints, one of which strikes west-northwest, and the

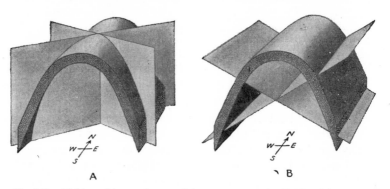

Fig. 103. Folds with conjugate joint systems. *A.* Fold with vertical diagonal joints. *B.* Fold with strike joints dipping about 30 degrees.

other of which strikes east-northeast. The attitude of the folds indicates that the compressive force was acting along east-west lines. In the light of experimental observations, the joints could be interpreted as shear fractures that developed due to a compressive force acting in an east-west direction, with the easiest relief in a north-south direction. (See also Chapter 10.)

Figure 103B is a block diagram of an area in which the horizontal fold axes trend north-south and in which the axial planes are vertical. Two sets of joints strike north-south, but one set dips about 30 degrees east, whereas the other set dips about 30 degrees west. Such a conjugate system can also be interpreted as shear fractures due to an east-west compressive force, but under such conditions that the easiest relief was upwards. (See also Chapter 10.)

Shear joints can result from a couple. Figure 104, for example, is a map of an area in which there are two sets of vertical joints, one set striking east-northeast, the other striking west-northwest.[4] These joints

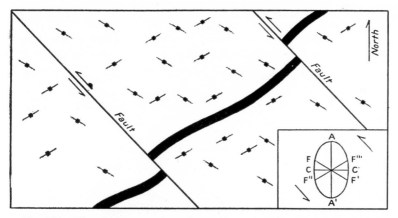

Fig. 104. Map showing vertical shear joints caused by a horizontal couple. Solid black is key bed. Faults are vertical; movement parallel to strike of faults.

are in a block bounded by two northwesterly-striking vertical faults, along both of which the northeasterly wall has moved northwest relative to the southwest wall. The central block was subjected to a couple; utilizing the concept of the strain ellipsoid, as illustrated in the lower right-hand corner, the intermediate axis would be perpendicular to the surface of the earth, and the strain axes AA' and CC' would trend respectively north-south and east-west. The shear fractures would be essentially parallel to FF' and $F''F'''$.

Although such explanations of conjugate joint systems as those given on the preceding pages are plausible and account for all the facts, other interpretations cannot always be eliminated. A conjugate system might conceivably form if the rocks are subjected to tension which acts in one direction at one time and in a different direction at another time. In such a case, the younger set would generally abut against the older set. Dikes

[4] For a somewhat comparable situation see Wager, L. R., "Jointing in the Great Scar Limestone of Craven, and Its Relation to the Tectonics of the Area," *Quarterly Journal of the Geological Society of London*, Vol. 87, pp. 392–424, 1931.

PLATE XII.   *Joints. Paleozoic gneiss. Highway 2, Acton, Massachusetts. Joints dip steeply to left.* (Photo by L. D. Leet.)

or veins might fill some joints in one set, but none in the second. If, however, the two sets of joints are shear fractures, no essential difference in age should be apparent. Although individual joints of one set may be younger or older than joints of the other set, there should be no systematic age difference.

The analysis of faulting given in Chapter 10 can also be applied to joints, inasmuch as both faults and joints are ruptures.

In general, the structural geology of a large area must be well understood in order that the joints may be interpreted correctly. Even under such circumstances, several interpretations may explain the facts equally well, and a unique solution cannot be obtained.

SHEETING

Sheeting, a form of rupture similar to jointing, is best exposed in artificial openings such as quarries (Plate XIII). The sheeting surfaces are somewhat curved and are essentially parallel to the topographic surface, except in regions where there has recently been rapid erosion. The fractures are close together at the surface of the earth, and in many places the interval between them is measured in inches. The interval increases with depth, and a few tens of feet beneath the surface the visible sheeting disappears. At greater depths, however, invisible planes of weakness parallel to the sheeting are utilized by quarrymen in their work. Although sheeting is best developed in granitoid rocks, it is also observed in sandstone.

Various hypotheses have been developed to explain sheeting. According to one of these, the sheeting in granite is parallel to the upper contact of the intrusive body and formed as tension cracks during the cooling of the rock after it had crystallized. In such an interpretation the topography is controlled by the sheeting rather than the sheeting by the topography. Numerous field examples, however, show that this hypothesis is untenable because the sheeting is unrelated to the igneous contacts.

According to a second hypothesis, the sheeting is a tensional phenomenon due to the release of load during erosion. Although it is evident that a mass of rock approaching the surface is under a constantly decreasing load and will expand, it is difficult to understand why the expansion should lead to rupture. Nevertheless, as has been stated on p. 96, the release of the compressional force on specimens that have been under high confining pressure sometimes causes ruptures perpendicular to the axis of compression.

A third hypothesis is similar in some respects to the second hypothesis. Because of progressive lowering of the surface of the earth due to erosion and consequent decrease in the confining pressure, the rock expands in all directions. The vertical expansion is unimpeded, and only air

PLATE XIII.　*Sheeting. In granite near Marlboro, New Hampshire.* (Photo by E. M. Heinrich.)

has to be pushed away. The horizontal expansion is hindered by rock. Compressional forces parallel to the surface of the earth develop and cause rupture. Shear fractures would be inclined at angles of about 30 degrees to the surface of the earth. Extension fractures, as described on p. 96, would be parallel to the surface. This is the most acceptable interpretation of sheeting.

CHAPTER 8

Description and Classification of Faults

GENERAL CHARACTERISTICS

Faults are ruptures along which the opposite walls have moved past each other. The essential feature is differential movement parallel to the surface of the fracture. Some faults are only a few inches long, and the total displacement is measured in fractions of an inch. At the other extreme, there are faults that are hundreds of miles long with a displacement measured in miles and even tens of miles.

The *strike* and *dip* of a fault are measured in the same way as they are for bedding or jointing. The strike is the trend of a horizontal line in the plane of the fault. The dip is the angle between a horizontal surface and the plane of the fault; it is measured in a vertical plane that strikes

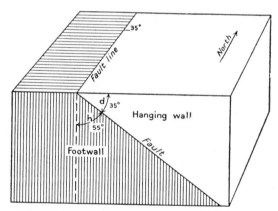

Fig. 105. Terminology for a fault plane. $d = $ dip, $h = $ hade.

at right angles to the fault. The *hade* is the complement of the dip; that is, the hade equals ninety degrees less the angle of dip. The hade may also be defined as the angle between the fault plane and a vertical plane that strikes parallel to the fault. Hade is a relatively obsolete term, but is common in the older literature. In Fig. 105 the front of the block is a plane that strikes east-west and dips vertically. The right-hand side of the block strikes north-south and has a vertical dip. The fault is an inclined plane that strikes north-south, dips 35 degrees east, and has a hade of 55 degrees east.

The block above the fault is called the *hanging wall* (Fig. 105); the block below the fault is the *footwall*. A person standing upright in a tunnel along a fault would have his feet on the footwall, and the hanging wall would hang over him. It is obvious that vertical faults have neither a footwall nor a hanging wall.

Although many faults are clean-cut, in many instances the displacement is not confined to a single fracture, but is distributed through a *fault zone*, which may be hundreds, even thousands, of feet wide. The fault zone may consist of numerous interweaving small faults, or it may be a confused zone of breccia or mylonite (p. 151). *Distributive faulting* occurs if the differential movement takes place by systematic small displacements along a large number of closely spaced fractures.

The intersection of the fault with the surface of the earth is known as the *fault line, fault trace,* or *fault outcrop* (Fig. 105). In most instances, the fault line, as it appears on a map, is reasonably straight or somewhat sinuous. If, however, the dip of the fault is low and the topographic relief high, the fault line may be exceedingly irregular.

NATURE OF MOVEMENT ALONG FAULTS

Translational and Rotational Movements

The movement along faults may be translational or rotational. In Fig. 106, diagrams *A* and *B* illustrate translational movement, whereas diagrams *C* and *D* illustrate rotational movement.

In *translational movement* there has been no rotation of the blocks relative to each other; all straight lines on opposite sides of the fault and outside the dislocated zone that were parallel before the displacement are parallel afterwards.

In Fig. 106A, two points, *a* and *a′*, contiguous before faulting, have been separated by the faulting. The right-hand block has moved directly down the dip of the fault relative to the left-hand block. The lines *bc* and *c′d*, which were parallel before faulting, are also parallel after faulting. In Fig. 106B, the right-hand block has moved diagonally down the fault; the lines *bc* and *c′d*, parallel to each other before faulting, are also parallel after faulting.

Rotational movements are those in which some straight lines on opposite sides of the fault and outside the dislocated zone, parallel before the displacement, are no longer parallel afterwards. In Fig. 106C, the right-hand block has gone down relative to the left-hand block, but the displacement increases toward the front; at point *a* there has been no displacement, but *b* and *b'* were contiguous before faulting. Lines *ca* and *ad*, parallel before faulting, are not parallel after faulting. In Fig. 106D, the back part of the right-hand block has gone up relative to the left-hand block, but the forward part of the right-hand block has gone down. The lines *dc* and *c'e*, parallel before faulting, are no longer parallel after faulting.

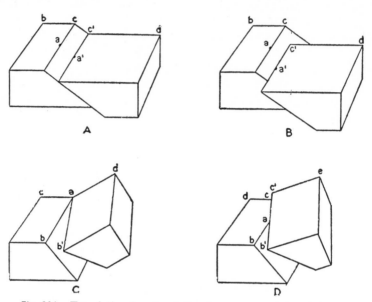

Fig. 106. Translational and rotational movements. *A* and *B*, translational movements. *C* and *D*, rotational movements. Small letters are referred to in text.

In a sense, all faults have a certain amount of rotational movement. The displacement increases or decreases along the strike of all faults, and the blocks must rotate somewhat relative to one another. But if the rotation is not too great, the movements at any one locality may be treated as if the fault were a translational one.

Relative Movements

A rather elaborate terminology has, of necessity, been devised to describe the movement along faults and the effects on disrupted strata. The terminology has been devised primarily for translational movements, but it may be used with modifications for rotational movements.[1]

[1] Throughout this book the terminology advocated by a committee of the Geological Society of America has been followed. A few additional terms proposed since the committee made its report have been incorporated in the nomenclature that follows, but the basic classification is unchanged. See Reid, H. F., *et al.*, "Report of the Committee on the Nomenclature of Faults," *Bulletin Geological Society of America*, Vol. 24, pp. 163–186, 1913.

Faults in themselves never offer any direct evidence as to which block actually moved. Thus in Fig. 106A, the right-hand block may have gone down and the left-hand block may have remained stationary, or the left-hand block may have gone up and the right-hand block may have moved down; both blocks may have gone down, but the right-hand block may have gone down more than the left-hand block, or both blocks may have gone up, but the left-hand block may have gone up more than the right-hand block. Because in most cases no direct evidence is available concerning the absolute movements, the terminology is based chiefly on relative movements.

Figure 107 illustrates some of the various kinds of relative movements that may take place along a translational fault. In diagram A the hanging wall has moved directly down the dip relative to the footwall; in diagram B the hanging wall has moved parallel to the strike; and in dia-

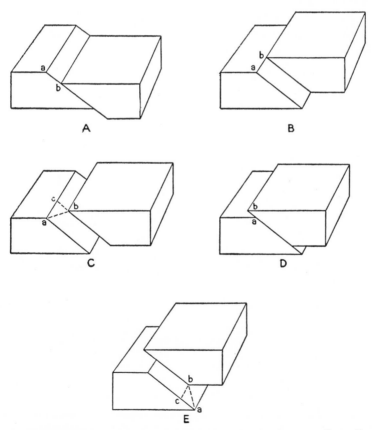

Fig. 107. Net slip, Dip slip, and Strike slip. A. ab = net slip = dip slip; strike slip is zero. B. ab = net slip = strike slip; dip slip is zero. C. ab = net slip; cb = dip slip; ac = strike slip. D. ab = net slip = dip slip; strike slip is zero. E. ab = net slip. bc = strike slip, ac = dip slip.

gram *C* the hanging wall has moved diagonally down the fault plane. In diagram *D* the hanging wall has moved directly up the dip of the fault, and in diagram *E* the hanging wall has moved diagonally up the fault plane.

The term *slip* is used to indicate the relative displacement of formerly adjacent points on opposite sides of the fault, and it is measured in the fault surface. The *net slip* (*ab* of Fig. 107) is the total displacement; it is the distance measured on the fault surface between two formerly adjacent points situated on opposite walls of the fault. It is defined in terms of the distance and the angle it makes with some line in the fault plane, such as a horizontal line or a line directly down the dip. In Fig. 107C, the net slip *ab* makes an angle of 35 degrees with a horizontal line in the fault plane; the distance depends, of course, on the scale. It is also necessary to state the relative movement; in this case the hanging wall went down relative to the footwall. It is equally correct to say that the footwall went up relative to the hanging wall. The *strike slip* is the component of net slip parallel to the strike of the fault; it is indicated by *ac* in Fig. 107C. The *dip slip* is the component of the net slip measured parallel to the dip of the fault plane; it is *bc* of Fig. 107C. In Figs. 107A

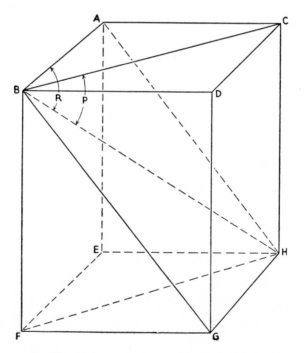

Fig. 108. Rake and plunge. The line *BH* lies in the plane *ABGH* Angle *ABH* = rake; angle *CBH* = plunge.

and 107D, the dip slip equals the net slip, and the strike slip is zero. In Fig. 107B, the strike slip equals the net slip *ab* and the dip slip is zero. In Fig. 107E, inasmuch as the movement is diagonal, there is both a dip slip component *ac* and a strike slip component *bc* to the net slip *ab*.

The *rake*[2] is the angle that a line in a plane makes with a horizontal line in that plane. Thus in Fig. 108, the plane *ABGH* dips to the right and contains the line *BH*. The angle *ABH* is the rake of *BH*. Plunge was defined on p. 46; the only vertical plane in Fig. 108 that contains *BH* is the plane *BCFH*. The angle *CBH* is the plunge. The rake, the angle *ABH*, as measured in the plane *ABGH*, is about 57 degrees; the plunge, the angle *CBH*, as measured in the plane *BCFH*, is about 45 degrees.

In Fig. 107C, the rake of the net slip is the angle *bac*; in Fig. 107E, the rake is the angle *cba*.

In Fig. 109A, the fault intersects a bed or vein, which is shown in solid black; the fault dips toward the reader. The *trace slip* is that component of the net slip parallel to the trace of the bed on the fault. In Fig. 109A, the net slip is *ab*, the strike slip is *ac*, and the dip slip is *bc*. The trace slip

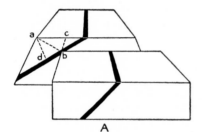
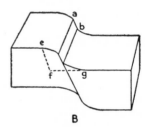

Fig. 109. Slip and shift. *A*. Fault dips toward reader; black is a stratum of rock. *ab* = net slip, *ac* = strike slip, *cb* = dip slip, *db* = trace slip, *ad* = perpendicular slip. *B*. *ab* = net slip = dip slip; strike slip is zero. *ef* = net shift = dip shift; strike shift is zero.

is *db*. The *perpendicular slip* is that component of the net slip measured perpendicularly to the trace of the bed on the fault; it is *ad* of Fig. 109A.

A vertical plane perpendicular to the strike of the fault contains the dip slip. The front of the block shown in Fig. 110 represents such a plane, and *ad* is the dip slip. The *vertical slip*, *ae*, is the vertical component of the net slip and dip slip.[3] The *horizontal slip* is the horizontal component of the net slip. The *horizontal dip slip*, *ed*, is the horizontal component of the dip slip. By some geologists *ed* is called the heave and *ae* is called the throw. As will be shown later, however, this usage is undesirable.

The slip refers to the displacements along the fault plane itself. If

[2] Often called *pitch*. Because pitch has been used in so many different ways, a committee of the U. S. Geological Survey has recently recommended that rake be used instead.

[3] Gill, J. E., "Fault Nomenclature," *Transactions of the Royal Society of Canada*, 3rd series, section IV, Vol. XXXV, pp. 71–85, 1941.

there is drag along the fault, however, the total displacement may be of more significance than the slip. The term *shift* is used to refer to the displacement on opposite sides of the fault and outside the dislocated zone. Figure 109B illustrates a fault along which there has been drag; the movement has been directly down the dip. The dip slip *ab* equals the net slip in this case. The net shift is *ef*; the dip shift is the same. The strike shift in this case is zero.

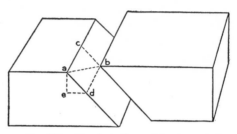

Fig. 110. Vertical slip and horizontal dip slip. *ab* = net slip; *ac* = strike slip, *cb* = *ad* = dip slip. *ae* = vertical slip, called *throw* by many geologists. *ed* = horizontal dip slip, called *heave* by many geologists.

Effects on Disrupted Strata

The above discussion has been confined to the relative movements along faults, and it has not considered the effects on the disrupted strata or veins. The apparent movement of the disrupted stratum may be very different from the net slip. This point is very important and cannot be overemphasized. The apparent movement is a function of many variables, and depends not only on the net slip, but also on the strike and dip of the fault, the strike and dip of the disrupted stratum, and the attitude of the surface on which the observations are made. It is possible for the apparent movement to be zero, although the net slip may be great.

Figures 111 to 120 show the relationship between the net slip and the apparent movement under different conditions. In Fig. 111, the beds are horizontal, and the net slip *ab* is directly down the dip. Figure 111A

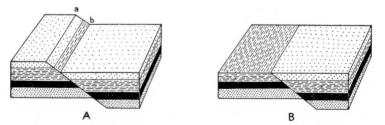

A   B

Fig. 111. Apparent movement in a vertical section equals the net slip. *A*. Before erosion; *ab* = net slip = dip slip. *B*. After erosion of top of footwall block.

illustrates relations before erosion, and Fig. 111B illustrates the relations after the left-hand block has been eroded down to the level of the right-hand block. On the map—the upper surface of Fig. 111B—different beds outcrop on opposite sides of the fault. On the front of the blocks, the apparent movement equals the net slip. A deep valley or an artificial opening, such as a quarry or mine, might produce an exposure of this sort.

In Fig. 112, the net slip *ab* is parallel to the strike of the fault. In Fig. 112B, the front of the left-hand block has been eroded back to coincide with the front of the right-hand block. Such an exposure might be found on the side of a valley or in an artificial opening. The apparent move-

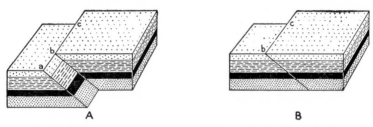

Fig. 112. Apparent movement in a vertical section is zero. *A*. *ab* = net slip = strike slip. *B*. After removal of front of footwall block.

ment in such a section is zero, although the net slip may be considerable. If the net slip were diagonally down the fault plane, a vertical section at right angles to the strike of the fault would show an apparent movement, but the value would be less than the net slip.

Figures 113 to 116 illustrate faults that strike at right angles to the strike of the bedding. In Fig. 113, the net slip *ab* is directly down the dip.

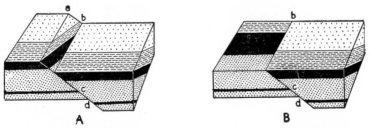

Fig. 113. Apparent movement in vertical section equals net slip. *A*. *ab* = *cd* = net slip = dip slip. *B*. After erosion of top of footwall block. A right-handed fault.

Figure 113A shows the relations before erosion; Figure 113B shows the relations after the left-hand block has been eroded down to the level of the right-hand block. On the map—the upper surface of Fig. 113B—the apparent movement is such as to suggest that the left-hand block moved back a considerable distance parallel to the strike of the fault. If the beds have a low dip, a comparatively small net slip down the dip can give a large apparent displacement on the map. The apparent movement on the front of the blocks, Fig. 113, equals the net slip.

In Fig. 114, the net slip is parallel to the strike of the fault; Figure 114A depicts the relations before erosion; Figure 114B indicates the relations after the front of the left-hand block has been eroded back to

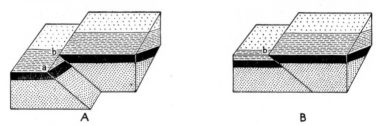

A   B

Fig. 114. Apparent movement in a vertical section gives erroneous impression that hanging wall has gone up. A. ab = net slip = strike slip. B. After removal of front of footwall block. A left-handed fault.

coincide with the front of the right-hand block. On the map the apparent movement equals the net slip. But the apparent movement on the front of the block, Fig. 114B, gives the false impression that the hanging wall has moved up.

In Fig. 115, the net slip n has been diagonally down the dip. After the surface and front of the left-hand block have been eroded to the surface and front of the right-hand block, respectively, the relations are

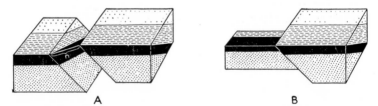

A   B

Fig. 115. Apparent movement in vertical section is less than net slip. A. n = net slip. B. After removal of top of footwall block.

those illustrated in Fig. 115B. On the map, the left-hand block has apparently moved back; in the structure section the right-hand block has apparently moved down.

Figure 116 illustrates the special case in which the net slip is parallel to the trace of the bedding on the fault plane. Fig. 116B shows the relations after erosion of the top and front of the left-hand block. There is no apparent movement either on the map or on the front of the block. In fact, the generalization may be made that wherever the net slip is parallel to the trace of the disrupted stratum on the fault plane, there is no apparent movement on the map or cross sections.[4] Figure 112 also illustrates this principle.

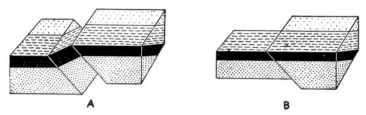

Fig. 116. Net slip parallel to trace of bedding on fault. Apparent movement in a vertical section and in map is zero. *A.* Immediately after faulting. *B.* After removal of top and front of footwall block.

Figure 117 is an example of a fault that strikes parallel to the strike of the disrupted strata. The hanging wall has gone down relative to the footwall. The apparent movement in the front of the block in Fig. 117A equals the net slip. On the map of Fig. 117B, some of the beds are repeated because of the faulting. If the net slip were parallel to the strike of such a fault, there would be no apparent movement because the net slip would be parallel to the trace of the beds on the fault. If the hanging

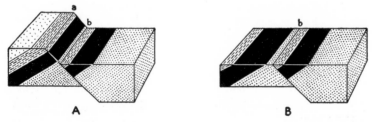

Fig. 117. Apparent movement in vertical section equals net slip. *A.* $ab =$ net slip $=$ dip slip. *B.* After removal of top of footwall block.

wall were to move diagonally down the dip, some of the beds would be repeated, but the apparent movement on a cross section at right angles to the strike of the fault would be less than the net slip.

Figure 118 illustrates a fault that strikes parallel to the strike of the strata, but the hanging wall has moved up relative to the footwall. The net slip is the same as the apparent movement on the front of the block in Fig. 118A. If the right-hand block is eroded to the level of the left-hand block, the bed shown in solid black does not crop out at the surface.

[4] Beckwith, R. H., "Trace-slip Faults," *Bulletin American Association Petroleum Geologists,* Vol. 25, pp. 2181–2193, 1941.

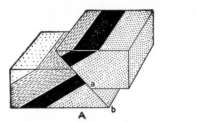
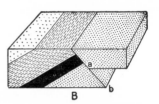

Fig. 118. Apparent movement in vertical section equals net slip. *A. ab* = net slip = dip slip. *B.* After removal of top of hanging wall block.

Figure 119 is the special case in which the fault and the strata have not only the same strike, but have also the same dip. It is obvious that, in such a case, the apparent movement on the map and in the cross section is zero, regardless of the value of the net slip.

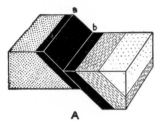
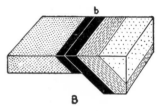

Fig. 119. Fault is parallel to bedding, and hence there is no apparent movement. *A. ab* = net slip = dip slip. *B.* After removal of top of footwall block.

Figure 120 represents the case where the fault strikes diagonally to the strata, and where the hanging wall has moved directly down the dip of the fault. After erosion, as shown in Fig. 120B, the apparent movement on the map suggests that the hanging wall has moved back relative to the footwall.

These numerous examples have been cited to emphasize that the apparent movement may be very deceiving. Moreover, it is disconcerting to realize that even if we know the dip and strike of the fault, the dip and strike of the disrupted strata, and the apparent movement, it is

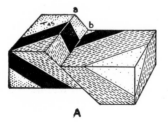
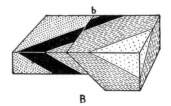

Fig. 120. Apparent movement on map does not equal the net slip. *A. ab* = net slip = dip slip. *B.* After removal of top of footwall block.

nevertheless impossible to determine the net slip. Suppose, for example, that the geologist mapped an area such as that shown on the top of the block diagram in Fig. 113B. The attitude of the bedding and of the fault are known; moreover, the apparent movement along the fault is given by the map. Actually, the net slip was directly down the dip. But the observed, apparent movement on the map could have resulted equally well from a horizontal movement parallel to the strike of the fault— that is, if the left-hand block moved backward relative to the right-hand block. Moreover, diagonal movement down the dip of the fault would have produced the same effect on the map.

Calculation of Net Slip

The amount and nature of the movement can be determined, however, if the strike and dip of the fault and the strike and dip of two or more planes with different attitudes are broken by the fault. Figure 121A is an example of two veins, $aa'a''a'''$ and $bb'b''b'''$, that have different attitudes and are displaced along a fault. This problem can be solved by

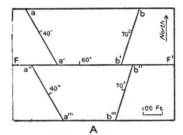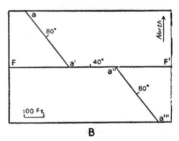

A   B

Fig. 121. Calculation of net slip. *A.* $aa'a''a'''$ and $bb'b''b'''$ are two veins displaced along the fault FF'. With these data the net slip can be calculated. *B.* $aa'a''a'''$ is a vein displaced along the fault FF'. The net slip cannot be calculated unless some additional data are available.

graphical methods; the rake of the net slip is 85 degrees toward the northeast, and the hanging wall (north block) has moved up relative to the footwall; the value of the net slip is 175 feet. The disrupted bands may be dikes, veins, bedding planes, or older faults. (See also pages 469 to 477.)

Even if data are available for only one disrupted band, the problem can be solved if the direction of movement is known. The striations on a slickensided surface (p. 149) may show the direction of movement, but this method is dangerous, for as is stated on p. 149, slickensides may record only the last movements along the fault plane. Figure 121B shows how this method may be used. In addition to the data indicated on the map, it is known that the striations rake 45 degrees toward the northeast. The net slip may be calculated by graphical methods to be 260 feet.

Separation

Separation indicates the distance between two parts of the disrupted horizon measured in any indicated direction. The *horizontal separation* is the separation measured in any horizontal direction. Figure 122A is a map of a fault and a disrupted horizon. The line *we* is the horizontal separation in an east-west direction. The line *ns* is the horizontal separation in a north-south direction. The strike separation, *hi*, is the horizontal separation parallel to the strike of the fault.[5] The strike separa-

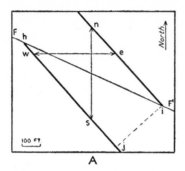 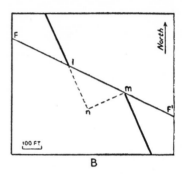

A   B

Fig. 122. Separation as shown on geological map. Heavy black band is disrupted bed. *FF′* = fault trace. *A. ns* = north-south horizontal separation; *we* = east-west horizontal separation; *hi* = strike separation; *ji* = offset; *hj* = overlap. *B.* Geological map. *lm* = strike separation; *mn* = offset; *ln* = gap.

tion in Fig. 122A may be described as *right-handed* or *right-lateral* because an observer following the bed along the strike must turn to the right to find the same bed across the fault. Similarly, the strike separation in Figure 122B is *left-handed* or *left-lateral*. The *offset* or *normal separation* is measured perpendicular to the disrupted horizon; *ji* in Fig. 122A is the offset. The overlap is *hj*. In Fig. 122B *mn* is the offset and *ln* is the *gap*.

The *vertical separation* is the separation measured along a vertical line. In Fig. 123B, which is a vertical section perpendicular to the strike of the fault, *eg* is the vertical separation. The *dip separation* is the separation measured directly down the dip of the fault.[6] In Fig. 123B, *ej* is the dip separation.

Faults bring beds into contact that are normally separated by intervening strata with a definite thickness. The thickness of these intervening beds is the *stratigraphic separation* or *stratigraphic throw* along the fault. Figure 124 shows how the stratigraphic separation may be determined. Along the fault, bed *m* in the right-hand block is brought into

[5] Hill, M L., "Classification of Faults," *Bulletin American Association of Petroleum Geologists*, Vol. 31, pp. 1669–1673, 1947.
[6] Hill, M. L., *op. cit.*

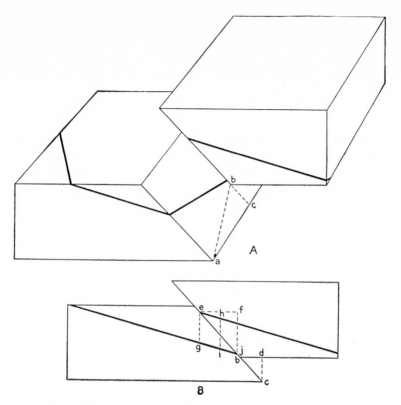

Fig. 123. Separation. Heavy black band is disrupted bed. *A.* Block diagram; $ab =$ net slip; $bc =$ dip slip; $ac =$ strike slip. *B.* Vertical cross section perpendicular to strike of fault. $eg = hi =$ vertical separation; eb $=$ apparent movement $=$ dip separation; $fj =$ throw; $ef =$ heave.

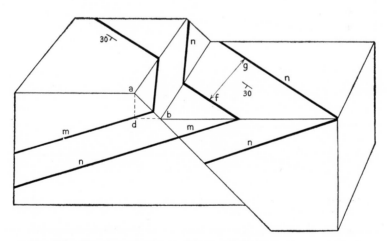

Fig. 124. Stratigraphic throw. Heavy black lines are two disrupted beds, *m* and *n*. $ab =$ net slip $=$ dip slip; ad and db are the vertical and horizontal slips. $gf =$ breadth of outcrop between beds *m* and *n*. Stratigraphic throw can be calculated as shown in text.

contact with bed *n* in the left-hand block. From the top of the right-hand block it is possible to calculate the thickness of the beds between *m* and *n,* according to the equation

$$t = gf \times sin \; \delta$$

In this equation t = thickness of beds between *m* and *n*; gf = breadth of outcrop between *m* and *n* measured perpendicularly to the strike of the strata; and δ = angle of dip of beds. The stratigraphic separation is one of the most important measurements of all, because in sedimentary rocks it can be determined with precision if the stratigraphy is known.

Throw and Heave

The *throw* and *heave* are measured in a vertical section that is perpendicular to the strike of the fault. The throw is the vertical component of the dip separation in such a section; heave is the horizontal component of the dip separation.

Figures 125 and 126 illustrate these terms. Figure 125 is an example in which the fault strikes parallel to the strata, and in which the movement has been directly down the dip. Figure 125A is a block diagram, and Fig. 125B, a cross section at right angles to the fault, is the same

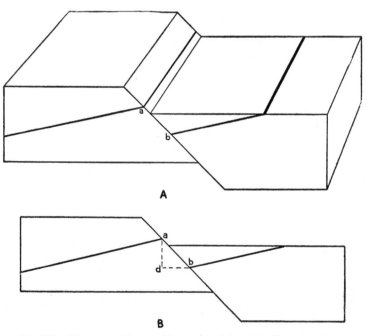

A

B

Fig. 125.   Throw and heave. Heavy black band is disrupted stratum. *A.* Block diagram; ab = net slip = dip slip. *B.* Vertical cross section perpendicular to strike of fault. Same as front of block diagram above. ab = net slip = dip slip, ad = throw, db = heave.

as the front of the block diagram. The throw (*ad*) is the vertical component of the dip separation (*ab*). The heave, *db*, is the horizontal component of the dip separation. In this particular case, they are respectively the same as the vertical slip and horizontal dip slip. However, this is not always true. Figure 126 shows a fault that is diagonal to the strike of the disrupted stratum. Figure 126A is a block diagram, and

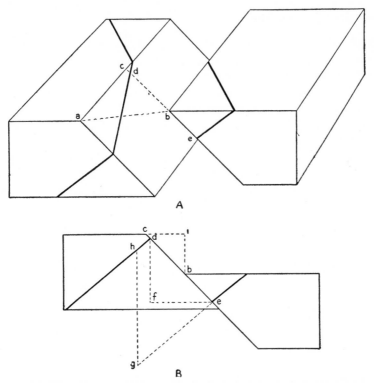

Fig. 126. Throw and heave. Heavy black band is disrupted stratum. *A*. Block diagram; *ab* = net slip, *ac* = strike slip, *cb* = dip slip. *B*. Vertical cross section perpendicular to the strike of the fault; along same plane as front of hanging wall block of block diagram. *cb* = dip slip; *ib* = vertical slip, *throw* to some geologists; *ci* = horizontal dip slip, *heave* to some geologists; *de* = apparent movement = dip separation; *df* = throw; *fe* = heave; *hg* = vertical separation.

Fig. 126B is a vertical section perpendicular to the strike of the fault; the throw is *df*, and the heave is *fe*. The vertical slip is *ib*, and the horizontal dip slip is *ci*. They are obviously different from the throw and heave.

It is clear that throw and heave refer to the effects on the disrupted band. If two bands with different attitudes, such as two dikes, are broken by a fault, each has a different value for the throw and heave. Many geologists feel that the terms should refer only to the movement along the fault and that they should be independent of the effect on the disrupted bands. These geologists use throw for the vertical slip (ib of Fig. 126B) and they use heave for the horizontal dip slip (ci of Fig. 126B).

CLASSIFICATIONS

Geometrical Classifications

Bases of classifications. Faults, like joints, may be classified on the basis of their geometry or their genesis. Because no interpretation is involved, geometrical classifications are obviously less hazardous than genetic classifications. It is partly for this reason that the geometrical classifications will be considered first.

The bases of five different geometrical classifications are: (1) the rake of the net slip; (2) the attitude of the fault relative to the attitude of the adjacent rocks; (3) the pattern of the faults; (4) the angle at which the faults dip; and (5) the apparent movement on the fault.

Classification based on rake of net slip. A *strike-slip fault* is one in which the net slip is parallel to the strike of the fault (Fig. 114A); that is, the strike equals the net slip and there is no dip-slip component. The rake of the net slip is therefore zero.

A *dip-slip fault* is one in which the net slip is up or down the dip of the fault (Fig. 113A); that is, the dip slip equals the net slip and there is no strike-slip component. The rake of the net slip is therefore 90 degrees.

A *diagonal-slip fault* is one in which the net slip is diagonally up or down the fault plane (Fig. 115A). There is both a strike-slip and dip-slip component; the rake of the net slip is greater than zero but less than 90 degrees.

Classification based on attitude of fault relative to attitude of adjacent beds. The second of these geometrical classifications, which is based on the attitude of the faults relative to the attitude of the adjacent rocks, would be highly involved if all the variables were considered. In general, therefore, the terms refer merely to the relations as observed in plan— that is, on a geological map. A *strike fault* is one that strikes essentially parallel to the strike of the adjacent rocks. Figures 117 and 118 are examples of strike faults. The strike of the adjacent rocks is ordinarily measured on the bedding, but if the bedding is absent, the strike may be measured on the schistosity of metamorphic rocks or on the flow structure of igneous rocks.

A *bedding fault*[7] is a variety of strike fault that is parallel to the

[7] Behre, C. H., "Bedding Plane Faults and Their Economic Importance," *American Institute Mining and Metallurgical Engineers, Technical Publication 767*, pp. 9–13, 1937.

bedding; Figure 119 is an example of a bedding fault. A *dip fault* strikes essentially parallel to the direction of dip of the adjacent beds; that is, its strike is perpendicular to the strike of the adjacent beds. Figure 114, 115, and 116 are examples of dip faults. An *oblique* or *diagonal fault* is one that strikes obliquely or diagonally to the strike of the adjacent rocks; Figure 120 is an example of a diagonal fault.

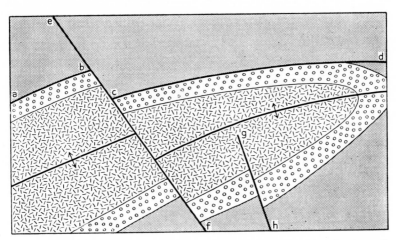

Fig. 127. Longitudinal and transverse faults. Anticline plunging toward the east (right) is broken by faults. *abcd* = longitudinal fault; *ebcf* and *gh* are transverse faults.

A *longitudinal fault* strikes parallel to the strike of the regional structure; *abcd* of Fig. 127 is an example of a longitudinal fault. Along most of its course it is a strike fault, but locally the adjacent rocks may strike at a high angle to the fault. A *transverse fault* strikes perpendicularly or diagonally to the strike of the regional structure; *ef* and *gh* of Fig. 127 are examples of transverse faults. Along most of its course a transverse fault is a dip or diagonal fault, but locally the adjacent rocks may strike parallel to the fault.

Classification based on fault pattern. A third geometrical classification is based on the pattern shown by the faults; ordinarily the classification is based on the pattern on a map, but it may be based on the pattern in a cross section. The attitude of the adjacent rocks is unimportant. In some localities, the faults have essentially the same dip and strike; they thus belong to a set of *parallel faults* (Fig. 128A). If the strikes are the same but the dips differ, the faults are assigned to two or more sets of parallel faults. *En échelon faults* are relatively short faults that overlap each other (Fig. 128B). *Peripheral faults* are circular or arcuate faults that bound a circular area or part of a circular area (Fig. 128C). *Radial faults* belong to a system of faults that radiate out from a point (Fig. 128D).

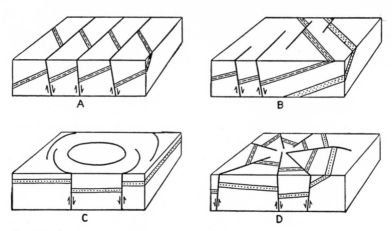

Fig. 128. Geometrical classification of faults by pattern. *A.* Parallel faults. *B. En échelon* faults. *C.* Peripheral faults. *D.* Radial faults.

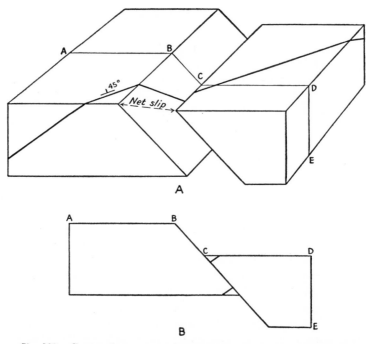

Fig. 129. Contrasting true and apparent movement on a fault. *A.* Block diagram. Heavy black band is disrupted bed. *B.* Vertical cross section along *ABCDE* of the block diagram. Although the hanging wall has gone down relative to footwall, the disrupted horizon suggests the opposite.

In some areas, the strike and dip of the faults may differ so markedly that the arrangement appears to be quite haphazard. In many such cases, however, the faults may be grouped into several sets.

Classification based on value of dip of fault. The fourth geometrical classification is based on the angle of dip of the fault. *High angle faults* are those that dip greater than 45 degrees; *low angle faults* are those that dip less than 45 degrees.

Classification based upon apparent movement. A fifth geometrical classification is based upon the apparent movement in vertical sections at right angles to the fault. A *normal fault* is one in which the hanging wall has apparently gone down relative to the footwall. A *reverse fault* is one in which the hanging wall has apparently gone up relative to the footwall. Normal faults are illustrated by Figs. 111, 113, 115, and 117. Reverse faults are illustrated by Figs. 114 and 118. It should be noted that the apparent movement is not necessarily the same as the true movement. In Fig. 114 the movement along the fault was parallel to the strike of the fault. In Fig. 129 the hanging wall actually moved down, but in the vertical section at right angles to the strike of the fault (Fig. 129B), the hanging wall appears to have moved up.

Summary. It is obviously hopeless to attempt to establish a single set of terms that will take into consideration all the factors enumerated above. A far better system is to describe faults by using several terms from the various classifications given above. Thus the faults in one locality may be described as high angle, *en échelon,* dip faults. In another locality the faults may be low angle, parallel, longitudinal faults.

Genetic Classifications

Ideal classification. The most satisfactory classifications in natural science are those based on genesis. An ideal genetic classification of faults would be based primarily on the nature of the forces involved. Such a classification should consider not only whether the forces were compressional, tensional, shearing, or torsional, but it should consider also the direction in which these forces were acting. In the present state of our knowledge, however, such a classification is impossible.

Classification based on relative movements. The most satisfactory genetic classification that can be established at present is based on the nature of the relative movement along the fault.

A *thrust fault* or *thrust* is a fault along which the hanging wall has moved up relative to the footwall. Thrust faults indicate shortening of the crust of the earth.

A *gravity fault* is a fault along which the hanging wall has moved down relative to the footwall. They indicate lengthening of the crust of the earth.

Strike-slip faults are those along which the displacement has been essentially parallel to the strike of the fault—that is, the dip-slip component is small compared to the strike-slip component. The term *wrench fault* has also been used for faults of this type, especially if the dip is nearly vertical and the strike is transverse to the regional structure.[8] A *sinistral* or *left-handed strike-slip fault* is shown in Fig. 130. If the observer looks along the strike of the fault, the relative movement has been such that the block on his left has moved toward him, whereas the block on his right has moved away from him. If an observer looks along the strike of a *dextral* or *right-handed strike-slip fault*, Fig. 130, the movement is such that the block on his left has moved away from him, whereas the block on his right has moved toward him. Usually a sinistral

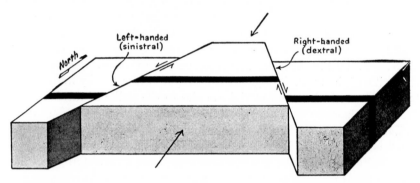

Fig. 130. Strike-slip faults. Formed by north-south compression with easiest relief in east-west direction. The fault striking N. 30° W. shows right-handed separation; the fault striking N. 30° E. shows left-handed separation.

fault will have a left-lateral separation and a dextral fault will have a right-lateral separation. In fact, the names sinistral and dextral were chosen because of the separations. However, a clear distinction should be made between separation and the net slip. In Fig. 121A the bed $aa'a''a'''$ shows a right-lateral separation, but bed $bb'b''b'''$ shows a left-lateral separation. It would obviously be meaningless to describe the fault as a left-lateral or right-lateral fault. As shown on page 135, the net slip in this case is essentially parallel to the dip of the fault; the hanging wall has moved up relative to the footwall. Fig. 116 is a sinistral strike-slip fault (with a slight dip-slip component), but there is no strike separation —that is, no offset of the beds along the fault. The terms left-lateral and right-lateral should be used only to describe the separation, whereas sinistral and dextral should be used to describe the relative direction of the strike slip.

Because the relative movement along the fault plane is not necessarily parallel to either the strike or the dip, but may be diagonal, the termi-

[8] Anderson, E. M., *The Dynamics of Faulting and Dyke Formation, with Application to Britain,* 2nd ed. Edinburgh: Oliver and Boyd, 1951.

nology should make allowance for these possibilities. The most satisfactory solution is to divide the fault plane into four quadrants by two
lines making an angle of 45 degrees with a horizontal line on the fault
plane. This has been done in Fig. 131, which represents the footwall of
the fault. If the relative movement of the hanging wall is such that the
net slip is toward the upper quadrant, the fault is a thrust fault; if the
net slip is toward the lower quadrant, the fault is a gravity fault; if
the net slip is toward the right or left quadrants, the fault is a strike-slip
fault. If the net slip is not directly down the dip or parallel to the strike,
a modifying clause should be added to the appropriate term. Thus if the

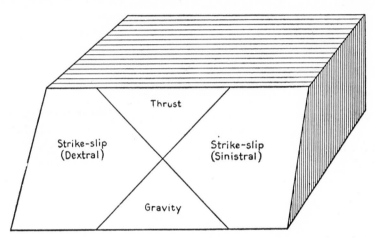

Fig. 131. Genetic classification of faults. Fault dips toward reader,
and hence the block represents the footwall. If hanging wall moves into
top sector, the fault is a thrust; if hanging wall moves into lower sector,
the fault is a gravity fault; if hanging wall moves into either the right
or left sectors, the fault is a strike slip fault.

net slip is in the upper quadrant but makes an angle of 60 degrees with a
horizontal line in the fault plane, the fault can be called a thrust fault with
a large component parallel to the strike of the fault.

Classification based on absolute movements. The classification outlined above is based on relative movements. A more elaborate classification would be based on absolute movements relative to some datum
plane, such as sea level. Thus five kinds of gravity faults might be recognized: (1) those in which the footwall did not move, but in which the
hanging wall moved down; (2) those in which the footwall moved up,
while the hanging wall remained stationary; (3) those in which the hanging wall moved down and the footwall moved up; (4) those in which both
blocks moved down, but in which the hanging wall moved a greater
amount; and (5) those in which both blocks moved up, but in which the
hanging wall moved less than the footwall.

Similarly, five kinds of thrust faults might be established.

In most instances, however, data are not available to indicate the absolute movement on faults. Many attempts have been made to establish criteria based on the pattern of the faults, the dip of the fault plane, or the comparative intensity of the deformation in the two blocks. Knowledge of that phase of mechanics known as *statics* indicates that such criteria are unreliable.

In a few instances, where movements along faults near the ocean have occurred within historic times, it is possible to ascertain which block moved. Moreover, from a consideration of crustal forces, it is sometimes possible to theorize about the absolute movements along faults. Under certain conditions, therefore, terms based on absolute movements may be of value. *Upthrusts* are high angle faults along which the relatively uplifted block has been the active element. If the hanging wall of a high angle thrust fault has moved up while the footwall stayed in place, or if the footwall of a high angle gravity fault has moved up while the hanging wall stayed in place, the fault is an upthrust.

Sometimes the term *underthrust* is used for those thrust faults in which the footwall has been the active element, whereas *overthrust* is used for those thrust faults in which the hanging wall has been the active element.

CHAPTER 9

Criteria for Recognition of Faults

INTRODUCTION

Faults may be recognized in various ways. If a fault is exposed in a cliff, a road cut, or a mine working, it may be readily observed, and precise data may be obtained concerning its attitude and the separation of the disrupted strata. In other instances the observations may not be so direct, but careful field work may bring to light data which permit a complete analysis of the fault. In still other cases some information about the fault may be obtained, but a complete analysis may be impossible.

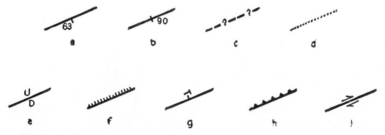

Fig. 132. Map symbols for faults. *a.* Fault showing strike and dip. *b.* Strike of vertical fault. *c.* Doubtful or probable fault. *d.* Concealed fault, i.e., overlain by younger deposits not affected by fault. *e.* Gravity fault, *U* on upthrown block, *D* on downthrown block. *f.* Another symbol for gravity fault, hachures on downthrown side. *g.* Thrust, *T* on upthrown block. *h.* Another symbol for thrust, saw-teeth on upthrown block. *i.* Relative movement on fault; can be used on maps or cross sections; if a map, indicates a strike-slip fault. (Modified from map symbols of U. S. Geological Survey.)

Finally, there may be instances where the data are so incomplete that it is impossible to decide whether a fault is present or not. On some maps separate symbols are used to differentiate observed faults, inferred faults, and possible faults from each other (Fig. 132).

The criteria for the recognition of faults may be considered under the following headings: (1) discontinuity of structures; (2) repetition or omission of strata; (3) features characteristic of fault planes; (4) silicification and mineralization; (5) sudden changes in sedimentary facies; and (6) physiographic data. LeRoy, *et al.,*[1] list additional criteria that are useful in subsurface geology.

Some of the features characteristic of faults are also typical of unconformities, and in some places it is difficult to determine whether a fault or an unconformity is present. Methods of distinguishing between the two cannot be considered intelligently, however, until unconformities have been discussed. Criteria for distinguishing between faults and unconformities will be discussed in Chapter 15.

DISCONTINUITY OF STRUCTURES

If strata suddenly end against different beds, a fault may be present. On a map, cliff, or artificial exposure, the discontinuity occurs along a line, but this is merely the trace of a surface of discontinuity. In some instances the disrupted strata may be found in the same outcrops or in nearby exposures, but usually this is not so. The discontinuity of strata along faults is illustrated in Figs. 111, 113–115, and 117–118. Dikes, veins, or older faults also may end suddenly along some line, and the displaced parts may appear elsewhere. In such cases, however, the observer must realize that dikes, veins, or faults may form with a discontinuous pattern. Moreover, discontinuity of structures is, in itself, not proof of faulting; the truncation of structures is also typical of unconformities (p. 242), intrusive contacts (p. 290), and, on a small scale, cross-bedding.

In summary, discontinuity of structures is characteristic of faults, but it is a proof of faulting only if other possible interpretations have been eliminated.

REPETITION AND OMISSION OF STRATA

Figure 133 is a geological map of a region of folded and faulted sedimentary rocks. A syncline lies near the center of the map, as is

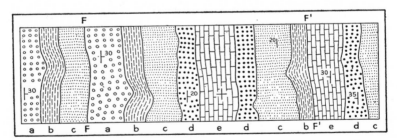

Fig. 133. Faults indicated by repetition and omission of strata. Strata, from oldest to youngest, are *a, b, c, d,* and *e. FF* and *F'F'* are faults. Dip-strike symbols indicate attitude of bedding.

[1] LeRoy, *et al., Subsurface Geologic Methods,* 2nd ed. Golden, Colorado: Colorado School of Mines, 1156 pages, 1950.

shown by the dips, and the formations are progressively younger from *a* to *e*. In certain places, however, one or more formations are missing, as, for example, along the line *FF*, where formation *b* is absent, and along the line *F'F'*, where *c* and *d* are missing. The lines *FF* and *F'F'* must be the traces of faults, but no data are given to indicate the direction and value of the dip of the faults.

The omission of strata, however, may be due to an unconformity (Chap. 15).

FEATURES CHARACTERISTIC OF FAULT PLANES

Many faults are accompanied by such distinctive features as slicken-sides, grooving, gouge, breccia, and mylonite; these features are conclu-sive proof of faulting, but some of them may be confused with phe-nomena of a different origin.

Slickensides are polished and striated surfaces that result from friction along the fault plane. The scratches or striations are parallel to the direction of movement, but caution is necessary in employing such information because some faults show many slickensided layers, in each of which the striations have different trends. Moreover, a slickensided layer may record only the last movements along the fault, and the earlier displacements may have been in some other direction.

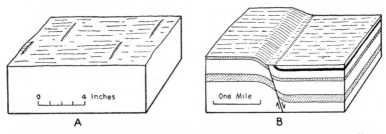

Fig. 134. Features associated with faults. *A.* Slickensides with small as-sociated steps; lines parallel to front of block are scratches; at right angles to them are small "steps." *B.* Drag along a fault. Stippling and solid black represent special beds.

Many slickensided surfaces are accompanied by sharp, low steps that trend at right angles to the striations (Fig. 134A). These sharp little rises are commonly only a fraction of an inch high and may be so small that they are difficult or even impossible to see. These rough surfaces can be used to determine the relative movement along the fault plane, in much the same way that *roches moutonnées* indicate the direction in which glacial ice was moving. In Fig. 134A, the upper block, which is not shown, moved from left to right relative to the lower block, on which the slicken-sides are shown. Even if the small irregularities are not visible, however, a person with sensitive fingers may be able to tell the direction of movement. The surface feels smooth if the fingers slide in the direction that the missing block was displaced, whereas in the reverse direction the fault feels rough.

Some faults show large grooves or furrows several feet from crest to crest and several inches deep; they are parallel to the direction of displacement.

Drag is in some cases an aid in divulging the relative motion along the fault, as is shown in Fig. 134B. Because of friction the beds in the hanging wall are dragged up in this particular case, whereas the beds in the footwall are dragged down. This method is subject to the same limitation as are slickensides because the observed drag may be due to the last movements along the fault and may even be the opposite of the major movement.

Some of the rock along a fault may be pulverized to a fine-grained *gouge*, which looks and feels like clay. In fact, gouge differs in no important way from clays of glacial origin because both are pulverized rock.

Breccia consists of angular to subangular fragments of various sizes, characteristically associated with a more finely crushed matrix. The fragments typically range from an inch to several feet in diameter, but much larger blocks may occur. Fault breccias may be many tens of feet thick.

Large blocks may be caught along faults. Such blocks are separated from the foot and hanging walls by faults that may or may not be accompanied by breccia. Such large blocks are called *horses* or *slices*. The term *horse* usually refers to such a block caught along a gravity fault (p. 143), and *slice* refers to a block caught along a thrust fault (p. 143). This distinction is of no great importance, and merely reflects the fact that the terms were first used in two different countries.

In the Death Valley region of California a remarkably coarse breccia is associated with thrust faults. This coarse breccia has been mapped as the Amargosa *chaos*. The characteristic features are as follows:[2]

"(1) The arrangement of the blocks is confused and disordered-chaotic. (2) The blocks, though mostly too small to map, are vastly larger than those in anything that could be called a breccia; most of them are more than 200 feet in length, some are as much as a quarter of a mile, and a few are more than half a mile in length. (3) They are tightly packed together, not separated by much finer-grained material. (4) Each block is bounded by surfaces of movement—in other words, each is a fault block. (5) Each block is minutely fractured throughout, yet the original

[2] Noble, L. F., "Structural Features of the Virgin Spring Area, Death Valley, California," *Bulletin Geological Society of America*, Vol. 52, pp. 941-1000, 1941.

bedding in each block of sedimentary rock is clearly discernible and is sharply truncated at the boundary of the block. Commonly the bedding, even of incompetent beds, is not greatly distorted."

A *mylonite* is a microbreccia that maintained its coherence during the deformation.[3] It is characteristically dark and fine-grained and may be difficult to distinguish from sedimentary or volcanic rocks. The brecciated character is generally apparent only from microscopic study. Although usage varies, the term *mylonite* should be restricted to those microbreccias with a streaked or platy structure; they may look like slate. Uncrushed fragments of the parent rock can be recognized under the microscope. An *ultramylonite* forms if the crushing is so complete that no such fragments remain. An ultramylonite may be difficult to recognize unless transitions to mylonite and the parent rock are preserved. *Flinty crush-rock* and *pseudo-tachylite* are massive microbreccias that lack the platy structure. Flinty crush-rock looks like chert. Pseudo-tachylite looks like tachylite, which is a variety of basaltic glass. Flinty crush-rock and pseudo-tachylite that are exceedingly fine-grained—the individual grains are 0.001 millimeter in diameter—may fill irregular fractures near the fault and may simulate dikes of igneous rocks. Although some geologists believe that these rocks were actually molten at one time, there is no unanimity of opinion on this matter.

Although slickensides, gouge, breccia, mylonite, and related phenomena are found along many faults, they are not necessarily present. It is often assumed that the larger the fault, the greater the amount of breccia, gouge, and mylonite. This is by no means true. In general, gouge and breccia form near the surface of the earth, where the confining pressures are comparatively small, and mylonite forms at greater depth, where the confining pressure forces the rocks to retain their coherence. Parts of some of the great overthrusts in the Alps are so devoid of slickensides, gouge, breccia, and mylonite that they passed unnoticed and were for a time mapped as sedimentary contacts. It was only after paleontological evidence was obtained and after areal mapping was extended that the existence of the great faults was recognized.

SILICIFICATION AND MINERALIZATION

Faults, because they are extensive fractures or branches of large fractures, are often the avenues for moving solutions. The solutions may replace the country rock with fine-grained quartz, causing *silicification*. This phenomenon in itself is not proof of faulting, but in some localities

---

[3] Waters, A. C., and C. D. Campbell, "Mylonites from the San Andreas Fault Zone," *American Journal of Science,* Vol. 29, pp. 473–503, 1935.

it may be highly suggestive. *Mineralization* along faults is typical of many mining districts.[4]

DIFFERENCES IN SEDIMENTARY FACIES

A fault with a large horizontal displacement, such as an overthrust (p. 184), is suggested if contiguous strata of exactly the same age show very different *sedimentary facies*.[4a] Figure 135 illustrates a basin of deposition in which sandstones are deposited near shore, shales farther out, and limestones farthest from shore. The transition from sandstone to shale, and from shale to limestone, will be gradual and there will be considerable interfingering of beds. The rocks of this particular age are

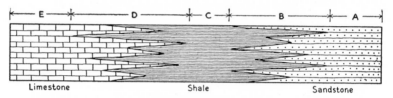

Fig. 135. Changes in sedimentary facies across a basin of deposition. $A =$ Sandstone facies, $B =$ sandstone-shale facies, $C =$ shale facies, $D =$ shale-limestone facies, $E =$ limestone facies.

said to be represented by a sandstone facies in region A, a sandstone-shale facies in region B, a shale facies in region C, a shale-limestone facies in region D, and a limestone facies in region E. Even if the strata are strongly folded and exposed by erosion, the various facies will grade into each other. On the other hand, a large overthrust (Chap. 11) may bring the sandstone facies of region A into contact with the limestone facies of region E. Conversely, if contemporaneous strata are represented in the same area by radically different sedimentary facies, a fault of large displacement is suggested. It is not possible to deduce the amount of the displacement because at present we do not know precisely the distances involved in the change from one facies to another. The Alps are a classic area for the juxtaposition of different facies due to overthrusting Similar relations are found in Nevada.[5]

[4] Newhouse, W. H., *et al., Ore Deposits as Related to Structural Features.* Princeton: Princeton University Press, 1942; especially pp. 126–137, 147–243.
    Wilson, M. E., *et al., Structural Geology of Canadian Ore Deposits.* Montreal: Canadian Institute of Mining and Metallurgy, 948 pages, 1948.
[4a] Longwell, C. R., *et al.,* "Sedimentary Facies in Geologic History," *Geological Society of America, Memoir 39,* 1949.
[5] Ferguson, H. G., R. J. Roberts, and S. W. Muller, "Golconda Quadrangle, Nevada: Geologic Quadrangle Maps of the United States," *U. S. Geological Survey,* 1952.

PHYSIOGRAPHIC CRITERIA

The more direct geological evidences of faulting may be unobtainable, particularly if the downthrown block is completely buried by alluvium. But some of the topographic features may indicate the presence of a fault. The physiographic criteria include offset ridges, scarps,[6] scarplets, triangular facets, truncation of structure by a mountain front, modified drainage patterns, and springs.

Resistant sedimentary formations are generally expressed topographically by ridges (Fig. 74). A dip fault or diagonal fault will displace the strata, as in Fig. 113B, and, consequently, the ridge held up by some resistant bed will be discontinuous, and an *offset ridge* will result.

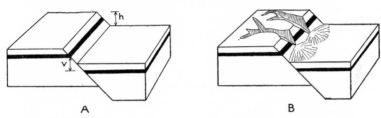

Fig. 136. Fault scarp. *A*. Before erosion; *h*, height of scarp, equals *v*, the vertical slip. *B*. After some erosion the material removed from deep valleys on the footwall block has been deposited as alluvial fans on hanging wall block.

A *scarp* is a relatively steep, straight slope of any height (Fig. 136). A scarp may be ten feet high or thousands of feet high (Plates I and XIV). Although the slope of a scarp is steep compared to that of the surrounding region, it may be only ten or twenty degrees; slopes steeper than 45 degrees are not common. As erosion wears a scarp back, the scarp may lose its straightness and become irregular, but there is no precise way of defining when it ceases to be called a scarp.

A scarp is not, of course, proof of the presence of a fault because scarps may develop quite independently of faulting. The steeper slope of a cuesta, formed by subaerial erosion, may be relatively straight and be a typical scarp. Marine erosion may form a wave-cut cliff, which may also have all the attributes of a scarp. Erosion may be locally controlled by a joint or by a series of joints, and a low scarp may develop. All too frequently a fault is assumed because of the presence of a scarp, but additional evidence is necessary to establish a fault. The essential point is that scarps, although compatible with faulting, are not proof of faulting.

[6] Cotton, C. A., "Tectonic Scarps and Fault Valleys," *Bulletin Geological Society of America*, Vol. 61, pp. 717-758, 1950.

PLATE XIV. *Fault Scarp. Bounding Kilauea caldera, Hawaii. Halemaumau lava pit in middle distance.* (Photo by Matson Lines.)

Scarps associated with faults are of three types: fault scarps, fault-line scarps, and composite fault scarps.

A *fault scarp* owes its relief directly to the movement along the fault, even though erosion may have greatly scarred the initial topography. The faults shown in Figs. 136–143 are gravity faults. However, many fault scarps are associated with thrust faults, especially high-angle thrusts (Fig. 155). Figure 136A illustrates a very fresh fault scarp. A surface of low relief has been broken by a gravity fault, and the height of the scarp (h) is equal to the vertical slip (v). If the rocks eroded from the upthrown block are deposited as alluvium on the downthrown block (Fig. 136B), the height of the scarp will gradually decrease. But in many places, such as New Zealand, streams that drain to the sea may remove whatever debris is carried to the down-faulted block. Erosion may even attack the downthrown block if it stands above base level.[7] As long as the slope retains any resemblance to straightness, it is classed as a scarp.

A *fault-line scarp* is a scarp that owes its relief to differential erosion along a fault-line. Figure 137 illustrates some of the ways in which fault-line scarps may form. In Fig. 137A, the initial relief due to faulting has been destroyed by erosion. The region is then bodily uplifted and a new baselevel of erosion established at *abc*. The soft rocks, shown by parallel lines, are rapidly reduced to the new baselevel, but the resistant sandstone, shown by dots, protects the left-hand block. The resulting scarp (Fig. 137B) is a *resequent fault-line scarp*.

Under certain conditions the downthrown block may be topographically higher than the upthrown block. After the stage illustrated in Fig. 137B, the whole area may be reduced to the baselevel *abc*, and the resistant bed is worn off the upthrown block. Because of still later uplift of the whole region, a new baselevel is established at *def*. In the ensuing erosion the resistant bed protects the downthrown block, and an *obsequent fault-line scarp* forms (Fig. 137C). In the example cited, more than one cycle of erosion has been assumed, but it is possible to develop an obsequent fault-line scarp from a fault scarp in a single cycle.

A *composite fault scarp* is one that owes its height partly to differential erosion and partly to actual movement on the fault. Figure 137B is an example of a fault-line scarp. If there were renewed movement on the fault—the right-hand block dropping still lower—the height of the scarp would be increased. Part of the height of such a scarp would be due to erosion along a fault-line, whereas the remaining part of the height would be due to movement on the fault. The scarp is therefore composite in character.

It is frequently difficult to distinguish fault scarps, fault-line scarps,

---

[7] Cotton, C. A., *op. cit.*

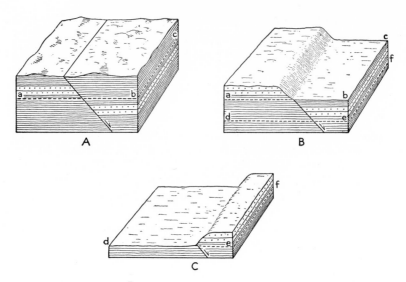

Fig. 137. Fault-line and fault-line scarp. *A.* Fault-line without scarp. Dotted formation is resistant to erosion; formations shown by parallel lines are not resistant to erosion; *abc* new baselevel of erosion. *B.* Resequent fault-line scarp. Easily eroded rocks on hanging wall block have been reduced to new baselevel; rocks resistant to erosion on footwall have been only partially eroded; the plane *def* represents a new baselevel of erosion. *C.* Obsequent fault-line scarp developed on the downdropped (relatively) block.

and composite fault scarps from each other. Criteria for doing so are discussed on pp. 160–163.

Scarplets, also known as *piedmont scarps,* are indicative of active faults. Scarplets lie at or near the foot of mountains, and they trend essentially parallel to the base of the range. The height is commonly measured in tens of feet, and scarplets over 100 feet high are rare. They are usually confined to unconsolidated deposits such as alluvial fans, glacial moraines, and lake terraces, but bedrock is exposed on some of them. It is evident that such scarps must be very young geologically because they would not have been long preserved in unconsolidated materials.

Some scarplets that cut unconsolidated deposits represent the emergence, at the surface of the earth, of a fault that cuts bedrock (Fig. 138A). This is necessarily true wherever bedrock is exposed on the face of the scarp. In the Owens Valley, California, some of the scarplets produced in the earthquake of 1872 may be traced along their strike from alluvium into bedrock without any change in the height of the scarp.[8] If the scarp cannot be observed to cross bedrock in any part of its course, the term *fan scarp* may be used

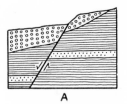 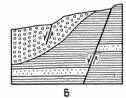 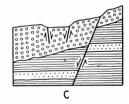

Fig. 138. Scarplets or piedmont scarps. Dotted and lined patterns represent bedrock. Open circles represent unconsolidated material. *A*. Scarplet that is direct continuation of a fault in the bedrock. *B*. Right-hand scarplet is direct continuation of fault in the bedrock, but left-hand scarplet is not. *C*. Graben bounded by faults that do not extend into bedrock.

In other instances the piedmont scarp may be only indirectly related to the master fault (Fig. 138B). Tension may develop in the alluvium because it tends to slide down hill when movements take place on the master fault. The passage of earthquake waves may develop brief, but significant, tensional forces. Some piedmont scarps face toward the mountain front (Fig. 138C); if there is also an outward-facing scarp nearer the mountains, the down-dropped block of alluvium constitutes a graben (see p. 203).

Piedmont scarps formed in historic time are known from several localities. During the Pleasant Valley, Nevada, earthquake in 1915, one of the piedmont scarps that formed was 18 miles long and had a maximum height of 15 feet.[9] In the Owens Valley earthquake of 1872, the maximum height of the scarps was 23 feet.[10]

Triangular facets are developed on some scarps associated with gravity faulting. Figure 139 illustrates how triangular facets may form. Figure 139A is the uneroded fault scarp, but such a perfect scarp is quite hypothetical—at least for scarps more than 100 feet high. The total movement on most faults is the result of many relatively small displacements, and erosion goes on during the whole period of movement. In Fig. 139B, deep V-shaped valleys have cut into the scarp and, in Fig. 139C, the valleys have been widened so that only half of the face of the original scarp remains. The spurs between the valleys are thus truncated by triangular facets, which have a broad base and an apex pointing upward. In Fig. 139C, the dip of the facets is the same as the dip of the fault, but this would be true only if erosion does not attack the face of the fault. In most cases, however, the upper part of the scarp is subjected to erosion, as is shown in Fig. 139D, and the slope of the scarp is less than the slope of the fault. In Nevada and Utah the scarps slope 20 to 35 degrees, but the associated faults dip 50 to 70 degrees.

[8] Hobbs, W. H., "The Earthquake of 1872 in the Owens Valley, California," *Beiträge zur Geophysik,* Vol. 10, pp. 352–385, 1910; p. 375 and Pl. XI.

[9] Jones, J. C., "The Pleasant Valley, Nevada, Earthquake of October 2, 1915," *Bulletin Seismological Society of America,* Vol. 5, pp. 190–205, 1915.

[10] Hobbs, W. H., *loc. cit.*

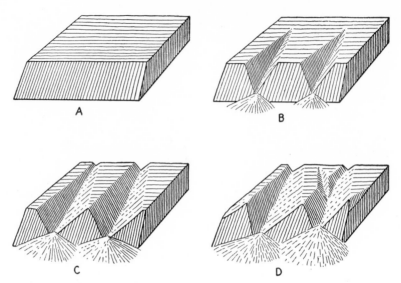

Fig. 139. Evolution of triangular facets. *A*. Fault scarp prior to erosion. *B*. Partially eroded fault scarp. *C*. Triangular facets representing remnants of original fault scarp. *D*. Triangular facets that represent the original fault scarp driven back somewhat by erosion.

Triangular facets may also develop along fault-line scarps. Moreover, they are not confined to scarps associated with faults. Wherever interstream spurs are truncated by erosion, such triangular facets may form. If a maturely dissected region is attacked by marine or lacustrine erosion, the triangular facets that develop on the ends of the interstream spurs are aligned, and the resulting scarp simulates a fault scarp. Glaciers also truncate interstream spurs to develop triangular facets.

It is apparent that triangular facets, although a characteristic feature of scarps associated with faults, may evolve in other ways. Triangular facets normally are associated with gravity faults; they are associated with thrust faults only under exceptional circumstances.

A *break in a stream profile* or an *offset stream* may occur at a fault-line. If the stream cannot erode with sufficient rapidity to maintain grade while faulting is in progress, the profile of the stream may be unusually steep in the vicinity of the fault. After the 1915 earthquake at Pleasant Valley, Nevada, a stream flowed over a waterfall 10 feet high.[11] Such breaks are not common, however, because faulting is relatively slow compared to the speed with which streams may be incised. Moreover, the deposition of alluvium on the downthrown block tends to smooth out the profile. Broken stream profiles, however, may be due to causes other than faulting.

Wherever the movement is dominantly horizontal and essentially parallel to the strike of high-angle faults, a map of the streams may show

[11] Jones, J. C., *loc. cit*.

distinct offsets. Such relations have been observed in California, where the northwesterly-trending Haywards fault zone near San Francisco is crossed by streams that flow southwestward.[12] Similar relations have been observed along the San Andreas and other faults in California.[13] The stream courses southwest of the fault are displaced toward the northwest 25 to 1,000 feet. In some instances the lower end of a valley has been abandoned, and the valley abuts directly against a scarp. But offsets in stream courses can also develop wherever a valley crosses a zone of weakness, such as a soft bed, a set of joints, or a fault.

The *truncation of the internal structure of the range at the mountain front* is highly suggestive of a fault. Figure 140 illustrates such a case.

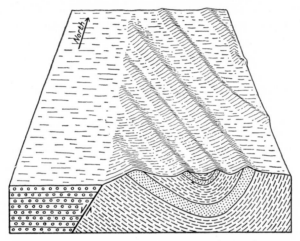

Fig. 140. Mountain front truncating internal structure of a range. Resistant sandstones, shown by dots, hold up ridges; main valley is underlain by unconsolidated alluvium, shown by open circles.

The western part of the region is an alluvial flat, but to the east a series of ridges trends northwest. The ridges are held up by resistant sandstones in a syncline trending northwest. All the ridges end suddenly at the north-south line that separates the alluvial flat from the mountains. Under normal conditions of erosion, the ridges would not end this way, and a fault separating the alluvial flat from the mountains is implied. Additional data would be necessary to determine both the direction and

[12] Russell, R. J., "Recent Horizontal Offsets Along the Haywards Fault," *Journal of Geology*, Vol. 34, pp. 507–511, 1926.

J. P. Buwalda, "Nature of the Late Movements on the Haywards Rift, Central California," *Bulletin Seismological Society of America*, Vol. 19, pp. 187–200. 1929.

[13] Wallace, R. E., "Structure of a Portion of the San Andreas Rift in Southern California," *Bulletin Geological Society of America*, Vol. 60, pp. 781–806, 1949.

M. L. Hill and T. W. Dibblee, Jr., "San Andreas, Garlock, and Big Pine Faults, California," *Bulletin Geological Society of America*, Vol. 64, pp. 443–458. 1953.

value of the dip of the fault, and the nature and amount of the displacement.

Springs in alignment along the foot of a mountain range are highly suggestive of faulting, especially if the water is hot. The alignment suggests the presence of a major plane of weakness, and the hot water indicates a fracture that permits deep penetration of circulating waters.

The physiographic criteria for faulting are important, but they must be employed with discretion. Some of the physiographic features mentioned, such as scarps, triangular facets, broken stream profiles, offset streams, and springs, may be unrelated to faulting and may be due to other causes. They are most significant when used in conjunction with other kinds of evidence, such as those described on pp. 147–152. Scarplets and the truncation of the internal structure of the range, on the other hand, are in themselves usually acceptable evidence for the presence of a fault.

Aerial photographs are, under some conditions, exceedingly useful in recognizing faults. The fault is usually a sharp line and in some instances a scarp is present on one side. Some faults, because of silicification, stand out as ridges. In a single photograph the fault may be traced for tens of miles. The continuity may be more readily seen on the photograph than in the field. Although the dip of the fault may sometimes be estimated, detailed work on the ground is usually necessary to determine the magnitude of the displacement. Remarkable examples of faults shown by aerial photographs have been described from the Canadian Shield.[14]

Aerial photographs have also been used for plotting lineaments.[15] A *lineament* is any topographically controlled line on an aerial photograph. Wilson preferred to describe such features as linears, but such usage is undesirable inasmuch as linear has been used in geology in a different sense (Chapter 21). Lineaments may be produced by faults, joints, bedding, foliation, or even lineation. They are plotted from the aerial photographs. Considerable work on the ground is necessary to interpret these lineaments.

DISTINCTION BETWEEN FAULT SCARPS, FAULT-LINE SCARPS, AND COMPOSITE FAULT SCARPS

It is difficult—and in many instances practically impossible—to distinguish fault scarps, fault-line scarps, and composite fault scarps from each other. Nevertheless, this is an important problem for both

[14] Joliffe, A. W., "Structures in the Canadian Shield," *Transactions American Geophysical Union* for 1942, pp. 699–707.

[15] Wilson, J. T., "Some Aspects of Geophysics in Canada with Special Reference to Structural Research in the Canadian Shield, Part 2: An Approach to the Structure of the Canadian Shield," *Transactions American Geophysical Union,* Vol. 29, pp. 691–726, 1948.

structural geologists and physiographers, and both should strive for a solution of the problem.[16]

Features suggesting that the scarp is a true fault scarp are: (1) piedmont scarps; (2) lakes; (3) frequent severe earthquakes; and (4) a poor correlation between rock resistance and surface form.

Piedmont scarps have been discussed above, and it has been shown that they are associated with active faulting. It is likely that the entire scarp, at the foot of which the piedmont scarp lies, is a fault scarp. Under certain conditions, however, if faulting is renewed along a fault-line scarp, a piedmont scarp would form, and the false impression would be given that the entire scarp is a fault scarp.

Lakes associated with a fault-line suggest a fault scarp. A lake may form if a fault cuts across a stream, and the block on the downstream side is uplifted (Fig. 141A). Depressions also develop if the down-dropped block settles different amounts along the strike of the fault,

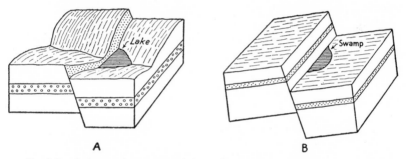

A   **B**

Fig. 141. Lakes and swamps along a fault scarp. *A.* Stream that flowed toward the left has been dammed by the fault scarp. *B.* Swamp occupies depression at foot of fault scarp caused by tilted fault blocks.

and lakes or swamps may occupy these depressions (Fig. 141B). *Sag ponds* occupy depressions along active faults in California. But lakes associated with faults are not likely to last very long because the outlet may be lowered very rapidly, or sediments from the nearby hills and mountains may fill up the lake.

Lakes are not a normal accompaniment of fluviatile erosion, and they are not to be expected along fault-line scarps. On the other hand, lakes at the foot of fault-line scarps may result from local overdeeping by glaciers, damming by landslides and lava flows, and from other causes.

Frequent severe earthquakes in the vicinity of a scarp associated with a fault indicate a fault scarp because the earthquakes are presumably due to movement along the fault. In Shensi and Kansu provinces,

[16] Blackwelder, E., "The Recognition of Fault Scarps," *Journal of Geology*, Vol. 36, pp. 289–311, 1928.

Cotton, C. A., *op. cit.*

China, recurrent destructive earthquakes at the base of high scarps are evidence that the mountains are young, active fault blocks.

A poor correlation between rock resistance and surface form suggests a fault scarp. If the scarp were due entirely to erosion, the hard formations would form hills and mountains, and the soft formations would be occupied by valleys. On the other hand, if the soft rocks rise above the hard rocks, a fault scarp is indicated. But it is obvious that such a situation could not long withstand the ravages of erosion.

There are several lines of evidence that may be used to show that a scarp is a fault-line scarp: (1) scarp on the downthrown side of the fault, (2) close correlation between rock resistance, structure, and topography; and (3) evidence of baseleveling subsequent to faulting.

It is self-evident that if the downthrown block is topographically higher than the upthrown block (Fig. 137C), the scarp is an obsequent fault-line scarp. The relief along the fault must be caused by differential erosion.

Locally the evidence may be noncommittal, as in the front part of the block diagram shown in Fig. 142. The scarp could be either a fault scarp or a fault-line scarp. At the back of the block, however, a younger conglomerate, shown by circles, overlies the older rocks and is unaffected

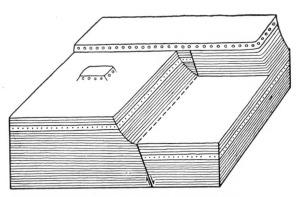

Fig. 142. Fault-line scarp. Dots = sandstone; parallel lines = shale; circles = conglomerate. (See text.)

by the fault. It is evident that the original topographic expression of the fault had been destroyed by erosion of the whole region to the surface directly beneath the conglomerate. The conglomerate was then deposited. Finally, in a renewed cycle of erosion, the conglomerate in the foreground, and many older beds in the right foreground were eroded, and a fault-line scarp developed.

A close correlation between topography and rock resistance is indicative of a fault-line scarp. The scarp is high and abrupt where the contrast in lithology is greatest, is more subdued where the contrast is slight, and may disappear if rocks on opposite sides of the fault are equally resistant.

The recognition of composite fault scarps must be based upon combinations of the criteria given above, and the local conditions are so

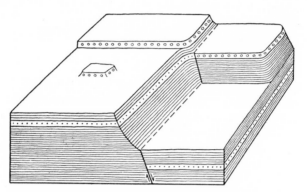

Fig. 143. Composite fault scarp. Dots = sandstone; parallel lines = shale; circles = conglomerate. (See text.)

variable that a general discussion here is inadvisable. One type of evidence is illustrated by Fig. 143, which may be considered a later stage than that illustrated by Fig. 142. Part of the height of the scarp in the foreground of Fig. 143 is directly due to movement along the fault because the conglomerate has been displaced by the fault.

CHAPTER 10

Mechanics of Faulting

INTRODUCTION

In Chapter 6 the relationship of rupture to stress and strain was considered. It was shown that fractures are of two general types, tension fractures and shear fractures. Along tension fractures the walls move apart. Along shear fractures the displacement is parallel to the walls, and there is no movement perpendicular to the fracture. Tension fractures are not faults, at least when they first form. It is entirely possible, of course, for later displacement to be parallel to the walls. The tension fracture could thus become a fault. Moreover, the displacement along shear fractures may be later than and independent of the stresses that produced the initial fracture.

Most of the present chapter will deal with those faults that were originally shear fractures. Moreover, it is assumed that the displacements are caused by the same stresses as those that produced the initial rupture. But it should be clearly understood that the displacement may be the result of stresses other than those that caused the original rupture. A discussion of this phase of the problem is reserved to the end of the chapter.

In any attempt to analyze faulting on the basis of mechanical principles, it is necessary to make some simplifying assumptions. For the present it is sufficient to say that the analysis treats the rocks as if they were isotropic, that is, as if their properties were the same in all directions. A more detailed discussion of the nature of these assumptions and their possible significance is also discussed near the end of the chapter.

DIRECTION OF DISPLACEMENT

In Chapter 6 we were concerned only with the formation and orientation of the shear fractures. We were not concerned with the nature of the displacement that followed the rupture. As shown on page 95 and in Fig. 81, the shear fractures make angles of about 30 degrees[1] with the

[1] Hereafter the figure 30 degrees will be used without qualification, but it should always be understood that it is only an approximation.

greatest principal stress axis and are parallel to the intermediate principal stress axis.

The nature of the ensuing displacement that follows rupture is illustrated in Fig. 144. In this case a compressive force is applied vertically and the block is restrained on the front and back, but is free to move to the right and left. The orientation of the stress ellipsoid (page 99) is shown on Fig. 144A; the greatest principal stress axis (*P*) is vertical, the intermediate stress axis (*Q*) is perpendicular to the plane of the paper, and the least principal stress axis (*R*) is horizontal in the plane of the paper. As shown in Fig. 144B, two sets of shear fractures (*FF'* and

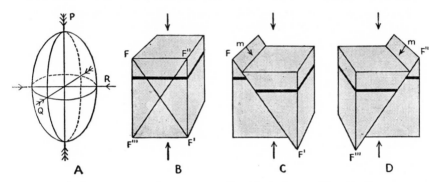

Fig. 144. Relation of faults to stress ellipsoid. *A.* Stress ellipsoid: *P* = greatest principal stress axis, *Q* = intermediate principal stress axis, *R* = least principal stress axis. *B.* Orientation of shear fractures. *C.* Along *FF'* the right-hand block has moved down. *D.* Along *F"F'"* the left-hand block has moved down.

F"F'") may form, making angles of 30 degrees with the greatest principal stress axis. If the force continues to be applied after a through-going rupture has formed, faulting will take place, as shown in Fig. 144C and 144D. The direction of displacement will be parallel to the trace (*m*) of the greatest principal stress axis on the shear fracture. Perhaps a simpler statement is to say that the direction of displacement lies in the plane of the rupture and is perpendicular to the intermediate principal stress axis. Along fracture *FF'* (Fig. 144C) the right-hand block has moved down, whereas along fracture *F"F'"* (Fig. 144D) the left-hand block has moved down.

STRESS AND FAULTING

Introduction

The objective of this analysis is to determine the attitude of faults and the direction of displacement along them when the rocks are subjected to stress. Those cases in which one of the principal stress axes is vertical will be investigated first. This will be followed by a study of those cases in which one of the principal stress axes is horizontal. Then the general case will be discussed. Finally, some consideration will be given to those factors that complicate the application of such analyses to the study of faults.

Cases in Which One Principal Stress Axis Is Vertical

The stress ellipsoid may have any conceivable orientation in the crust of the earth. The simplest case, which will be analyzed first, is that in which one of the principal stress axes is vertical; obviously the other two principal stress axes will be horizontal and make an angle of 90 degrees with one another.[2] We must first consider the *standard state,* which al-

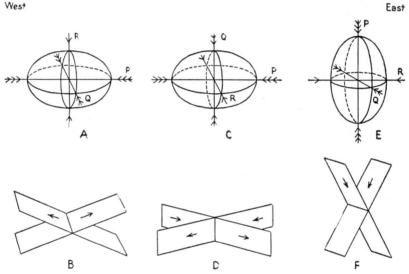

Fig. 145. Type of fault depends upon orientation of stress ellipsoid. $P =$ principal stress axis, $Q =$ intermediate stress axis, $R =$ least stress axis. *A.* Least principal stress axis vertical. *B.* Thrusts form under conditions postulated in *A.* *C.* Intermediate stress axis is vertical. *D.* Strike-slip faults form under conditions postulated in *C.* *E.* Greatest principal stress axis vertical. *F.* Gravity faults form under conditions postulated in *E.* (After E. M. Anderson.)

though idealized, offers a convenient standard of reference. It is a condition in which the lithostatic pressure is uniform on all sides of any imaginary block in the crust. This uniform pressure increases regularly with depth and ideally is equal to the weight of the overlying column of rock.

Let us first imagine a situation at some depth in the earth whereby the net effect of all the forces is to produce an additional pressure paral-

[2] E. M. Anderson, *The Dynamics of Faulting and Dyke Formation with Applications to Britain,* 2nd ed. London: Oliver and Boyd, 1951.

lel to a horizontal east-west line and a somewhat smaller pressure parallel to a horizontal north-south line. The stress ellipsoid is now oriented (Fig. 145A) with the least principal stress axis vertical (R), the intermediate principal stress axis horizontal north-south (Q), and the greatest principal stress axis horizontal east-west (P). When the greatest principal stress P is increased to such an extent that the stress difference, $P - R$, exceeds a critical value, the rocks will rupture if they are sufficiently brittle. These fractures will be parallel to Q and make an angle of 30 degrees with P (Fig. 145B). That is, in geological terminology, the fractures will strike north-south; one set will dip 30 degrees east, the other set 30 degrees west. Moreover, as shown on Fig. 145B they will be thrusts; in both sets the hanging wall will move relatively upward over the footwall.

Let us now imagine a similar situation where, starting with the standard state, an additional pressure is applied parallel to a horizontal east-west line (Fig. 145C). But this time let us assume that there is a decrease in pressure—to some value less than that of the standard state—in a horizontal north-south direction. The vertical pressure is assumed to remain unchanged. The greatest principal stress axis (P) is horizontal east-west, the intermediate principal stress axis (Q) is vertical, and the least principal stress axis (R) is horizontal north-south. When the stress difference, $P - R$, exceeds a critical value, the rocks will rupture. The shear fractures will be vertical, one set striking ENE, the other set striking WNW (Fig. 145D). If faulting takes place, the ENE set will be right-handed strike-slip faults; the WNW set will be left-handed strike-slip faults.

Let us now imagine a situation where, starting with the standard state, the net effect of all the forces is to produce a decrease in pressure parallel to the horizontal east-west direction and also a smaller decrease in pressure parallel to the horizontal north-south direction. The vertical pressure is assumed to remain unchanged. The greatest principal stress axis (P) is now vertical, the intermediate principal stress axis (Q) is horizontal north-south, and the least principal stress axis (R) is horizontal east-west (Fig. 145E). When the stress difference exceeds a critical value, the rocks will rupture. In geological terminology, the fractures will strike north-south; one set will dip 60 degrees to the east, the other set will dip 60 degrees to the west (Fig. 145F). If displacement occurs, the fractures will become gravity faults, the hanging walls moving down with reference to the footwalls.

Of course, the choice of an east-west direction for one of the principal stress axes and a north-south direction for the other was merely for simplifying the discussion. The two horizontal stress axes could assume any directions, provided that they are at right angles to each other. Thus the faults may strike in any direction, depending upon the orientation of the stress axes. Moreover, the only necessary condition is that the stresses parallel to the principal stress axes be unequal. This may be accomplished in many ways, only a few of which were discussed above. The stresses parallel to all the axes might be increased, but some less than others. Or the stresses parallel to all the axes might decrease, but some more than others. Various combinations are possible.

Cases in Which Intermediate Principal Stress Axis Is Horizontal

The analysis given in the preceding section accounts for thrust faults that dip about 30 degrees, gravity faults that dip about 60 degrees, and vertical strike-slip faults which, under the simplest conditions, make an angle of about 60 degrees with the fold axes (page 212). Anderson, in his study of the faults of Britain, assumed that deviations from these attitudes were the result of rotation of the fault planes because of later deformation.

A more complete analysis of the problem shows that none of the principal stress axes need be vertical. Hafner[3] has shown that the faults may have an infinite variety of dips, depending upon the stresses involved. As before, certain simplifying assumptions are necessary. One is that the rocks are isotropic. Moreover, the analysis is made in two dimensions. In the illustrations given in Figs. 146–149 this means that the intermediate stress axis is assumed to be horizontal; that is, it is perpendicular to the plane of the paper.

In the case illustrated in Fig. 146 an additional horizontal pressure is superimposed upon the standard state. This superimposed horizontal

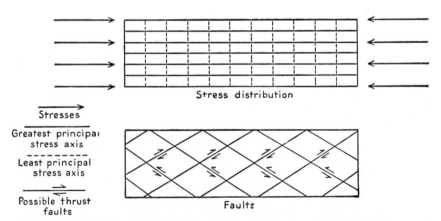

Fig. 146. Faults if superimposed horizontal stress is same at all depths. Upper diagram shows trajectories of stress axes; lower diagram shows attitude of possible thrust faults. (Based on description by W. Hafner.)

[3] The analysis in this section is based upon that presented by W. Hafner, "Stress Distributions and Faulting," *Bulletin Geological Society of America*, Vol. 62, pp. 373–398, 1951.

pressure is assumed to have the same value at all depths. The pressure at both ends of the block must be the same, otherwise the block would move.

The upper diagram shows the distribution of the stresses. The solid horizontal lines represent the *trajectories*—that is, the paths—of the greatest principal stress axes. They are everywhere horizontal parallel to the plane of the paper. The broken lines are the trajectories of the least principal stress axes. They are everywhere vertical. The intermediate principal stress axes are everywhere perpendicular to the plane of the paper.

If the additional superimposed pressure becomes great enough, the rocks will rupture. As shown in the lower diagram of Fig. 146, there will ideally be two sets of fractures making angles of 30 degrees with the greatest principal stress axes. The direction of displacement will be parallel to the trace of the greatest principal stress axes on the fractures. In geological terminology the hanging walls move up with reference to the footwalls. Thus the faults are thrusts. Of course, the regular spacing of the faults is entirely diagrammatic. Moreover, under natural conditions one set may develop in preference to the other.

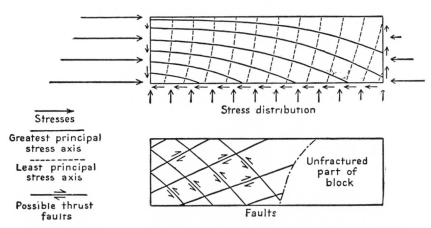

Fig. 147. Faults if superimposed horizontal stress increases downward. Rupture strength assumed to be 3,000 kg./cm.² Upper diagram shows trajectories of stress axes; lower diagram shows attitude of possible thrust faults; details depend on several variables, including strength of rocks. (After W. Hafner.)

In the case illustrated in Fig. 147 an additional horizontal pressure is superimposed upon the standard state. It is assumed that this additional pressure increases downward; this is indicated at the left end of the upper diagram by the increased length of the arrows toward the bottom. It is also assumed that the effectiveness of the superimposed pressure decreases in intensity from left to right; this fact is indicated by the greater length of the horizontal arrows on the left side of the diagram compared to those on the right. The additional stresses, which are shown in the diagram and which are necessary to preserve equilibrium, need not concern us here.

The solid lines in the upper diagram show the orientation of the trajectories of the greatest principal stress axes. The broken lines are the trajectories of the least principal stress axes. The intermediate principal stress axes are everywhere parallel and are perpendicular to the plane of the paper.

If the supplementary stress becomes great enough, the resulting shear fractures will be oriented as shown in the lower part of Fig. 147. Inasmuch as the plunges of the greatest principal stress axes differ from

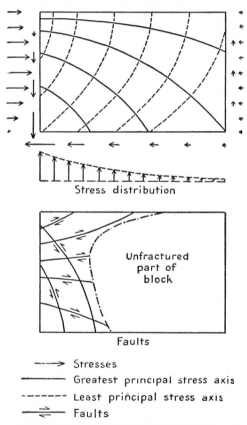

Fig. 148. Faults if supplementary stress decreases exponentially from left to right. Rupture strength assumed to be 3,000 kg./cm.² Upper diagram shows trajectories of stress axes. Lower diagram shows attitude of possible faults; one set consists of high-angle thrusts; second set consists of low-angle faults, which are thrusts above, gravity faults below. (After W. Hafner.)

place to place, the dips of the faults will also differ. As shown at the left end of the lower diagram, one set of faults dips 30 degrees to the left, the other set 30 degrees to the right, because the greatest principal stress axes are here horizontal. At the right-hand end of the diagram, because the greatest principal stress axes plunge to the right, one set of faults dips about 20 degrees west, the other set about 40 degrees east. All the faults are thrusts. Because the supplementary pressure was applied to the left end of the block, and its effectiveness is assumed to decrease in intensity to the right, the right-hand end of the block does not fracture. The boundary between the fractured and unfractured parts of the blocks depends upon a number of factors.

In Fig. 148 the superimposed horizontal stress decreases exponentially in a horizontal direction from left to right. In this case the trajectories of the greatest principal stress axes plunge to the right. As before, the fractures will be inclined 30 degrees to the greatest principal stress axes. There will be one set of high-angle thrusts and one set of low-angle thrusts. In fact, progressing downward in the diagram the low-angle thrusts become horizontal faults and at the bottom of the diagram become low-angle gravity faults. The right-hand part of the block is not fractured. The location of the boundary between the fractured and unfractured part of the block depends upon a number of factors.

In Fig. 149 it is assumed that the supplementary pressure system consists of two parts. One is a variable vertical stress represented in the upper diagram by the vertical arrows under the block. A variable shearing stress is shown by the horizontal arrows at the bottom of the block. In order to give the diagram some geological significance, Hafner[4] assumed that the block was 10 miles thick. In the upper diagram the trajectories of the greatest principal stress axes are shown by solid lines. They plunge toward the center of the diagram at relatively low angles at the margins and at progressively higher angles toward the center. Conversely, the trajectories of the least principal stress axis form a gigantic arch. The resulting faults are shown in the lower diagram. In the upper central part of the diagram they are high-angle gravity faults. Toward the margins one set of these gravity faults dip at progressively lower angles. The second set becomes progressively steeper, eventually passes through the vertical, and nearer the margins becomes high-angle thrust faults. Subsequent erosion may expose various levels.

This two-dimensional analysis of faults shows that both thrusts and gravity faults may dip at angles ranging from 0 degrees to 90 degrees. We thus find a rational theoretical basis for field observations. Strike-slip faults have not been mentioned in this section because, in order to restrict the discussion to reasonable lengths, it has been assumed that the intermediate principal stress axis was always horizontal. If, however, the

[4] Hafner, W., *op. cit.*

intermediate principal stress axis were vertical, then the diagrams in Figs. 146–149 could be looked upon as if they were maps rather than sections.

General Case

In the analysis on pages 166 to 168 it has been assumed that one of the principal stress axes was vertical. In the analysis on pages 168 to 172 it has been assumed that the intermediate principal stress axis was horizontal. Under either of these assumptions the net slip of thrust and gravity faults would plunge directly up or down the dip of the faults. The net slip of strike-slip faults would be horizontal. In neither of these analyses is any provision made for diagonal-slip faults. Such faults would form, however, if none of the principal stress axes were vertical or horizontal.

MODIFYING FACTORS

Introduction

It has been necessary in the preceding sections to make a number of simplifying assumptions. Consequently the patterns shown by faults in the field will undoubtedly be more complex and variable than those shown in the diagrams. Again it should be emphasized that the regular distribution of the faults is entirely diagrammatic. Some of the other factors that make the problem more complex are discussed below.

Applied Force

The forces along the margins of the blocks in the preceding figures have a symmetry and regularity that is very unlikely within the crust of the earth. Thus the distribution of stress within the blocks would be more complex.

Inhomogeneity

It has already been emphasized that the crust of the earth lacks homogeneity. This would have an important effect on the distribution of the stresses even if the applied forces varied in some uniform and systematic way. Moreover, inhomogeneities influence the orientation of the shear fractures. For example, if the theoretical shear fractures at some place are horizontal, but the bedding dips 10 to 20 degrees, the actual fracture would probably follow the bedding. Foliation planes, joints, and older faults influence the orientation of new fractures.[5]

Effects of Rupture

Once the rocks have ruptured the stress distribution may be pro-

---

[5] Seigel, H. O., "A Theory of Fracture of Materials and Its Application to Geology," *Transactions American Geophysical Union*, Vol. 31, pp. 611–619, 1950.

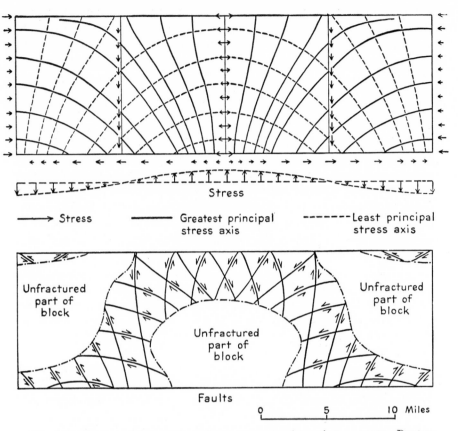

Fig. 149. Faults when supplementary stress consists of two parts. Rupture strength assumed to be 3,000 kg./cm². Upper diagram shows trajectories of stress axes. Supplementary stresses are: (a) a variable vertical stress represented by vertical arrows; (b) a variable shearing stress represented by arrows at bottom of block. Lower diagram shows attitude of possible faults. (After W. Hafner.)

foundly modified.[6] A few small fractures in a large block would not be significant, but obviously a few large ruptures would exert a great influence on the behavior of the rocks. If large blocks become completely isolated from one another by fractures, the stress distribution might differ considerably from what it was originally.

Plasticity

In the preceding analyses it was tacitly assumed that the rocks were relatively brittle, with little or no plastic deformation preceding the rupture. At depths of 5 or 10 miles many rocks are relatively plastic. If they are sufficiently plastic they might never fail by rupture during the period of deformation; they would continue to flow indefinitely. Such cases need

[6] McKinstry, H. E., "Shears of the Second Order," *American Journal of Science,* Vol. 251, pp. 401–414, 1953.

not concern us here. But we are concerned with rocks that yield plastically a considerable amount before they rupture. Even in such cases the principles enunciated above are pertinent because they deal with the stresses just before and at the time of rupture. Nevertheless, it must be emphasized that a considerable plastic deformation may precede the rupture.

Tension Fractures

As indicated at the beginning of this chapter, it has been tacitly assumed that all faults are initially shear fractures. It is clear, however, that tension fractures may also become faults. A specific example of this is shown in Fig. 174. Because the cracks are open, they must be tension fractures. However, the blocks on opposite sides of the tension cracks have moved up and down relative to one another, as much as a foot in some cases. This is because the isolated vertical sheets of unconsolidated material were very unstable and slumped different amounts. Under the conditions postulated in Figs. 146–149, tension cracks would form at right angles to the least principal stress axes. In Fig. 146 they would be horizontal. In Figs. 147–149 they would form at right angles to the least principal stress axes (the broken lines); that is, in these two-dimensional analyses they would be parallel to the solid lines.

Later Deformation

As already indicated, the attitude of a fault plane may be modified by later deformation. A vertical fault might cut horizontal sediments; if the sediments are later folded to a vertical position, the fault will be horizontal. Low-angle thrust planes may be subsequently folded, in some cases to assume very high dips (see pages 184 to 193).

A shear fracture may form, with or without faulting, under one condition of stress. Subsequently, under very different conditions of stress, displacement may take place. For example, a vertical strike-slip fault, along which there had been relatively little displacement, might be utilized later for large differential vertical movements.

Conclusions

It is apparent from the preceding discussion that no simple rules can be established to determine the nature and magnitude of the forces involved in the formation of a fault. The geological history of the region must be known. It may be necessary to extend the study to a relatively large area. Moreover, several alternate hypotheses may explain the observed facts. Nevertheless, any conclusions must be based not only on field observations, but also on a mechanical basis such as that outlined above.

APPLICATIONS OF THEORY

The application of the theoretical principles enunciated above will become more apparent in the following chapters. Nevertheless, a brief discussion of a few applications is desirable at this point.

If sufficient data are available, the orientation of the stress ellipsoid in a region may be determined. Of course, the orientation may vary throughout geological time; consequently in this discussion we are referring to the orientation when the faults being considered were active. Moreover, although the stress ellipsoid may be properly oriented, it may be impossible to reach any definite conclusions concerning the forces that produced the stress.

The following generalizations may be made. (a) The intermediate principal stress axis lies in the plane of the fault and at right angles to the net slip. (b) The greatest principal stress axis lies in the plane that is perpendicular to the intermediate principal stress axis. It makes an angle of about 30 degrees with the fault plane. For gravity faults or faults with a gravity component, it lies in the same direction as that in which the fault dips (Figs. 145E and F); that is, if a gravity fault dips east, the angle of 30 degrees is measured in an easterly direction. For thrust faults or faults with a thrust component, the greatest principal stress axis lies in the opposite direction of that in which the fault dips (Figs. 145A and B); that is, if a thrust fault dips west, the angle of 30 degrees is measured in an easterly direction. (c) The least principal stress axis is at right angles to the other two.

Figure 150 shows an artificial gravity fault produced by moving a rigid partition toward the right in a box of sand.[7] Assume for the moment, however, that the mechanics of formation of the fault is unknown in order to see whether we can reach any conclusions from the principles given above.

The intermediate stress axis (Q) must lie in the plane of the fault and be horizontal because the net slip is directly down the dip of the fault. The greatest principal stress axis should make an angle of about 30 degrees with the fault and lie in a plane parallel to the page, which is the plane perpendicular to the intermediate stress axis. Moreover, as stated above, this angle must be measured in the same direction as that in which the gravity fault dips, that is, toward the east. Thus the greatest principal stress axis is vertical. With the other two axes defined, the least principal stress axis (R) is horizontal in the plane of the paper. The stress ellipsoid therefore has the orientation shown in the right-hand part of Fig. 150.

[7] Hubbert, M. K., "Mechanical Basis for Certain Familiar Geologic Structures," *Bulletin Geological Society of America*, Vol. 62, pp. 355–372, 1951.

Without further information we could not determine the ultimate forces involved. Starting from the standard state, such an orientation of the stress ellipsoid could theoretically be the result of an increase in pressure parallel to P, a small increase parallel to Q, and no change parallel to R. This could be caused by an active compressive force from below. A second possibility is a decrease in pressure parallel to R, a slight decrease parallel to Q, while there is no change parallel to P. We know that the second interpretation is correct because of the conditions of the experiment.

Gravity faults in the western United States are illustrated in Figs. 167, 171, 172, and 179. The faults dip about 60 degrees, and the net slip, insofar as it is known, is essentially down the dip. The stress ellipsoid is thus oriented as shown in Fig. 145E. But what was the ultimate cause of this distribution of stress? One interpretation is that, starting with the standard state, there was a decrease in pressure parallel to R, a slight

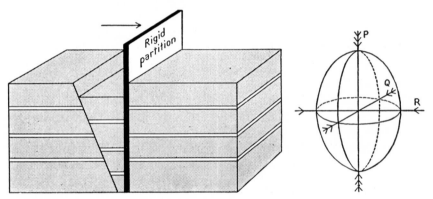

Fig. 150. Gravity fault. Develops when rigid partition is moved to right in unconsolidated sand. Stress ellipsoid is for area to left of partition. (After W. K. Hubbert.)

decrease parallel to Q, and no change parallel to P. In other words, the crust was extended parallel to R. A second possibility is that illustrated in Fig. 149, where differential vertical movements played a dominant role in the development of the faults.

Figure 151 illustrates some artificial thrusts produced many years ago by Cadell[8] in connection with a study of the structure of the Northwest Highlands of Scotland. A series of thrusts dip from 20 degrees to 40 degrees to the right. They were produced by a block pushed from the right against artificial sediments. Assume for the moment, however, that the mechanics of formation of these faults is unknown in order to see whether we can reach any definite conclusions.

The intermediate principal stress axis (Q), inasmuch as it must lie in the plane of the fault and be perpendicular to the net slip, is perpendicu-

[8] Cadell, H. M., "Experimental Researches in Mountain Building," *Transactions Royal Society of Edinburgh*, Vol. XXXV, Part i, p. 337, 1889.

lar to the plane of the paper. The greatest principal stress axis (P) must lie in the plane of the paper and be 30 degrees from the fractures. Moreover, as indicated above, this angle must be measured in the opposite direction of that in which the fault dips. Thus the greatest principal stress axis is horizontal and lies in the plane of the paper (right-hand diagram of Fig. 151). The least principal stress axis is vertical.

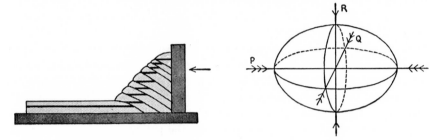

Fig. 151. Thrust faults. On left: rigid block moved to left against weak sediments. (After W. Cadell.) On right: stress ellipsoid.

It is thus possible to deduce the orientation of the stress ellipsoid. But if we assume an initial standard state, such an orientation could result from a large decrease in pressure parallel to the vertical axis (R), a slight decrease parallel to Q, and no change parallel to P. A second possibility is a large increase in pressure parallel to P, a slight increase parallel to Q, and no change parallel to R. From the conditions of the experiment we know that the second interpretation is correct.

The thrusts in Fig. 156 dip 25 to 55 degrees. For the reasons given above, the least principal stress axis is vertical, the intermediate principal stress axis is perpendicular to the plane of the paper, and the greatest principal stress axis is horizontal in the plane of the paper. Although such a distribution of stress could be explained in various ways, the most logical conclusion is that the thrusts are due to horizontal compression, analogous to the examples shown in Fig. 146.

Low-angle thrusts, such as that illustrated in Fig. 162 indicate that the stress ellipsoid is differently oriented than in the previously cited examples. It may be safely assumed that this thrust was nearly horizontal before it was folded. If we may assume that the net slip is due east, it follows that the intermediate principal stress axis is horizontal north-south, whereas the greatest principal stress axis plunges 30 degrees to the east. As in the previous examples, several different conclusions may be reached concerning the external forces. They may have been similar to those illustrated in Fig. 148.

FAULTING AND THE STRAIN ELLIPSOID

The emphasis in the preceding part of this chapter has been on the relation between stress and faulting. This method has the advantage that the problem can be analyzed quantitatively. In the future, as additional quantitative data on the physical properties of rocks become available, the method will become even more useful. But a qualitative analysis can be made by use of the strain ellipsoid. In fact, in American geology this method of study has been the one most commonly employed. Consequently a brief discussion is highly desirable even though it may seem in part repetitious of the earlier part of the chapter.

Figure 152A is a stress ellipsoid. The symbol P is the greatest stress axis, Q is the intermediate stress axis, and R is the least stress axis. Under such conditions of stress an imaginary sphere will be converted into the strain ellipsoid shown in Fig. 152B. The A is the greatest strain axis, B is the intermediate strain axis, and C is the least strain axis. The intermediate axes of the stress and strain ellipsoids, Q and B, respectively coincide. The greatest stress axis P coincides with the least strain axis C. The least stress axis R coincides with the greatest strain axis A. The nature of the net slip is shown in Figs. 152C and D.

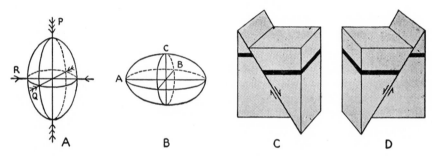

Fig. 152. Relation of faults to stress and strain ellipsoids. *A.* Stress ellipsoid: $P =$ greatest principal stress axis, $Q =$ intermediate principal stress axis, $R =$ least principal stress axis. *B.* Strain ellipsoid; $A =$ greatest strain axis, $B =$ intermediate strain axis, $C =$ least strain axis. Axes of stress and strain ellipsoids are parallel only if orientation of stress axes is constant throughout deformation. *C.* Gravity fault in which right-hand block moved down. *D.* Gravity fault in which left-hand block moved down.

The following generalizations may be made. (a) The intermediate strain axis lies in the plane of the fault and is at right angles to the net slip. (b) The least strain axis lies in a plane perpendicular to the intermediate strain axis and makes an angle of about 30 degrees with the fault plane. For gravity faults or faults with a gravity component, it lies in the same direction as that in which the fault dips. For thrust faults or faults with a thrust component, it lies in the opposite direction of that in which the fault dips. (c) The greatest strain axis is at right angles to the other two.

Of course, the stress and strain axes are mutually parallel only if the stress axes occupy the same position throughout the deformation. If the attitude of the stress ellipsoid changes during the deformation it is apparent that the strain ellipsoid will occupy some position intermediate between the first and last positions of the stress ellipsoid.

A few examples will show how these principles may be employed. The upper part of Fig. 153A is a gravity fault that dips east and in which the net slip is directly down the dip. It follows that the intermediate strain axis B is perpendicular to the plane of the paper (lower diagram). The least strain axis C is 30 degrees in the direction in which the fault dips and hence is vertical. The greatest strain axis (A) is horizontal in the

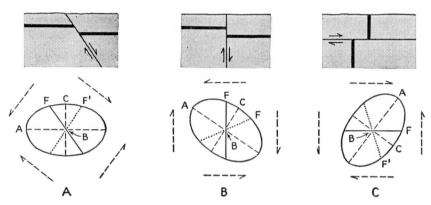

Fig. 153. Relation of faults to strain ellipsoid. Upper diagrams are faults. Lower diagram shows inferred orientation of strain ellipsoid; nature of external forces discussed in text.

plane of the paper. The next step is to try to deduce the forces that oriented the strain ellipsoid in this way. As in the case of the stress ellipsoid, there are several possibilities. Active tension parallel to A would produce the observed orientation. But so also would compression parallel to C. Various couples such as those shown by the arrows in broken lines should be considered. Some additional data would be necessary to reach a conclusion.

The upper part of Fig. 153B is a vertical fault in which the net slip is directly down the dip. The intermediate strain axis (B) is consequently perpendicular to the plane of the paper. The least strain axis is about 30 degrees from the fault. If the fault dipped 89° E., the fault would be classified as a gravity fault; in this case the angle of 30 degrees would be measured in the same direction as that in which the fault dips; that is, it would be measured toward the east. If the fault dipped 89° W., it would be classified as a thrust fault. In this case the angle of 30 degrees would be measured in the opposite direction from that in which the fault dips; that is, the angle would be measured toward the east. The orientation of the strain ellipsoid is shown in the lower diagram of Fig. 153B.

Such an orientation could be the result of tension parallel to A, compression parallel to C, or couples such as those shown by the broken lines.

Figure 153C is a horizontal fault in which the net slip is parallel to the plane of the paper. The orientation of the strain ellipsoid is shown in the lower diagram. This orientation could be the result of tension parallel to A, compression parallel to C, or couples such as those shown by the arrows represented by the broken lines.

The upper diagrams of Figs. 146–149, which show the trajectories of the stress axes, can be readily converted into strain diagrams. In fact, the solid lines are the least strain axes, and the broken lines are the greatest strain axes.

It is apparent from the above discussion that, just as in the case of the stress ellipsoid, a unique solution of the forces that caused the structure may be difficult to find. Additional structural information may offer the clue to the answer.

CHAPTER 11

Thrust Faults

INTRODUCTION

Thrust faults, often simply called *thrusts*, are those faults in which the hanging wall moves up relative to the footwall. This involves crustal shortening and implies compression. Ordinarily, it is impossible to ascertain which wall has been the active element; but, as has already been stated, if it is possible to determine which block moved, an underthrust is one in which the footwall is thrust under the hanging wall, whereas an overthrust is one in which the hanging wall is thrust over the footwall. Overthrust is also used in another sense (p. 184). The term *upthrust* may be used for high-angle thrust faults in which the hanging wall is the active element.

ORIGIN

Some thrusts develop when a fracture forms at a high angle to the bedding across one limb of a fold (Fig. 154A); the relative movement is such that the strata nearer the center of the anticline move over the strata nearer the center of an adjacent syncline. Another type of thrust forms when the inverted limb of an overturned or recumbent fold becomes so stretched that it finally ruptures (Fig. 154B). The relative motion is such that the strata nearer the center of the anticline move over those nearer the center of the adjacent syncline.

Some thrusts are not directly related to folding. In many cases the fracture cuts across horizontal strata (Fig. 154C). In other instances the fracture cuts across strata that have already been folded (Fig. 154D).

A thrust that follows a bedding plane is known as a *bedding thrust*. On p. 89 it has been shown that all folding involves some slipping of the beds past each other, but ordinarily the amount is so slight that it is measured in fractions of an inch. If, however, the movement is great enough to cause slickensiding, brecciation, or a displacement of at least several inches, the surface may be properly called a bedding thrust wherever the hanging wall moves up relative to the footwall.

In areas of flat or gently dipping strata, a fracture may follow a bedding plane for a long distance, and the upper formations may slide thousands of feet or even miles over the lower beds (Fig. 154E). Although such fractures are bedding thrusts, they are a special kind and may be called *décollements* (see also p. 60). In many instances, especially if the upper block is rigid and cannot fold, the frontal part of the fracture (*bc*

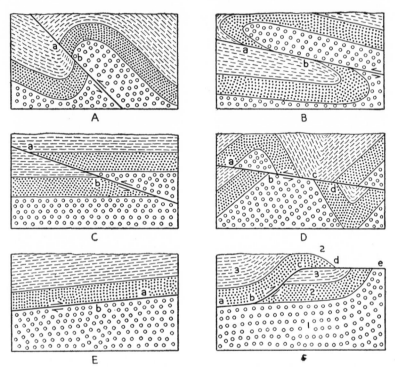

Fig. 154. Thrust faults. *A*. Thrust plane diagonal to limb of anticline; *ab* = net slip. *B*. Thrust formed by stretching of overturned limb of fold; *ab* = net slip. *C*. Thrust that forms without prior folding; *ab* = net slip. *D*. Thrust that forms later than folding; *ab* = net slip; at *c* younger rocks are thrust over older; at *d* the rocks above and below the thrust plane are the same age; between *a* and *b* older rocks are thrust over younger. *E*. Bedding thrust. *F*. Erosion thrust; *1* = oldest beds, *2* = beds of intermediate age, *3* = youngest beds. Although between *a* and *b* the fault is a bedding thrust, between *c* and *d* it is an erosion thrust. If thrust block moves to *e*, younger rocks would be thrust over older.

of Fig. 154F) must cut across the strata. Thrusts of this type in Nevada have been described.[1]

Thrust faults may emerge at the surface of the earth to form fault scarps. Scarps associated with high-angle thrusts (Fig. 155) may be similar to those associated with high-angle gravity faults. The blocks

[1] Longwell, C. R., "Thrust Faults of Peculiar Type," *Bulletin Geological Society of America*, Vol. 44, p. 93 (abstract), 1933.

on either side of the fault may be tilted, and tilted fault blocks may be expressed topographically, just as in the case of tilted fault blocks associated with gravity faults (Fig. 168). Many of the topographically expressed fault blocks in New Zealand are bounded by high-angle thrusts.[2]

If a low-angle thrust fault emerges at the surface of the earth, the hanging wall may move horizontally a considerable distance over an erosion surface. Such faults are *erosion thrusts* (*cd* of Fig. 154F). If the advancing thrust sheet undergoes erosion, a veneer of gravel or alluvium may be deposited in front of it; the thrust sheet ultimately overrides these gravels.[3]

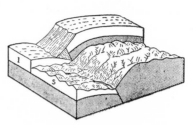

Fig. 155. Fault scarp along a high angle thrust. *I* = initial form, with some talus (shown by shortest dashed lines); *S* = form after some erosion. (After C. A. Cotton.)

Older rocks are thrust over younger formations along the thrusts illustrated in Fig. 154A, B, and C. In fact, thrusts are commonly recognized by the fact that the rocks in the hanging wall are older than those in the footwall. It is apparent, however, that under certain conditions, younger rocks may be thrust over older rocks. In some thrusts, as at *c* in Fig. 154D, younger rocks rest on older rocks; elsewhere, as at *a*, older rocks are on younger rocks; and locally, as at *d*, the rocks above the thrust are the same age as those beneath it. Along erosion thrusts, younger rocks may lie on older ones. In Fig. 154F, older rocks are on younger rocks at *c* and *d*; if, however, the hanging wall were to move over the erosion surface as far as *e*, formation *2* would lie on formation *1*. Thrusts in which younger rocks rest on older rocks may be difficult to recognize, and it may be particularly hard to distinguish such thrusts from unconformities.[4]

Folded thrusts are not uncommon. One example is shown at the right-hand end of Fig. 45. The data here are particularly good because a tunnel gives a continuous section some distance beneath the surface of the earth, and it crosses the thrust in three places. Other examples of folded thrusts are discussed on p. 184 and are illustrated by Figs. 157, 159, 162, 164, and 186.[5] Such folded thrusts are relatively even planes at one stage in their development; they are later folded.

---

[2] Cotton, C. A., "Tectonic Scarps and Fault Valleys," *Bulletin Geological Society of America*, Vol. 61, pp. 717–758, 1950.

[3] Longwell, C. R., "Structure of the Northern Muddy Mountain Area, Nevada," *Bulletin Geological Society of America*, Vol. 60, pp. 923–968, 1949.

[4] Billings, M. P., "Thrusting Younger Rocks Over Older," *American Journal of Science*, 5th ser., Vol. 25, pp. 140–165, 1933.

[5] See also King, P. B., *et al.*, "Geology and Manganese Deposits of Northeastern Tennessee," *Tennessee Division of Geology, Bulletin 52*, 1944.

Imbricate structure, sometimes called *shingle-block structure,* consists of several thrust faults dipping in the same direction. Ordinarily, the strata dip in the same direction as the thrusts and at similar, but not necessarily identical, angles. Excellent examples of imbricate structure are found in the Valley and Ridge Province of the Southern Appalachian Mountains[6] and in the Canadian Rockies (Fig. 156).[7]

Fig. 156. Imbricate structure in the Canadian Rockies. Formations in order of decreasing age are *1, 2, 3, 4,* and *5. 1 =* Cambrian, Ordovician, Devonian; *2 =* Carboniferous, *3 =* Triassic, *4 =* Jurassic, *5 =* Cretaceous. (After Raymond and Willard.)

OVERTHRUSTS

Overthrusts are spectacular geological features along which large masses of rock are displaced great distances. An *overthrust* may be defined as a thrust fault with an initial dip of 10 degrees or less and a net slip that is measured in miles. For another usage of the term, see p. 146. The *overthrust sheet* or overthrust block is the block above the fault plane. Although the initial dip is low, the overthrust may be folded to assume a steep dip, and it may even become overturned.

Our knowledge of overthrusts results largely from the fact that they are folded and eroded. Figure 157 is a map and structure section of a folded overthrust in a region of low relief. The attitude of the thrust plane is given by dip-and-strike symbols. The rocks above are shown by a dotted pattern, whereas those beneath the thrust plane are shown by diversely oriented short dashes. The overthrust sheet originally extended as far west as the line *xy,* but has been subsequently eroded from the central part of the area. The broken line in the upper part of the structure section shows the original top of the overthrust sheet. The symbol *K* is a remnant of the overthrust sheet, now isolated by erosion from the main thrust sheet. It is called a *Klippe* (a German word for *cliff*) because many such erosional remnants of overthrust sheets in northern Switzerland are high mountains bounded by steep cliffs. Erosion has broken through the upper sheet at *F,* exposing the rocks beneath the fault. This area is a *Fenster* or *window* because it is possible to look through the upper sheet to the lower. In Fig. 157, in which the surface of the

[6] Rodgers, John, "Geologic Map of East Tennessee, with Explanatory Text," *Tennessee Division of Geology, Bulletin 58,* 168 pages and 14 maps, 1953. See especially pl. 15.

[7] Raymond, P. E., and B. Willard, "A Structure Section across the Canadian Rockies." *Journal of Geology,* Vol. 39, pp. 97–116, 1931.

earth is flat, the Klippe is preserved in a doubly plunging syncline, and the Fenster is due to a doubly plunging anticline. Erosion alone may be

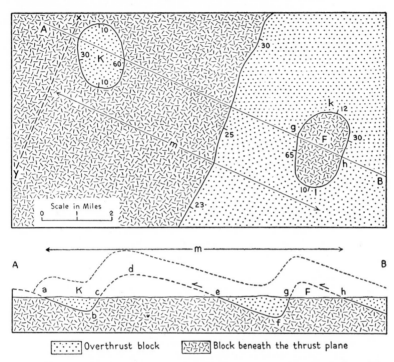

Fig. 157. Folded overthrust. Map above, structure section below. Dip of thrust plane shown by figures. K = Klippe, F = Fenster (window). AB = line of structure section. m = minimum breadth of overthrust block. xy = original western limit of overthrust block. Other letters are referred to in text.

chiefly responsible for a Klippe or Fenster in regions of high relief. The term *window* is frequently misused in American geological literature to refer to inliers, which occur in a normal stratigraphic sequence wherever erosion has broken through the younger strata to expose a circular, elliptical, or irregular area of older rocks.

The *root zone* of an overthrust is the exposure of the overthrust nearest its source. Thus in Fig. 157 the root zone is at h.

The stratigraphic throw along overthrusts may be many thousands of feet, and in many instances it may be determined with considerable precision.

The calculation of the net slip on an overthrust may be difficult. It is apparent, however, that if the strata were essentially flat when thrusting began and that if the dip of the fault plane were low, the net slip would be many times the stratigraphic throw. In fact, a simple trigonometric relation exists, and, as shown in Fig. 158:

$$ab = \frac{ac}{\sin \delta}$$

In this equation ab = net slip, ac = stratigraphic throw, and δ = dip of the fault plane. This assumes that the movement is directly up the dip of the fault; that is, there is no strike slip component.

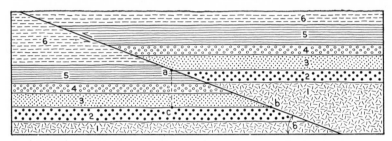

Fig. 158. Calculation of net slip from a cross section. Formations in order of decreasing age are *1, 2, 3, 4, 5,* and *6*. ab = net slip; ac = stratigraphic throw; δ = dip of thrust plane.

Even if the fault and the beds have been subsequently folded, δ may be taken as the angle between the bedding and the fault. In practice this method can seldom be applied because measurement of this critical angle may be impossible due to the drag and brecciation along the fault.

If sufficient data are available to prepare an adequate structure section, the net slip may be measured by noting the position of some key horizon both above and below the plane of the overthrust. In the structure section of Fig. 159, the net slip ab is five miles. The bottom of formation *3* below the thrust plane is truncated by the fault at point b. The same horizon above the thrust is truncated by the fault at a. For a specific example of such a thrust see Fig. 186.

The erroneous assumption is often made that a minimum value for the net slip may be obtained by measuring m (Figs. 157 and 159); this is the distance between the most advanced exposure of the fault in a Klippe and the most recessive exposure in a window, and it is measured at right angles to the strike of the main outcrop of the overthrust. Actually, m, as measured on the map, is the horizontal component of a somewhat greater distance measured along the fault plane. In Fig. 157, for example, m of the map is the horizontal component of *abcdefgh* of the structure section; in the structure section of Fig. 159, m is the horizontal component of *cabde*. The distance m may be called the *minimum breadth* of the overthrust. The true breadth of the overthrust is a much larger value and would be measured along the plane of the fault from the original most advanced position of the thrust block to that unknown place within the crust where the fault originated. Obviously, it is impossible to measure

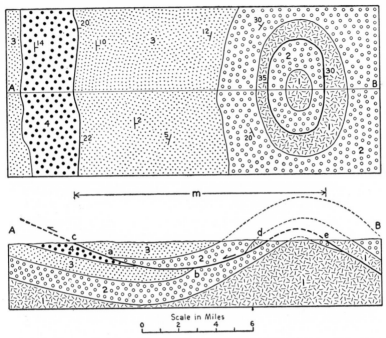

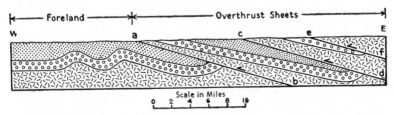

Fig. 159. Measuring net slip on an overthrust. Map above, structure section beneath. Formations in order of decreasing age are *1, 2, 3,* and *4.* Thrust is shown in heavier black line, with figures to indicate dip. *ab =* net slip. *m =* minimum breadth of overthrust block is really horizontal component of *cabde.*

the true breadth of overthrusts. In Fig. 159, the distance *m* is 13.7 miles, but the net slip *ab* is only 5 miles.

In many regions there may be more than one overthrust. In Fig. 160, three overthrusts, *ab, cd,* and *ef,* dip east, and along each of them the net slip is measured in miles. Each block between two overthrusts is an overthrust sheet; there are three overthrust sheets in Fig. 160.

The region in front of the overthrusts is often called the *foreland* (Fig. 160). Small thrusts, with a net slip of hundreds or even thousands of feet, may occur in the foreland, but there are no overthrusts.

The rocks of the foreland are essentially where they were deposited

Fig. 160. Foreland of an overthrust belt. *ab, cd,* and *ef =* thrust planes.

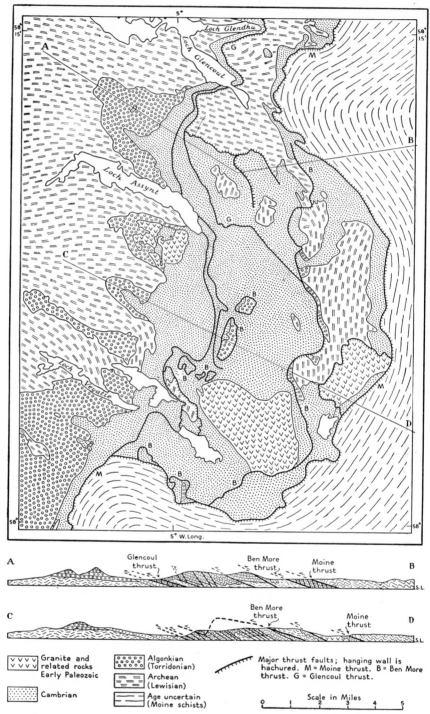

Fig. 161. Overthrusts of the Assynt District in the Northwest Highlands of Scotland. (Simplified from the Geological Survey of Scotland, Assynt district, 1923.)

and are said to be *autochthonous*—that is, developed where found; these rocks are sometimes called the *autochthon*. Although *foreland* and *autochthon* are somewhat similar terms, the former refers to the place, the latter to the rocks in that place.

The rocks in the overthrust sheets have traveled many miles from their original place of deposition and are said to be *allochthonous*—that is, formed somewhere else; these rocks are sometimes called the *allochthon*.

A *nappe* is a large body of rock that has moved forward more than one mile from its original position, either by overthrusting or by recumbent folding. The term is thus not synonymous with either *overthrust sheet* or *recumbent fold*. A large recumbent fold is a nappe, but a small one is not.

Some overthrusts are shown in Figs. 161, 162, 163, and 164. The Northwest Highlands of Scotland, a classic region of overthrusting[8] are illustrated by a map and structure sections of the Assynt district in Fig. 161. To the west is the foreland, composed of Archean, Algonkian, and Cambrian rocks. The western edge of the overthrust belt trends somewhat east of north across the center of the map. The Moine overthrust, designated by the letter *M*, is the major overthrust, and along it the Moine schists have been thrust westward. It is apparent that the Moine schists at one time extended at least as far west as Loch Assynt, but they have been removed from the central part of the area by erosion. Evidence to the north of the Assynt district indicates that the net slip along the Moine overthrust is at least 15 miles.

The Ben More thrust, designated by the letter *B*, outcrops west of the Moine thrust. Several Klippe of the Ben More thrust lie in the vicinity of section line *CD*.

The lowest thrust, separating the rocks that are essentially in place from those that have been moved, is known as a *sole*. Many minor thrusts, all dipping steeply to the east, produce a well-developed imbricate structure.

The Bannock overthrust [9] of southeastern Idaho is illustrated by Fig. 162. The main trace of the overthrust is very sinuous, extending southwestward from the northeast corner of the map. The irregularities are due to erosion of a folded overthrust. A large window appears in the northwest part of the map, and a smaller window appears in the north-central part.

Another example of a series of thrust sheets on top of one another is

[8] Peach, B. N., J. Horne, W. Gunn, C. T. Clough, L. W. Hinxman, and J. J. H. Teall, "The Geological Structure of the North-West Highlands of Scotland," *Memoir Geological Survey of Great Britain*, pp. 463–594. Glasgow: 1907.

[9] Mansfield, G. R., "Geology, Geography, and Mineral Resources of Southeastern Idaho," *U. S. Geological Survey Professional Paper 152*, pp. 150–159, 1929.

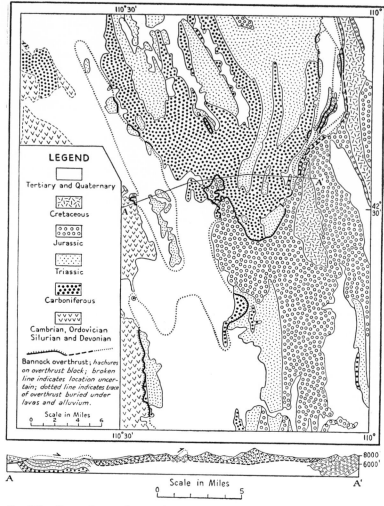

Fig. 162. Bannock overthrust of southeastern Idaho. (Simplified from G. R. Mansfield.)

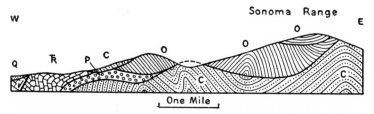

Fig. 163. Thrusts in Winnemucca Quadrangle, Nevada. Direction of displacement unknown. $O =$ Ordovician, $C =$ Carboniferous, $P =$ Permian, $Tr =$ Triassic, $Q =$ Quaternary. (After H. G. Ferguson, S. W. Muller, and R. J. Roberts.)

given in Fig. 163; no arrows are shown because the relative direction of thrusting is unknown.[10]

Some of the great overthrusts of the Glarus district of Switzerland [11] are shown in Fig. 164. The autochthonous rocks in the lower part of the section are separated from the allochthonous rocks in the upper part by a great overthrust, along which the net slip is at least 20 miles. The great drag folds in the autochthon show that the relative movement of the overthrust sheets was toward the north.

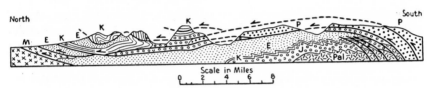

Fig. 164. Overthrusts of the Glarus District, Switzerland. Thrusts shown in heavy black. Pal = Paleozoic, P = Permian, J = Triassic and Jurassic, K = Cretaceous, E = Eocene, M = Miocene. (After J. Oberholzer.)

It is not always easy to determine the direction of movement along overthrusts. The early geologists assumed that the net slip was directly up the dip of the fault. This would probably be correct for an unfolded overthrust. Figure 157 is a hypothetical case in which the overthrust sheet moved from southeast to northwest parallel to the line AB. The present dip of the overthrust has little significance with reference to the direction of movement. Around both the Klippe and the window, the strike of the overthrust boxes the compass.

At h on the map of Fig. 157, the net slip is up the dip; at g, it is down the dip; and at k and l, it is parallel to the strike of the overthrust.

It is believed that in most instances the movement was essentially at right angles to the average strike of the overthrust. Thus in Fig. 161, the movement was essentially parallel to CD. More precise evidence is offered, however, by drag folds and minor thrusts beneath the overthrust. Drag folds are overturned in the direction of movement (Figs. 164 and 165). Minor thrusts dip in the direction from which the overthrust was moving (Fig. 161). An excellent example of the use of minor structures, such as drag folds, striations, cleavage, lineation, and boudinage (pages

[10] Ferguson, H. G., S. W. Muller, and R. J. Roberts, "Winnemucca Quadrangle, Nevada," *Geologic Quadrangle Maps of the United States, U. S. Geological Survey,* 1951.

[11] Bailey, E. B., *Tectonic Essays, Mainly Alpine,* pp. 36–56. Oxford: Clarendon Press, 1935.

Heim, A., *Geologie der Schweiz,* Vol. 1 and Vol. 2. Leipzig: C. H. Tauchnitz, 1919, 1921, and 1922.

Oberholzer, J., "Geologie der Glarneralpen," *Beiträge Geologischen Karte der Schweiz,* Neue Folge, Lieferung 28, 1933.

352 to 355, and 361), to tell the direction of overthrusting has been described from England.[12]

Some of the large overthrusts may be followed for long distances along the strike. The Bannock overthrust of Idaho is at least 270 miles long,[13] and the Lewis overthrust along the Rocky Mountain front in Montana is at least 135 miles long, and is probably more than 300 miles long.[14]

The stratigraphic throw may amount to several miles. Along the Bannock overthrust, the maximum stratigraphic throw is 15,000 feet;[15] along the Lewis overthrust, the stratigraphic throw is approximately 40,000 feet.[16] In the Muddy Mountains of Nevada there are two major overthrusts. Along the larger of these the stratigraphic throw is at least 11,000 feet and the net slip is at least 15 miles.[17] Near Buffalo Mountain, Tennessee, where lower Cambrian quartzites are thrust over Ordovician limestone and shales, the stratigraphic throw is approximately 14,000 feet.[18]

The net slip along some of the large overthrusts is to be measured in miles and even tens of miles. Unfortunately, however, many of the data in the geological publications are unreliable because the observers have actually measured the minimum breadth (p. 186), but have erroneously stated it to be the net slip. A minimum displacement of 12 miles along the Bannock overthrust is well authenticated; a larger figure of 35 miles, which is also cited in the geological literature, is actually the value for the minimum breadth. A minimum figure for the net slip along the Lewis overthrust is 15 miles. Although the net slip along the overthrust in the vicinity of Buffalo Mountain, Tennessee, is approximately 6 miles, the minimum breadth is 12 miles, and this figure has been erroneously stated to be the net slip. A structure section of the Glarus district in the Alps (Fig. 164) indicates that the net slip along the Glarus overthrust is not less than 20 miles.

Figure 165 shows two large overthrust sheets in the Swiss Alps 15

---

[12] Wilson, Gilbert, "The Tectonics of the Tintagel Area, North Cornwall," *Quarterly Journal of the Geological Society* of London, Vol. CVI, pp. 393–432, 1951.

[13] Mansfield, G. R., *op. cit.*

[14] Billings, M. P., "Physiographic Relations of the Lewis Overthrust in Northern Montana," *American Journal of Science*, 5th series, Vol. 35, pp. 260–272, 1938.

[15] Mansfield, G. R., *op. cit.*, p. 158.

[16] Clapp, C. H., "Geology of a Portion of the Rocky Mountains of Northern Montana," *Montana Bureau of Mines and Geology, Memoir 4*, p. 25, 1932.

[17] Longwell, C. R., "Geology of the Muddy Mountains, Nevada," *U. S. Geological Survey Bulletin 798*, p. 110, 1928; "Structure of the Northern Muddy Mountain Area, Nevada," *Bulletin Geological Society of America*, Vol. 60, pp. 923–968, 1949.

[18] Keith, A., "Roan Mountain Folio, No. 151," *Geologic Atlas of the United States, U. S. Geological Survey*, 1907.

King, P. B., *et al.*, "Geology and Manganese of Northeastern Tennessee," Tennessee Division of Geology, Bulletin 52, 275 pages, 1944.

miles southeast of Lake Geneva.[19] Cretaceous rocks have been pushed over Eocene formations along the lower thrust; Cretaceous rocks have been thrust over Cretaceous and Eocene formations along the upper thrust. The thrusts dip north, and the overthrust sheets have traveled northward relative to the underlying formations. The drag folds are consistent with this interpretation.

It was long assumed that overthrust blocks moved forward because pressure was being exerted on the back of the block. For example, in Fig. 158, it would be commonly assumed that a horizontally directed force was acting toward the left on the right end of the block. An alternative possibility would be that displacements beneath the left-hand block dragged it toward the right. Still another possibility would be that rocks

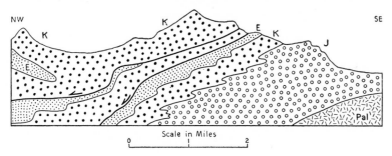

Fig. 165. Overthrusts in high calcareous Alps of Switzerland. Thrusts shown in heavy black. *Pal* = Paleozoic, *J* = Triassic and Jurassic, *K* = Cretaceous, *E* = Eocene. (Simplified from M. Lugeon.)

above the right-hand block dragged it toward the left. Where the upper block appears to have moved "downhill," as in the middle of Fig. 159, it has been supposed that the thrust plane was folded subsequent to the thrusting. But Fig. 165 suggests another possibility. Could the blocks above the thrust planes have slid downhill under the influence of gravity, in the same way that a landslide moves? This possibility is discussed on page 234. There it is also pointed out that some Klippe may not be erosional remnants of a once continuous thrust sheet, as shown in Fig. 157, but may merely be gigantic landslide blocks.

PALINSPASTIC MAPS

Most students of geology are familiar with paleogeographic maps, which show the geography at some specified time in the past.[20] Most

[19] Lugeon, M., "Les Hautes Alpes Calcaires entre la Lizerne et la Kander," *Matériaux pour la carte géologique de la Suisse. Nouvelle Series,* Vol. 30, 94 pp. Berne: 1914.

[20] Dunbar, C. O., *Historical Geology.* New York: John Wiley and Sons, Inc., 567 pages, 1949. Especially pp. 1–6.

such maps merely show the distribution of land and sea. Others are more elaborate,[21] showing in addition the location of mountain ranges and the thickness of the sediments that accumulated. A *paleogeologic* map purports to be a geologic map of an area as it would have appeared at some specified time in the past. For example, a geologic map of North America at the beginning of Tertiary time would obviously show no Tertiary or Quaternary rocks. Moreover, all rocks eroded away since the beginning of the Tertiary would be restored.

However, such maps ordinarily make no allowance for the shortening that has resulted from folding and overthrusting. On the ordinary paleogeographic map a geosyncline that was originally 200 miles wide but has been reduced to 150 miles by folding and thrusting is shown as 150 miles wide. Kay[22] has pointed out that it would be more correct to "unfold" and "unthrust" the rocks before preparing the paleogeographic maps. *Palinspastic maps* place rocks in their presumed positions prior to folding and thrusting. Commendable as this ideal may be, it is often difficult to put into practice because of lack of adequate information on the amount of crustal shortening.

[21] Eardley, A. J., *Structural Geology of North America.* New York: Harper and Brothers, 624 pages, 1951.
[22] Kay, Marshall, "Paleogeographic and Palinspastic maps," *Bulletin American Association Petroleum Geologists,* Vol. 29, pp. 426–450, 1945.

CHAPTER 12

Gravity or Normal Faults

INTRODUCTION

Gravity faults are those in which the hanging wall has gone down relative to the footwall; they involve lengthening of the crust of the earth. There are many possibilities concerning the actual movement as measured from some datum, such as sea level or the center of the earth. The footwall may remain stationary and the hanging wall go down; or the hanging wall may remain stationary and the footwall go up; or both blocks may move down, but the hanging wall more than the footwall; or both blocks may move up, but the footwall more than the hanging wall. In the present state of our knowledge it is impossible in most cases to determine the absolute movement, and hence an elaborate terminology is unnecessary and undesirable. In some instances, where there is evidence that the footwall has moved up along a high-angle gravity fault or that the hanging wall block has moved up along a high-angle thrust fault, the term *upthrust* may be used.

Many geologists use the term *normal fault* in preference to gravity fault, but as indicated on p. 143, normal fault has a different meaning. But most normal faults, as the term is defined in this book, are also gravity faults.

ATTITUDE, SIZE, AND PATTERN

The dip of gravity faults may range from almost horizontal to vertical, but dips greater than 45 degrees are more common than dips less than 45 degrees. Gravity faults may range from microscopic size to those that are tens of miles long and have a net slip that is measured in thousands of feet. The system of faults that bounds the Triassic rocks extending from New York to Virginia on the northwest is 340 miles long, according to the 1944 tectonic map of the United States. Gravity faults in the Colorado Plateaus of Arizona and Utah are shown on the same map to be 100 to 300 miles long. In most instances, such long faults are not single fractures throughout their length, but locally are fault zones. The gravity fault bounding the west side of the Wasatch Range of Utah is mapped by

Gilbert as a single, somewhat sinuous fault at least 80 miles long.[1] More detailed mapping by Eardley shows that at the south end of the range there are several *en échelon*, overlapping faults.[2]

The minimum net slip along a gravity fault bounding the Triassic rocks of Connecticut on the east side is 13,000 [3] feet and perhaps more.[4] The probable net slip along the gravity fault on the west side of the Wasatch Range of Utah is 17,900 feet.[5]

The pattern shown in plan by gravity faults is varied. The individual faults are generally rather straight, but they may be sinuous or irregular, with sudden changes in strike. In many instances two or more gravity faults are parallel to one another (Fig. 128A). *Step faults* are those in which the downthrow is systematically on the same side of several parallel faults. In many localities the gravity faults show an *en échelon* pattern (Fig. 128B). Elsewhere they may be peripheral (Fig. 128C), radial (Fig. 128D) or irregular.

The most conspicuous structural features that result from gravity fault are belts of *en échelon* faulting, tilted fault blocks, horsts, and graben.

EN ÉCHELON GRAVITY FAULTS

In some areas gravity faults show an en échelon pattern, such as that illustrated by Fig. 166A. The individual faults strike at an angle of approximately 45 degrees to the trend of the faulted belt as a whole. The active tension is in the direction TT' (Fig. 166B), but a regional tension acting in this direction would not account for the *en échelon* pattern. The long axis of a strain ellipse is oriented northeast (aa' of Fig. 166C). A couple caused by a northerly block moving toward the east relative to a southerly block would produce the type of fracture observed.

Faults of this type are common in northeastern Oklahoma.[6] The belts of faulting, of which there are several, trend north-south, whereas most of the individual faults trend north-northwest to northwest. The largest fault is $3\frac{1}{4}$ miles long, and the maximum stratigraphic throw is 130 feet.

[1] Gilbert, G. K., "Studies of Basin Range Structure," *U. S. Geological Survey Prof. Paper 153*, Fig. 12, 1928.

[2] Eardley, A. J., "Structure and Physiography of the Southern Wasatch Mountains," *Papers Michigan Academy Science, Arts, and Letters*, Vol. 19, pp. 377–400, 1933.

[3] Longwell, C. R., "Sedimentation in Relation to Faulting," *Bulletin Geological Society of America*, Vol. 48, pp. 433–442; cf. especially p. 436, 1937.

[4] Krynine, P. D., "Petrology, Stratigraphy, and Origin of the Triassic Sedimentary Rocks of Connecticut," *Bulletin 73, Connecticut State Geological and Natural History Survey*, 247 pp., 1950.

[5] Gilbert, G. K., *op. cit.*, p. 52.

[6] Fath, A. E., "The Origin of the Faults, Anticlines, and Buried "Granite Ridge" of the Northern Part of the Mid-Continent Oil and Gas Field," *U. S. Geological Survey Prof. Paper 128C*, pp. 75–84, 1920.
See also "Tectonic Map of the United States," *American Association of Petroleum Geologists*, 1944.

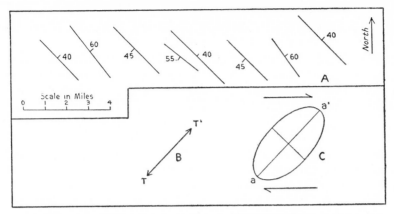

Fig. 166. *En échelon* gravity faults. *A.* Diagrammatic map of an area of *en échelon* gravity faults; each line represents a fault several miles long; angle of dip shown in degrees. *B.* Direction of active tension. *C.* Strain ellipse, caused by a couple.

A similar belt of *en échelon* faulting in central Montana, the Lake Basin fault zone, trends east-southeast for some 56 miles.[7] More than 90 northeasterly-trending faults have been mapped, many of them over 5 miles long, and one, at least, is 10 miles long. The dips of the faults range from 10 to 80 degrees, but average about 45 degrees; the maximum recorded stratigraphic throw is between 500 and 600 feet. Most of the faults are of the gravity type, but some are reverse faults, and in some there has been a strike slip component to the displacement. This belt of faulting is due to a couple, the southerly block moving east relative to the southerly block.

TILTED FAULT BLOCKS

Gravity faulting is accompanied in many instances by tilting of the blocks on one or both sides of the fault, and *tilted fault blocks* result. Examples are shown in Fig. 168. In many cases there is no topographic expression of the fault blocks (Figs. 168A and 168B). In other instances the topography expresses the underlying structure more or less faithfully (Figs. 168C and 168D). The situation is seldom as simple, however, as in these very diagrammatic figures because erosion attacks the highest areas.

[7] Hancock, E. T., "Geology and Oil and Gas Prospects of the Lake Basin Field, Montana," *U. S. Geological Survey Bull. 691*, pp. 101–147, 1918.

Chamberlin, R. T., "A Peculiar Belt of Oblique Faulting," *Journal of Geology,* Vol. 27, pp. 602–613, 1919.

Chamberlin, R. T., "Diastrophic Behavior around the Bighorn Basin," *Journal of Geology,* Vol. 48, pp. 673–716, 1940.

Also see "Tectonic Map of the United States," *op. cit.*

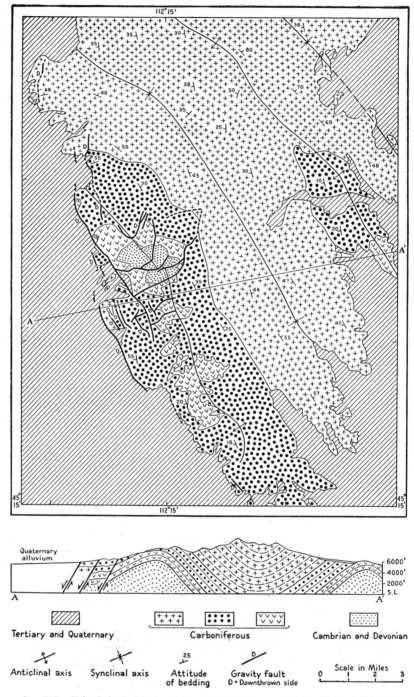

Fig. 167. Tilted fault block of the Oquirrh Range, Utah. (After Gilluly.)

The resulting debris may be deposited in the adjacent valleys as shown in Fig. 169A. On the other hand, streams may remove all the debris, and even the downthrown block may be eroded. The mountains that rise above the valleys in such cases are one variety of *fault block mountains*. Some fault block mountains are horsts (p. 208).

Tilted fault blocks are most readily recognized by the tilting of one or more datum planes, such as the bedding (Figs. 168A, 168B, and 168C). In some cases a late-mature or old-age erosion surface may be broken and tilted (Fig. 168D).[8] Such erosion surfaces are particularly useful in those

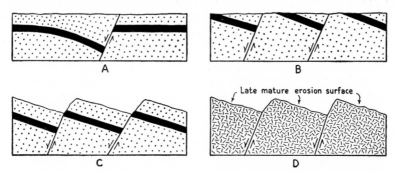

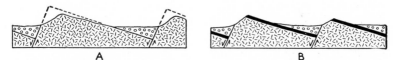

Fig. 168. Tilted fault blocks. Solid black = shale; dots = sandstone; diversely oriented dashes = granite. *A.* and *B.* Tilted fault blocks that are not expressed topographically. *C.* Topographically expressed tilted fault blocks. *D.* Topographically expressed tilted fault blocks developed on granite; a late mature erosion surface has been broken and tilted by the faulting.

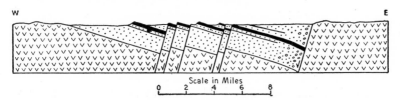

Fig. 169. Tilted fault blocks. Diversely oriented dashes are granite; circles are alluvium; solid black is lava. *A.* Alluvium derived from erosion of higher parts of the fault blocks accumuates in depressions. *B.* A broken and tilted lava bed that serves as a key bed.

Fig. 170. Tilted fault block of the Connecticut Valley, Connecticut. Checks = pre-Triassic crystalline rocks; dots = arkose, sandstone, shale; circles = conglomerate; solid black = volcanic rocks. (Modified from Barrell.)

[8] Pardee, J. T., "Late Cenozoic Block Faulting in Western Montana," *Bulletin Geological Society of America*, Vol. 61, pp. 359–406, 1950.

regions that are underlain by granitic rocks, or in those areas where the strata were highly deformed prior to the gravity faulting. In some mountains a thin lava flow may serve as the key bed that shows rupture and tilting (Fig. 169B).

The Triassic rocks of eastern North America display tilted fault blocks that have little topographic expression. In Connecticut (Fig. 170), the easterly-dipping Triassic rocks rest unconformably on the older crystalline rocks to the west. On the east a large, westerly-dipping gravity fault, with a net slip of at least 13,000 feet, separates the Triassic rocks from the crystalline rocks to the east. The Triassic strata dip toward the east at an angle of 20 degrees except near the fault, where the easterly dip reaches a maximum of 40 degrees. Longwell [9] has shown that the fault was active during deposition. A number of northeasterly-trending gravity faults lie within the Triassic rocks.

Tilted fault blocks that are expressed topographically are well developed in the Great Basin of the western United States.[10] Figure 167 shows the Oquirrh Range of central Utah.[11] These mountains rise 5,000 feet above the alluvial valley to the west, south, and east. The Paleozoic rocks are thrown into broad, open folds, the axes of which trend northwest. The western side of the range is broken by a series of gravity faults, the most significant of which trend north-northwest. Where the faults have actually been observed, the dip ranges from 40 to 64 degrees to the west-southwest, and it averages 57 degrees. In all instances the hanging wall has gone down relative to the footwall. The maximum measured stratigraphic throw, which is along the fault with the greatest length in Fig. 167, is 3,500 feet. The greatest displacement may be along the most southwesterly of the faults, but the downthrown block is buried under alluvium.

The manner in which the internal structure of the range is truncated by the western front of the mountains is clearly brought out by the map. A piedmont scarp, 40 feet high, which cuts alluvium, testifies to the recency of some of the movements. In general, however, the faults are not well expressed in the topography (see cross section in Fig. 167), and triangular facets are poorly defined. These facts indicate that considerable erosion has modified whatever scarps may have existed.

It is obvious that the mountain block has been uplifted along the faults many thousands of feet relative to the valleys to the west. A mature erosion surface, which developed on the site of the range prior to the normal faulting, has been tilted eastward at an angle of approximately 4 degrees.

[9] Longwell, C. R., *op. cit.*

[10] Nolan, T. B., "The Basin and Range Province in Utah, Nevada, and California," *U. S. Geological Survey, Prof. Paper 197*, pp. 141–193, 1943.

[11] Gilluly, James, "Geology and Ore Deposits of the Stockton and Fairfield Quadrangles, Utah," *U. S. Geological Survey Prof. Paper 173*, 1932.

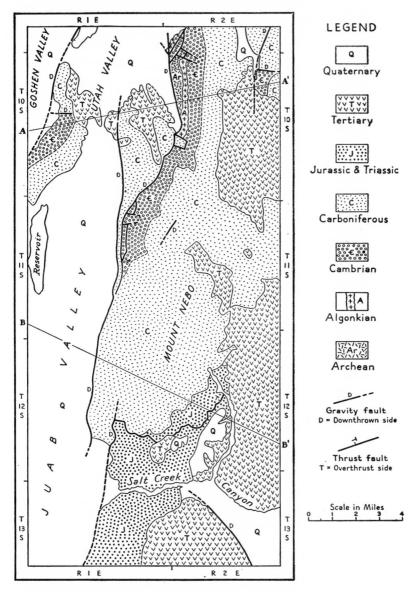

Fig. 171. Geological map of the tilted fault block of the southern part of the Wasatch Range, Utah. Cross sections along lines *AA'* and *BB'* are in Fig. 172. (After Eardley.)

The Wasatch Range of Utah is a tilted fault block[12] illustrated by Figs. 171–173. The Wasatch Mountains extend north from Salt Creek in the southern part of Fig. 171. The Juab Valley, which lies to the west of Mt. Nebo, the highest peak in this part of the Wasatch Range, is underlain by Quaternary alluvium many hundreds of feet thick.

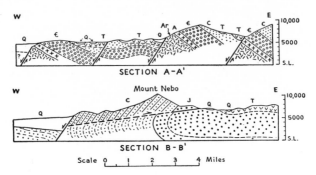

Fig. 172. Cross sections of the southern part of the Wasatch Range, Utah, along lines *AA'* and *BB'* of Fig. 171. *Ar* = Archean; *A* = Algonkian; *Ȼ* = Cambrian; *C* = Carboniferous; *J* = Triassic and Jurassic; *T* =Tertiary; *Q* = Quaternary. (After Eardley.)

The Jurassic and older rocks in the mountains were greatly deformed by the Laramide folding in the late Cretaceous; consequently, the Tertiary and Quaternary rocks rest unconformably (see Chapter 15) on the older rocks. Mt. Nebo has been eroded from the eastern limb of an overturned anticline; this is shown on section *BB'*, Fig. 172, where the

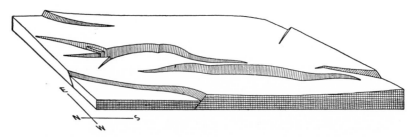

Fig. 173. Highly diagrammatic block diagram of the gravity faults of the southern part of the Wasatch Range, reviewed from west. The top of the block is an arbitrary surface, essentially horizontal. (After Eardley.)

younger, Jurassic rocks dip under the older, Carboniferous rocks. A major thrust of considerable breadth, but slight net slip, cuts the overturned

[12] Eardley, A. J., *op. cit.;* also, Eardley, A. J., "Geology of the North-Central Wasatch Mountains," *Bulletin, Geological Society of America,* Vol. 55, pp. 819–894, **1944.**

limb. Toward the north, the strata are less intensely overturned, and the dips progressively change from overturned toward the west into vertical and, finally, into easterly dips. Along the line of section AA', the Wasatch Range is carved out of the eastern limb of an anticline that is not overturned.

The gravity faults, the pattern of which is shown by the map, are much younger than the anticline and the thrust fault. Along the line of section BB', a single large fault bounds the range on the west. Farther north, however, another fault appears *en échelon* to the east, and north of section AA' this is the fault that bounds the range on the west. Two of the fault planes that may be observed dip 50 degrees west. The net slip on the major faults ranges from 6,500 to 7,800 feet. Figure 173 is a block diagram to illustrate the character of the gravity faults as seen from west of the area. The front of the block corresponds to the west side of the geological map, Fig. 171. The block diagram illustrates very strikingly the *en échelon* character of the faults. The surface of this block is an arbitrary horizontal datum plane, and in the area no such surface exists.

Many lines of evidence demonstrate the presence of the faults. Not only may the fault planes be observed, but triangular facets are well developed, and piedmont scarps cut alluvial fans, a fact that testifies to the recency of the movements.

Prior to gravity faulting, the region had been dissected to a mature topography with a relief of at least 3,000 feet.[13] Eardley has calculated that the fault block has been tilted to the east at an angle of 3 to 4 degrees.

GRABEN AND HORSTS

Many fault blocks are bounded on both sides by gravity faults along which the displacement is more or less equal, and consequently, there is little or no tilting. A *graben* is a block, generally long compared to its width, that has been lowered relative to the blocks on either side. A *horst* is a block, generally long compared to its width, that has been raised relative to the blocks on either side. The border faults are usually steep, and in most cases, if not all, they are either gravity faults or are essentially vertical. In some cases the border faults have been described as steep reverse faults, but the validity of these observations is questionable.

Graben and horsts, like most geological structures, may differ greatly in size. Figure 174, which is a map of small faults formed during the earthquake of December 20, 1932, near Cedar Mountain, Nevada, shows

[13] Eardley, A. J., "Strong Relief before Block Faulting in the Vicinity of the Wasatch Mountains, Utah," *Journal of Geology*, Vol. 41, pp. 243–267, 1933.

some small graben.[14] The black lines are open fissures that are essentially vertical; the weight of the line shows the relative strength of the fissures, but the width has been exaggerated. The surface of the ground was the datum plane displaced by the fissures. In the northeast corner of the map, a small graben, 35 feet wide and 140 feet long, is shown. The throw on the east wall is 12 inches, whereas on the west wall it is 5 inches. Some

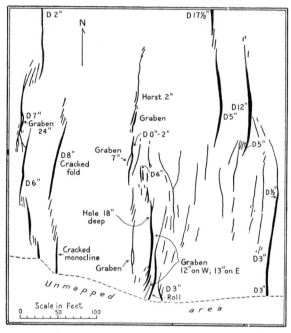

Fig. 174. Fissures, horsts, and graben formed during Cedar Mountain, Nevada, Earthquake. Solid black lines are open fissures; width of lines indicates relative magnitude of the fissures, but is not to scale. D = downthrown side of fissure, the amount being given in inches. (After Gianella and Callaghan.)

of the graben are even smaller; in the south-central part of the map, a graben is 120 feet long, 5 to 20 feet wide, and the displacement along the faults is approximately one foot.

In the Grand Canyon region in Arizona, 24 small graben that trend in a general northerly direction have been mapped.[15] The average length is 3½ miles, but the range in length is from 1 to 8 miles. Most of the

[14] Gianella, B. P., and E. Callaghan, "The Cedar Mountain, Nevada, Earthquake of Dec. 20, 1932," *Bulletin Seismological Society of America,* Vol. 24, pp. 345–377, 1934.

[15] Babenroth, D. L. and A. N. Strahler, "Geomorphology and Structure of the East Kaibab Monocline, Arizona and Utah," *Bulletin Geological Society of America,* Vol. 56, pp. 107–150, 1945.

graben are a quarter of a mile wide. The average net slip along the border faults is 100 feet, but ranges from 25 feet to 200 feet. Data are not given on the dips of the faults, but they are apparently steep.

In the Wasatch Plateau of Utah numerous graben that trend north-south cut the gently-dipping Mesozoic and Cenozoic strata. One of these, the Joe's Valley graben, is more than 60 miles long, and is 2 to $2\frac{1}{2}$ miles wide.[16] The *en échelon* pattern of the faults at the north end of this gra-

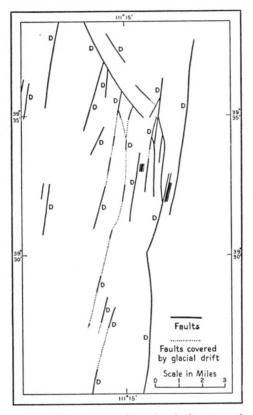

Fig. 175. Pattern of gravity faults at north end of Joe's Valley Graben, Utah. $D =$ downthrown side. (After Spieker and Billings.)

ben (Fig. 175) is similar to the pattern formed during the Cedar Mountain earthquake (Fig. 174). The maximum displacement on the faults throughout the entire graben ranges from 1,500 to 3,000 feet, but in the area covered by Fig. 175, it is from 1,400 to 1,600 feet. None of the faults has been observed, but the evidence indicates that the dips are steep.

A geologic map and structure section of part of a similar structural

[16] Spieker, E. M., and M. P. Billings, Glaciation in the Wasatch Plateau, Utah, *Bulletin Geological Society of America,* Vol. 51, pp. 1173–1198; especially Pl. 5, 1940.

feature in another part of the Wasatch Plateau, the Musinia graben,[17] are shown in Fig. 176. None of the faults have been observed, but the dips are essentially vertical. The displacement along the most easterly fault increases from south to north; at the south end of the map it is

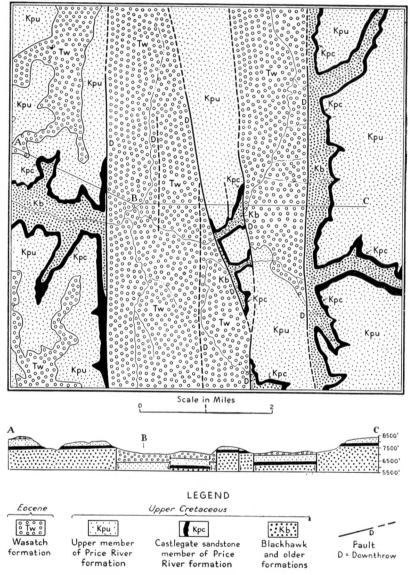

Fig. 176. Musinia Graben, Utah. (After Spieker and Baker.)

[17] Spieker, E. M., and A. A. Baker, Jr., "Geology and Coal Resources of the Salina Canyon District, Sevier County, Utah," *U. S. Geological Survey Bull. 796*, pp. 125–170, 1928.

only 500 feet, but at cross section *ABC* it is 1,300 feet; at the north end
of the map, the displacement increases to 2,500 feet. The displacement
along the western fault at structure section *ABC* is 2,000 feet. A notable
feature of this graben is a central horst, which increases in width toward
the north and which wedges out to the south.

The Rhine graben in Europe is 180 miles long and 20 to 25 miles wide.
The eastern border fault, where it is crossed by a tunnel, dips about 55
degrees toward the west, occupying a crushed zone about 50 feet wide.
The main part of the Great Graben, to the east of Lake Victoria in
Africa, is approximately 300 miles long and is as much as 35 miles wide.
The displacement along the faults bordering the Nyassa graben is as
much as 8,000 feet.

Most cross sections of graben are based on surface data, and little
information is available as to what happens at depth. Petroleum geology
has made great contributions to this phase of the problem. Figure 177 is
a section of a complex graben based on numerous drill holes.[18] The following points deserve special mention. (1) The graben is located on the
crest of an anticline. (2) The graben is about 1½ miles wide. (3) The

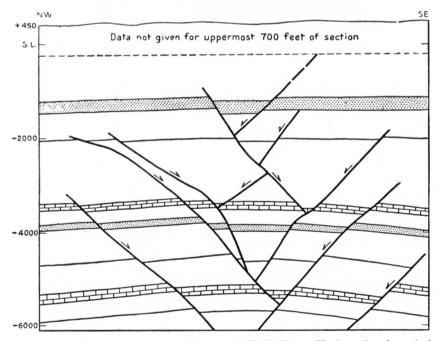

Fig. 177. Graben on anticline. Quitman Oil Field, Texas. Horizontal and vertical
scales are the same, shown in feet on left side of section. (After E. R. Scott; permission of American Association of Petroleum Geologists.)

[18] Scott, E. R., "Quitman Oil Field, Wood County, Texas," *Structure of Typical
American Oil Fields*, Vol. III, pp. 419–431. Tulsa: American Association Petroleum
Geologists, 1948.

throw on none of the faults exceeds 150 feet. (4) Many of the lesser faults terminate against larger faults.

In experimental graben, formed by subjecting clay to tension, *antithetic faults*[19] are extensively developed under certain conditions. These faults dip toward the master fault (Fig. 178), but the displacement along them is dominantly of the gravity type. Such antithetic faults are common in a tunnel section that cuts the eastern border fault of the Rhine graben.

Fig. 178. Edge of an artificial graben. Produced by subjecting clay to tension. The master fault and many subsidiary faults dip to the right. Antithetic faults dip to the left. All the faults are of the gravity type. (After H. Cloos.)

Horsts range in size from those that are only a few inches wide to those that are many miles wide. A small horst that occupies the center of the Musinia graben (Fig. 176) is at least 5 miles long, one mile wide at maximum; the displacement along the border faults is 1,000 to 1,500 feet.

The Ruby-East Humboldt Mountains of Nevada (Fig. 179) are essentially a large, complex horst that trends north-northeast for at least 53 miles and averages 7 miles in width.[20] The faults bounding the range are gravity faults that dip away from the mountains at angles of 60 to 70 degrees. The displacement on the eastern faults is 5,500 to 6,000 feet, whereas that on the western faults is only 2,000 feet. The range is thus a westward tilted horst. Many of the criteria given in Chapter 9 may be employed to prove the presence of the faults: the internal structure of

[19] Cloos, H., "Hebung, Spaltung, Vulkanismus," *Geologische Rundschau,* Band 30, Zwischenheft 4A, pp. 406–527, 1939; cf. especially p. 434.

[20] Sharp, R. P., "Basin-Range Structure of the Ruby-East Humboldt Range, Northeastern Nevada," *Bulletin Geological Society of America,* Vol. 50, pp. 881–920. 1939.

the range is truncated by the mountain front; piedmont scarps as much as 200 feet high cut bedrock, alluvium, and glacial moraines; triangular facets are exposed on the west side of the range; and in two localities the fault plane is exposed.

The Stillwater Range in central Nevada is another example of a horst

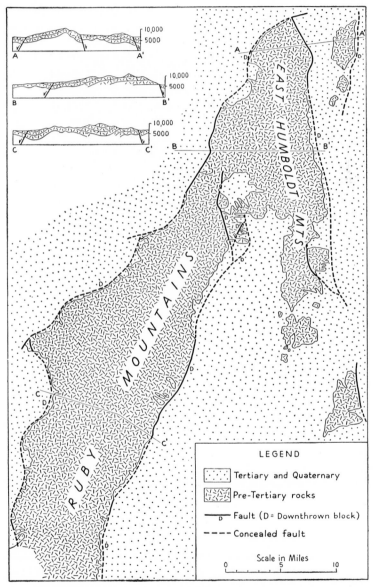

Fig. 179. Horst of the Ruby-East Humbolt Range, Nevada. (After R. P. Sharp.)

(Fig. 180). The Paleozoic and Mesozoic sedimentary rocks in the range
are thrown into folds trending north-northeast. A large body of Mesozoic
diorite cuts the folds in the southern part of the area. The gravity faults
are of various ages, but the most recent ones separate the range from
the valleys. "Longitudinal normal faults have determined the present
outline of the ranges. To some extent this faulting has taken place within

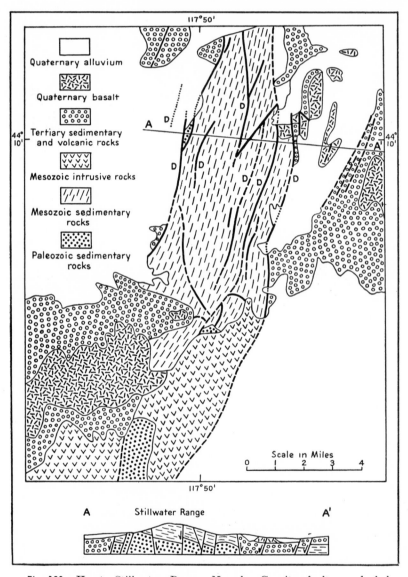

Fig. 180. Horst. Stillwater Range, Nevada. Gravity faults marked by
heavy lines, downthrown side indicated by *D*. (After H. G. Ferguson, S. W.
Muller, and R. J. Roberts.)

the present physiographic cycle, and the steep frontal scarps are at least in part the direct result of such movement." [21]

INTERMITTENT FAULTING

Movement along faults is intermittent, and a period of relatively rapid movements may be followed by a long interval of quiescence, during which erosion partially or completely destroys the topographic expression of the fault. In a renewed cycle of rapid movements a new scarp can develop.

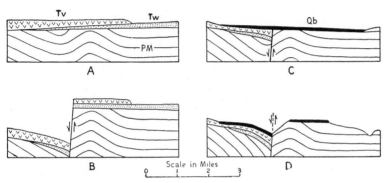

Fig. 181. Evolution of the Hurricane Fault, Utah and Arizona. $PM =$ Paleozoic and Mesozoic rocks; $Tw =$ Wasatch formation (Eocene); $Tv =$ Miocene (?) volcanics; $Qb =$ basalt (Quaternary). *A, B, C,* and *D* represent successive stages. (After L. S. Gardner.)

Figure 181 illustrates the intermittent character of movement along the Hurricane fault of Utah and Arizona.[22] This fault extends at least 170 miles in a direction somewhat east of north, and the displacement ranges from 1,500 to 10,000 feet. After eruption of Miocene (?) volcanics (Fig. 181A), the Hurricane fault formed in late Miocene or Pliocene time and the western block dropped 8,000 feet relative to the eastern block (Fig. 181B). In a subsequent interval of quiescence, all topographic expression of the fault was destroyed, and a surface of low relief developed. During Quaternary time basalts were erupted on this surface (Fig. 181C). During the last disturbance, which occurred during the Quaternary, the western block dropped 700 to 1,000 feet (Fig. 181D).

[21] Muller, S. W., H. G. Ferguson, and R. J. Roberts, "Geology of the Mount Tobin Quadrangle, Nevada," *Geologic Quadrangle Maps of the United States,* 1951.

[22] Gardner, L. S., "The Hurricane Fault in Southwestern Utah and Northwestern Arizona," *American Journal of Science,* Vol. 239, pp. 241–260, 1941.

CHAPTER 13

Strike-Slip Faults

ESSENTIAL FEATURES

Strike-slip faults are those along which the displacement is chiefly parallel to the strike of the fault. Most of them are steep and straight; crushing of the rocks in the vicinity is characteristic, and the larger faults of this type are usually fault zones rather than single, clean-cut fractures.

Although special terms have been proposed for the various faults that belong in this category, no general term is available other than strike-slip faults. Rifts are strike-slip faults that are parallel to the regional structure. Several names have been proposed for those strike-slip faults transverse to the regional structure, such as tear fault, flaw, wrench fault, and transverse fault.[1]

To demonstrate that a fault is a strike-slip fault may be difficult. Ideally two or more planar structures with different attitudes should be disrupted by the fault (p. 135 and pp. 474–481) in order to calculate the net slip.

Structural features that have been offset by some of the strike-slip faults described in geological publications are: (1) beds or formations; (2) dikes or veins; (3) axial planes and axes of folds; (4) sedimentary basins; (5) streams; (6) granitic stocks; and (7) zones of metamorphism.

STRIKE-SLIP FAULTS DIAGONAL TO FOLD AXES

Jura Mountains

Superb examples of strike-slip faults diagonal to fold axes have been described in the Jura Mountains of northern Switzerland and adjacent parts of France.[2] Mesozoic rocks display an Appalachian type of folding. The faults (Fig. 182) are diagonal rather than perpendicular to the fold axes. The faults are generally vertical and some of them have coarse

---

[1] Anderson, E. M., The Dynamics of Faulting and Dyke Formation, with applications to Britain, 2nd ed., p. 59. Edinburgh and London: Oliver and Boyd, 1951.

[2] Heim, Albert, *Geologie der Schweiz*, Vol. I, pp. 613–626, Leipzig: C. H. Tauchnitz, 1919

horizontal slickensides. Several of the faults are nearly 30 miles long. The average net slip, almost horizontal, is 0.6 mile, but along the south end of fault number *5* (Fig. 182) the net slip is 6 miles. Axes of folds are offset by the faults. In some instances the strata on one side of a fault are more intensely folded than those on the other side, indicating that folding continued after the fault was initiated. Most of the faults strike in a direction that is about 30° clockwise from lines drawn perpendicular to the fold axes. All these faults are left-handed. One fault and part of another strike about 30° counterclockwise from lines drawn perpendicular to the fold axes; these faults are right-handed. An explanation of

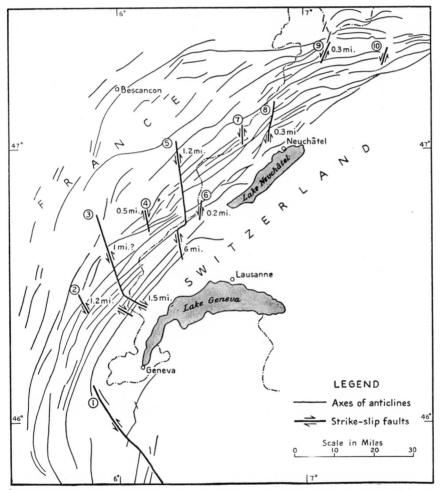

Fig. 182. Strike-slip faults of the Jura Mountains. Each fault is identified by a number in a circle. The relative direction of displacement is indicated by arrows and the maximum amount of the net slip, where known, is given in miles. (After A. Heim.)

these strike-slip faults in the Jura Mountains is given at the bottom of this page. It may at first seem incongruous that at the south end of fault number *3* the block to the west moves north, whereas at the north end of the fault the block to the west moves south. This is possible, however, because at the point where the fault takes a sharp bend the strata on the west side are more intensely folded than the strata on the east side.

Southwestern Wales

Another excellent example of strike-slip faults diagonal to fold axes is found in southwestern Wales (Fig. 183). The Paleozoic strata have been thrown into folds that strike N. 80° W.[3] Thrust faults have a similar strike and dip south. Two sets of diagonal strike-slip faults are present, but only a few of the larger faults could be shown on the scale of Fig. 183.

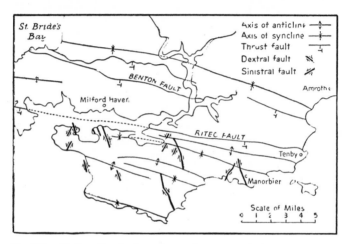

Fig. 183. Strike-slip faults of southwestern Wales. (Compiled from maps by E. M. Anderson, J. Pringle, and T. N. George.)

Anderson[4] says that of the 69 faults, 42 strike about N. 20° W. and 27 strike about N. 30° E. The dips are steep. The two sets of faults thus make an angle of about 50° with each other and about 25° with lines perpendicular to the fold axes. Of the 42 faults that strike N. 20° W., 40 are right-handed (dextral); of the 27 that strike N. 30° E., 22 and probably 24 are left-handed (sinistral). The maximum net slip is 1,200 feet. An explanation of these faults follows in the next section.

Origin of Diagonal Strike-Slip Faults

An explanation of diagonal strike-slip faults such as those in the Jura Mountains and in southwestern Wales has been given by E. M.

[3] Pringle, J., and T. N. George, *British Regional Geology, South Wales*, 2nd ed., (British) Geological Survey and Museum, 1948.
[4] Anderson, E. M., *op. cit.*, pp. 60–64.

Anderson.[5] If a series of sedimentary rocks is compressed along north-south lines, the axes of the resulting folds are oriented east-west. At times, however, the rocks may be sufficiently brittle to yield by rupture. In accordance with the principles developed in Chapter 10, two sets of shear fractures may form. If the direction of easiest relief is vertical—that is, the least stress axis is vertical—two sets of shear fractures striking east-west will form; one set will dip about 30° N., the other about 30° S. If displacement takes place along these fractures the hanging wall moves over the footwall to develop thrust faults. If, however, the easiest relief is in an east-west direction—that is, the least stress axis strikes east-west and is horizontal—the two sets of shear fractures will be vertical and will strike about N. 30° W. and N. 30° E. Any displacements along the fractures will be strike-slip movements. The N. 30° W. set will be right-handed, the N. 30° E. set will be left-handed (Fig. 130). Not only are the strike-slip faults in the Jura and in southwestern Wales oriented in accordance with theory, but the direction of the relative movements is also correct. In the Jura, however, for some unknown reason one set of strike-slip faults is much better developed than the other.

STRIKE-SLIP FAULTS PERPENDICULAR TO FOLD AXES

All transverse strike-slip faults are not diagonal to the fold axes. In the Gold Hill district of Utah, Nolan[6] has mapped a large number of strike-slip faults (Fig. 185). The structure is exceedingly complex because the rocks have been subjected to five major cycles of deformation during the late Mesozoic and early Tertiary, as well as later Tertiary deformation. Folds, thrusts, strike-slip faults, and gravity faults were developed during each of the five cycles. The folds trend north-south. Although many of the strike-slip faults strike 20° to 30° clockwise from lines perpendicular to the fold axes, the four major strike-slip faults, exposed for lengths of 3 to 8 miles, are perpendicular to the fold axes. Along the Dry Canyon fault the north block has moved 1,000 feet east, along the Blood Canyon fault the north block has moved 1 mile west, along the Clifton fault the north block probably moved 3 miles west, and along the Garrison Monster fault the north block has moved 1.5 miles east. Thus the displacement along the four major faults has not been systematic. A glance at the map also shows that along some of the faults that strike west-northwest, the northeast block has moved southeast, along others the northeast block has moved northwest.

It is apparent that these strike-slip faults do not bear the simple relations anticipated from the theory presented in the preceding section.

[5] Anderson, E. M., *op. cit.*, pp. 1–16.
[6] Nolan, T. B., "The Gold Hill Mining District, Utah," *U. S. Geological Survey, Professional Paper 177*, 1935.

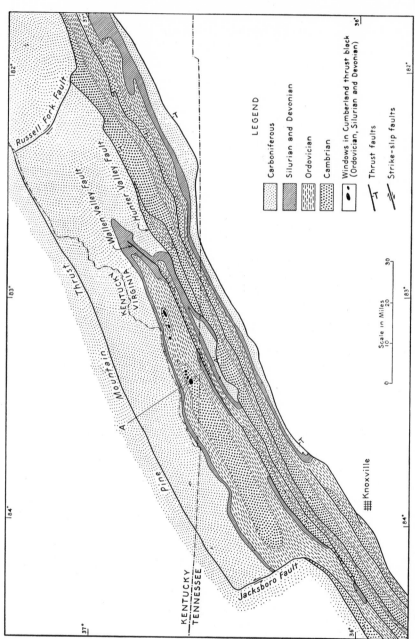

Fig. 184. Map of Cumberland thrust-block of southwestern Virginia and adjacent parts of Tennessee and Kentucky. For section *AA'* see Fig. 186. Compiled from maps by R. L. Miller, J. O. Fuller, W. P. Brosge, Geological Map of Virginia (1928) and Geological Map of Tennessee (1933).

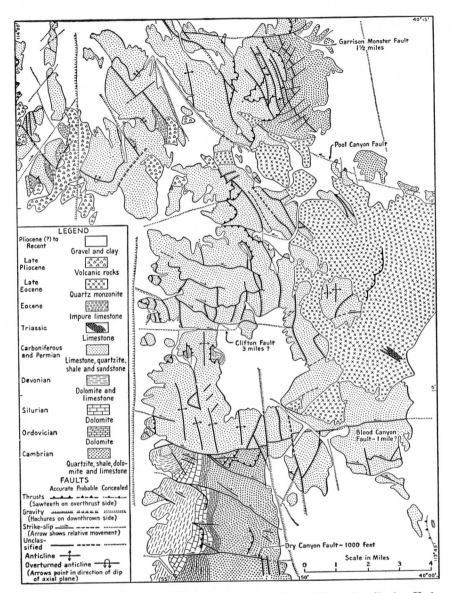

Fig. 185. Area of complex folding and faulting. Gold Hill mining district, Utah. Shows folds, thrust faults, gravity faults, and strike-slip faults; net slip along strike-slip faults shown in feet or miles. Thrust faults are fragmentary because of extensive displacement by later faulting, carrying them above or below present surface of erosion. (After T. B. Nolan.)

There are several possible reasons. (1) The theory assumes that the same forces caused the initial rupture and also caused the movement along that rupture; moreover, it is assumed that the faults are closely related genetically to the folds. However, the fractures may form under one set of forces but the actual movement may take place under different forces. For example, a steep gravity fault may later be utilized for strike-slip movements. (2) The theory assumes that the region being deformed was relatively homogeneous, or at least can be treated as a homogeneous region. The Gold Hill region is now an exceedingly heterogeneous portion of the crust of the earth; it reached that condition through five successive orogenic cycles. After the first cycle, if not before, it was heterogeneous rather than homogeneous.

STRIKE-SLIP FAULTS BOUNDING A THRUST BLOCK

A block bounded by two strike-slip faults may move forward between the relatively stationary terrains on either side. In many instances the moving block is also separated by a thrust fault from the stationary block beneath it. In a sense, therefore, the moving block is bounded by one scoop-shaped fracture, the bottom of the scoop corresponding to a thrust, the sides of the scoop to the strike-slip faults.

An unusually good example of such a structure is the Cumberland thrust block of southwestern Virginia and adjacent parts of Kentucky and Tennessee.[7] The fault block (Fig. 184), 125 miles long and 25 miles wide, has been thrust northwestward along the Pine Mountain thrust (Fig. 186). Along the line of the cross section in Fig. 184 the net slip is

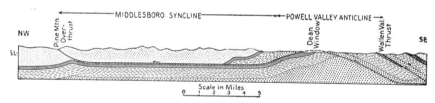

Fig. 186. Structure section of Cumberland thrust-block. Section is 27 miles long. Symbols same as in Fig. 184. Heavy dots = Cambrian; short lines = Ordovician; diagonal lines = Silurian and Devonian; light dots = Carboniferous. (After R. L. Miller and J. O. Fuller.)

[7] Butts, Charles, "Fensters in the Cumberland Overthrust Block in Southwestern Virginia," *Virginia Geological Survey, Bulletin 28,* 1927.

Rich, John L., "Mechanics of Low-Angle Overthrust Faulting as Illustrated by the Cumberland Thrust Block, Virginia, Kentucky, and Tennessee," *Bulletin American Association of Petroleum Geologists,* Vol. 18, pp. 1584–1596, 1934.

Miller, Ralph L., and J. Osborn Fuller, "Rose Hill Oil Field, Virginia," *U. S. Geological Survey, Oil and Gas Investigations, Preliminary Map 76,* 1947.

Miller, Ralph L., and William P. Brosge, "Jonesville District, Virginia," *U. S. Geological Survey, Oil and Gas Investigations, Preliminary Map 104,* 1950.

Wentworth, C. K., "Russell Fork Fault of Southwest Virginia," *Journal of Geology,* Vol. 29, pp. 351–369, 1921.

5.8 miles. Sixteen miles southeast of the front of the thrust block the Pine Mountain thrust reappears in a number of windows. The thrust block is bounded on the southwest by the Jacksboro strike-slip fault, along which the Cumberland thrust block has moved northwestward 10 miles. The thrust block is bounded on the northeast by the Russell Fork strike-slip fault, along which the Cumberland thrust block has moved northwestward about 2 miles. Thus, as indicated by Butts, the thrust block appears to have rotated as it moved northwestward, the southwest end traveling considerably farther than the northeast end.

LONGITUDINAL STRIKE-SLIP FAULTS

Rifts, that is, strike-slip faults parallel to the regional structure, are especially well displayed in California (Fig. 187). The largest of these, the San Andreas rift, extends 600 miles in a northwesterly direction. Gen-

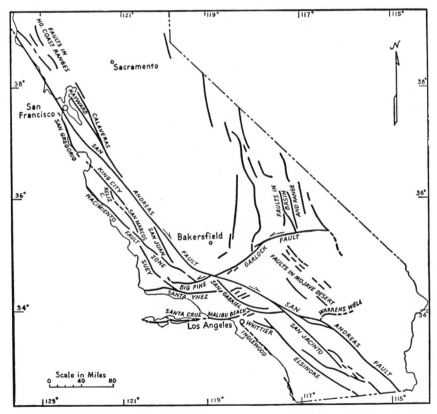

Fig. 187. Strike-slip and related faults of California. (After M. L. Hill and T. W. Dibblee. Jr.)

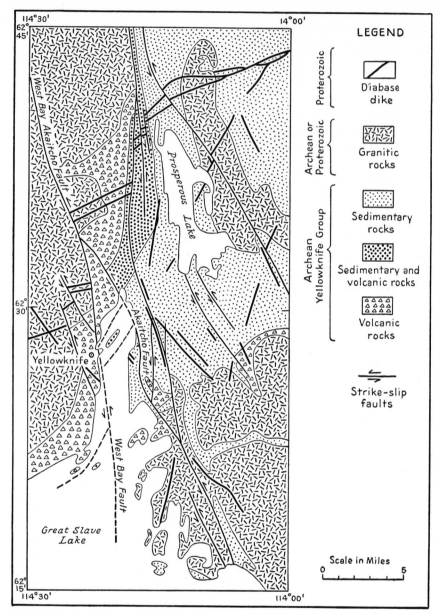

Fig. 188. Strike-slip faults of the Yellowknife District, North West Territories, Canada. (Compiled from A. W. Joliffe, and maps 709A and 868A. Geological Survey of Canada.)

erally the rift is a fault zone along which gouge or breccia is in places 100 yards wide. The disturbed zone may be much wider, but it is not clear how much of this is related to movement along the fault and how much represents deformation prior to the initiation of the fault. Topographically the fault is marked by scarps, ridges, sag ponds, and depressions, which are one to 100 feet deep. The fault plane is apparently very steep, inasmuch as in places it crosses rough topography without deflection.

Movement along this fault caused the San Francisco earthquake of April 18, 1906. The block on the northeast side of the fault moved southeastward relative to the block on the southwest side. Movement occurred on 270 miles of the fault, the average net slip (essentially horizontal) was 13 feet, and the maximum net slip was 21 feet. There is no agreement, however, as to how long the fault has been active nor as to the amount of the net slip. Some geologists believe that it did not form until the Pleistocene,[8] others believe that it originated as far back as the Cretaceous or Jurassic.[9] Offset streams suggest that total net slip is at least 700 feet. Reed [10] says the net slip "may be 10 miles or 24 miles, or more, but the evidence for any of these figures is inconlusive." Crowell [11] has recently shown that coarse clastic sediments of Miocene age on the southwest side of the San Gabriel fault, which parallels the San Andreas fault on the southwest (Fig. 187), have apparently been displaced 15 to 25 miles toward the northwest. It has been suggested that the net slip along the San Andreas fault may have been 120 miles since the Cretaceous and 350 miles since the Jurassic.[12]

Some geologists believe that the rifts of California are shear fractures formed by compressive forces acting in a north-south direction. Under such forces, if the easiest relief were east-west, two sets of vertical shear fractures would form, one set striking about N. 30° E., the other about N. 30° W. The former would be left-handed, the latter right-handed. The San Andreas and the San Gabriel faults conform to the second set. The Garlock and Big Pine faults could be the complementary set.[13] Although the angle between the two sets that is bisected by the supposed compressive force is 100 degrees rather than the 60 degrees or 70 degrees expected by theory, this is perhaps not a serious objection to the interpretation be-

[8] Taliafero, N. L., "Geologic History and Structure of the Central Coast Ranges of California," *California State Division of Mines, Bulletin No. 118*, pp. 119–162, 1943.

[9] Hill, Mason L. and T. W. Dibblee, Jr., "San Andreas, Garlock, and Big Pine Faults, California," *Bulletin Geological Society of America*, Vol. 64, pp. 443-458, 1953.

[10] Reed, R. D., *Geology of California*, p. 12. Tulsa, Oklahoma: American Association of Petroleum Geologists, 1933. Reprinted 1951.

[11] Crowell, John C., "Probable Large Lateral Displacement on San Gabriel Fault, Southern California," *Bulletin American Association of Petroleum Geologists*, Vol. 36, pp. 2026–2035, 1952.

[12] Hill, M. L., and T. W. Dibblee, *op. cit.*, p. 49.

[13] Hill, M. L. and T. W. Dibblee, Jr., *op. cit.*

cause the crust in southern California is exceedingly heterogeneous. A more weighty objection is the parallelism between the San Andreas fault and the folds of the Coast Ranges. The folds, which trend northwest, imply compressive forces acting along northeast-southwest lines.

STRIKE-SLIP FAULTS APPARENTLY YOUNGER THAN THE ASSOCIATED FOLDS

Yellowknife Area of Canada

A remarkable series of strike-slip faults in the Yellowknife area, North West Territories, Canada, has been described by Joliffe.[14] The faults strike N. to N. 30° W. (Fig. 188). The block to the east of each fault has moved north relative to the block to the west. Three kinds of planar features have been offset by the faults: (1) diabase dikes; (2) major stratigraphic units of the Yellowknife series; (3) and lava flows within the Yellowknife series. For example, a pair of diabase dikes has been offset several miles along the West Bay-Akaitcho fault (Fig. 188). Similar offsets are shown along the West Bay and Akaitcho faults by the formation shown in heavy dots. As shown on page 130, the offset along a fault is not necessarily the same as the net slip. By geometrical analysis of diversely oriented older dikes that are displaced by the fault, similar to the methods described on pages 469 to 477, Campbell [15] calculated that in the vicinity of the town of Yellowknife the block east of the fault moved upward toward the north. He computed the strike-slip to be 16,140 ± 690 feet. That is, the net slip is about 16,200 feet and plunges 5 or 6° S. These strike-slip faults are much younger than the folding of the volcanic and sedimentary rocks of the area. The folding was Archean, whereas the displaced diabase dikes are late Proterozoic.[16]

Wilson[17] has suggested that these left-handed strike-slip faults of the Yellowknife district are one of the two shear directions resulting from orogenic pressure directed west-northwest and south-southeast.

[14] Joliffe, A. W., "Structures in the Canadian Shield," *American Geophysical Union, Transactions of 1942*, pp. 699–707. Also maps 709A (1942) and 868A (1946), Geological Survey of Canada.

[15] Campbell, N., "West Bay Fault," *Structural Geology of Canadian Ore Deposits*, pp. 244–259. Montreal, 1948.

[16] Joliffe, A. W., "The North-western Part of the Canadian Shield," *International Geological Congress, Report of the Eighteenth Session*, Great Britain 1948, Part XIII, pp. 141–149, 1952.

[17] Wilson, J. Tuzo, "Some Aspects of Geophysics in Canada with Special Reference to Structural Research in the Canadian Shield (Part 2: An Approach to the Structure of the Canadian Shield)," *Transactions American Geophysical Union*, Vol. 29, pp. 691–726, 1948.

Scotland

W. Q. Kennedy[18] has shown from several lines of evidence that the Great Glen fault of Scotland is a large strike-slip fault (Fig. 189). He points out that the trace of the fault is a remarkably straight zone of crushed, sheared, and mylonitized rock, in places a mile wide. Several geological features are displaced by the fault, including: (1) a belt of highly injected schists; (2) metamorphic zones; (3) a granite stock; and

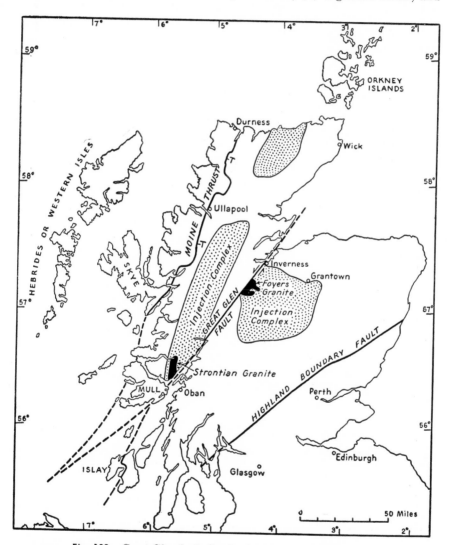

Fig. 189. Great Glen fault, Scotland. (After W. Q. Kennedy.)

[18] Kennedy, W. Q., "The Great Glen Fault," *Quarterly Journal of the Geological Society of London,* Vol. CII, pp. 41–76, 1946.

(4) possibly a thrust plane. The granite stock that has been split in two by the fault has many petrological peculiarities, and the two halves undoubtedly belong to the same original body. The part northwest of the fault is known as the Strontian granite, the part southeast of the fault is known as the Foyers granite (Fig. 189). The block northwest of the

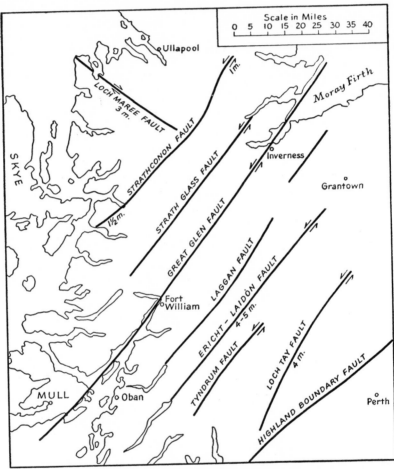

Fig. 190. Strike-slip faults of Scotland. Strike slip given in miles; strike slip along Great Glen fault is 65 miles. (After W. Q. Kennedy, E. M. Anderson, and Geological Map of Great Britain, 1948.)

fault has moved 65 miles southwest relative to the block southeast of the fault. There has also been some vertical movement, the southeast block having been downthrown 6,000 feet. North and south of the Great Glen fault (Fig. 190) six additional faults show similar trends. Wherever data are available the block northwest of each fault has moved relatively toward the southwest from 3 to 5 miles. Although the principal movement on the Great Glen fault was in the Late Devonian or Early Carboniferous, modern earthquakes along its trace indicate it is still active.[19] The strike-slip faults in Scotland are believed by Kennedy to represent one of the two theoretical shear fractures developed under north-south compression when the easiest relief was east-west. The complementary theoretical sets of shears trending northwest are absent except for the Loch Maree fault (Fig. 190).

SUMMARY

Strike-slip faults are an important type of deformation in the crust of the earth. Some, like those in the Jura and southwestern Wales are closely related to folds and are diagonal shear fractures developed under compression. Others, like those in the Gold Hill district of Utah and in California are geographically and presumably genetically associated with folds, but, inasmuch as they are perpendicular or parallel to the folds, they must be explained in a different way than the diagonal faults. The perpendicular faults may have been originally extension fractures or gravity faults that were later utilized for strike-slip movements. Some strike-slip faults such as those in Canada and in Scotland are in relatively rigid rocks at some distance from the active orogenic belt.

[19] Anderson, E. M., *The Dynamics of Faulting and Dyke Formation with Applications to Britain,* 2nd ed., Edinburgh: Oliver and Boyd, 206 pages, 1951; especially p. 125.

CHAPTER 14

Causes of Folding and Faulting

INTRODUCTION

Folds, as well as faults, are often classified as tectonic or nontectonic in origin. Those of *tectonic origin* result more or less directly from forces operating within the outer shell of the earth. Those of *nontectonic origin* are largely the result of movements under the influence of gravity near the surface of the earth, although the ultimate cause in many cases is tectonic. A clear distinction is by no means always possible. Even some of the larger structural features of the earth, such as the Jura Mountains (Fig. 45), formerly believed to be tectonic, have been recently considered to be nontectonic (p. 234).

In Chapter 10 we were primarily concerned with the stresses that produced faulting, but no attention was given to the causes of the stresses. In the present chapter we shall try to give some insight into the causes of faults as well as folds.

TECTONIC PROCESSES

Introduction

The tectonic processes that will be considered are: (1) horizontal compression, (2) horizontal tension, (3) intrusion of magma, (4) intrusion of salt, and (5) vertical forces of unspecified origin.

Horizontal Compression

Processes. By *horizontal compression* we mean a compressive force acting parallel to the surface of the earth. In other words, the greatest principal stress axis is parallel to sea level. The principle of horizontal compression is illustrated by Fig. 75A. In most cases the active force, analogous to a moving piston, operates on one side of the folded belt, whereas a resisting force is induced by a stationary block on the other side.

Laboratory experiments have been performed to produce folds by compression. The most exhaustive study was made approximately 60 years ago by Bailey Willis,[1] who sought to understand more thoroughly the folds of the Appalachian Province. The experiments were performed in a pressure box (Fig. 191), the interior of which was $39\frac{3}{8}$ inches long, 5 inches wide, and 20 inches deep. A movable piston was at one end. Alternating layers, representing sedimentary rocks, were laid in the box.

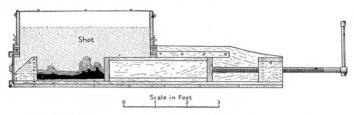

Fig. 191. Pressure box for producing folds. (After B. Willis.)

The various layers differed in thickness from $\frac{1}{16}$ of an inch to $2\frac{1}{2}$ inches. Each layer consisted of wax, plaster, and turpentine, the proportions having been varied in order to produce strata of different strength. A layer of B-B shot, more than a foot thick, was placed over the artificial sedimentary rocks. The piston was then slowly moved from right to left to produce folds such as those shown in Fig. 192. *A* represents the first stage,

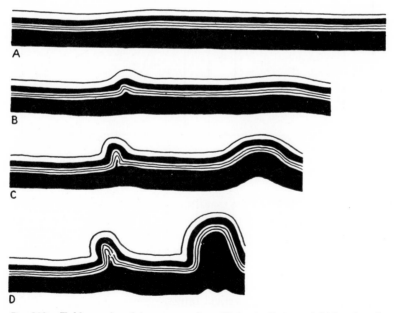

Fig. 192. Folds produced in pressure box. Piston active on right-hand end. (After B. Willis.)

[1] Willis, B., "The Mechanics of Appalachian Structure," *U. S. Geological Survey, 13th Annual Report,* Part 2, pp. 211–281, 1893.

D represents the last stage. The resulting folds, very similar to those in the Appalachian and Jura Mountains, indicate the effectiveness of horizontal compression to produce folds.

It is supposed, in applying this principle to orogenic belts, that the primary force acted at right angles to the trend of the folds.

If the intensity of the compressive force diminishes downward, the uppermost layers moving more than the lower layers, a couple is superimposed upon the simple compression (Fig. 75B). This causes asymmetry and overturning of the folds.

The primary forces in the Appalachian Province, where the folds trend northeast, were acting along northwest-southeast lines. In the North American Cordillera, where the folds trend northwest, the compressive forces acted along northeast-southwest lines.

Horizontal compression, however, may merely be the resultant of a *horizontal couple*. This has been shown experimentally by Mead.[2] A sheet of rubber is placed across a rectangular iron frame, with hinges at each of the four corners (Fig. 193A). A thin veneer of wax is placed on the rubber sheet, and the frame is then subjected to a couple (Fig. 193B)

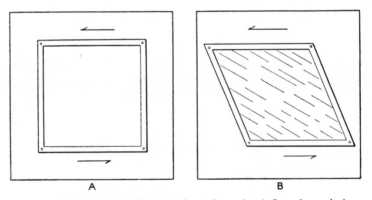

Fig. 193.   Folds produced by a horizontal couple. *A*. Iron frame before deformation. *B*. After deformation. (After W. J. Mead.)

The axes of the folds trend diagonally across the frame, making an angle of approximately 45 degrees to the direction in which the couple is acting. A circle under a similar force is deformed into an ellipse; the axes of the folds are parallel to the long axis of the ellipse.

Such folds may be minor features in a large orogenic belt. It has been suggested that some folds in California are due to a couple resulting from horizontal movement along vertical faults.

Some geologists, however, believe that entire orogenic belts are due to gigantic terrestrial couples. It has been suggested that the northwest-

[2] Mead, W. J., "Notes on the Mechanics of Geologic Structures," *Journal of Geology*, Vol. 28, pp. 505–523, 1920.

ward trending folds of the Sierra Nevada are due to a southward movement of the central part of North America relative to the Pacific Coast and that the northeastward trending ranges of China[3] are due to a southward movement of the interior of Asia relative to the Pacific Ocean.

Causes. A detailed consideration of the ultimate cause of the forces causing the horizontal compression is beyond the scope of this book, but a brief discussion should be of interest.

The *contraction theory* is classical.[4] This theory assumes that the interior of the earth has been growing progressively smaller throughout geologic time. This is supposedly due to one or more of the following reasons: (1) cooling; (2) formation of denser minerals; and (3) the extrusion of magma. The outer shell of the earth, compelled to accommodate itself to this smaller interior, has been subjected to strong compressive forces. Several objections have been made to this theory. One is that the amount of crustal shortening throughout geologic time greatly exceeds the amount that can be reasonably expected. A second objection has been that the theory fails to explain the concentration of deformation in relatively narrow belts, such as the Appalachians or the Rocky Mountains, with large intermediate undeformed areas. How can the stresses be transmitted for such long distances without causing folds in the intervening areas? The old analogy with a dried apple suggests that during a single period of deformation many small folds should be more or less evenly distributed over the earth. A third objection is that the hypothesis fails to explain the supposed recurrent character of deformation, that is, the occurrence of short periods of orogeny separated by long periods of quiescence. Gilluly[5] has pointed out, however, that orogeny may be more continuous than many geologists have thought in the past.

Continental drift has been considered important by some geologists.[6] The rigid continents are supposed to be sufficiently mobile to move about on the surface of the earth and to crumple up the sediments in front of them. There is considerable doubt, however, whether the continents move in this way, and no one has suggested an adequate force to cause the displacement. Under this hypothesis the horizontal compression is exerted by the moving continent.

Other hypotheses suppose that *melting of part of the crust initiates mountain-building.*

[3] Lee, J. S., *The Geology of China*, pp. 282–366. London: Thomas Murby and Co., 1939.

[4] Landes, K. K., "Our Shrinking Globe," *Bulletin Geological Society of America*, Vol. 63, pp. 225–240, 1952.

Scheidegger, A. E., and J. Tuzo Wilson, "An Investigation into Possible Methods of Failure of the Earth," *Proceedings Geological Association of Canada*, Vol. 3, pp. 167–190, 1950.

[5] Gilluly, James, "Distribution of Mountain Building in Geologic Time," *Bulletin Geological Society of America*, Vol. 60, pp. 561–590, 1949.

[6] Du Toit, A. L., *Our Wandering Continents*. Edinburgh: Oliver and Boyd, 366 pages, 1937.

"Atomic heating expands the crust and subcrust and melts a portion of the crust within a limited area, causing a domed regional uplift on a foundation of molten material having no permanent strength. Erosion of the uplifted area causes isostatic transfer, initiating an adjacent down-warp whose sinking is accentuated as it is filled with sediment. The crust creeps slowly down the slopes of the dome, and eventually thrust-faults toward the downwarp and folds its sedimentary rocks. Repeated movements occur, but finally crustal sliding off the dome causes tension and block-faulting in its central parts and copious emission of lavas and escape of heat. After this final orogenic spasm, the lateral creep of the crust ceases and the upwarped area subsides as the magma beneath it cools and congeals." [7] Under this hypothesis the horizontal compression is the result of the down-hill movement off the dome. The force available is a function of the weight of the sediments, the slope of the dome, and the friction between the stationary part of the dome and the sliding sediments.

In recent years a great deal of emphasis has been placed on *subcrustal convection currents.*[8] The outer shell of the earth under the continents is granitic in composition and some 25 kilometers thick. One variant of the theory supposes that the interior of the earth below this outer shell, down

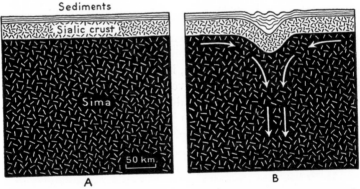

Fig. 194. Orogeny caused by subcrustal convection currents. *A.* Before orogeny; sialic crust, about 25 km. thick, overlain by sediments and underlain by sima. *B.* Convection currents (only small part of whole convection cell is shown) cause downward bending of crust and folding of sediments.

[7] Rich, John L., "Origin of Compressional Mountains and Associated Phenomena," *Bulletin Geological Society of America,* Vol. 62, pp. 1179–1222, 1951.

See also Wolfe, C. W., "The Blister Hypothesis and the Orogenic Cycle," *Transactions New York Academy of Sciences,* Ser. 2, Vol. 2, pp. 188–195, 1949.

[8] Griggs, David, "A Theory of Mountain Building," *American Journal of Science,* Vol. 237, pp. 611–650, 1939.

Vening Meinesz, F. A., "Major Tectonic Phenomena and the Hypothesis of Convection Currents in the Earth," *Quarterly Journal of the Geological Society of London,* Vol. CIII, pp. 191–207, 1948.

to a depth of 2,900 kilometers, is sufficiently homogeneous to behave as a single unit. Convection currents develop when the lower parts are sufficiently heated. These currents drag along the base of the crust (Fig. 194). The crust is downfolded to form a root and the overlying sediments, forced to occupy a smaller area than formerly, are thrown into folds. Moreover, some parts of the crust may be subjected to tension, which produces gravity faults. Although convection currents of the kind visualized are theoretically possible, even in a solid earth, it is doubtful that they can occur sufficiently often to explain the formation of folds and thrusts. (See page 394 for definition of "root.")

Horizontal Tension

Horizontal tension would cause gravity faults. In one sense it is not correct to speak of tension, except in the uppermost part of the crust. It would be more correct to say that the least principal stress axis is horizontal. In any case, the crust would fail along vertical tension fractures or along shear fractures dipping about 60 degrees. If the interior of the earth were to expand, an outer shell would be subjected to tension.[9]

The theories described in the preceding section were primarily designed to explain horizontal compression. However, this compression would be confined to certain parts of the crust. Elsewhere strong tensional forces might be set up. Subcrustal convection currents would in places tend to pull the crust apart. Although the sediments at the foot of a dome formed by melting would be subjected to compression, the sediments nearer the top of the dome would tend to be pulled apart.

Locally the tension may be caused by a couple. The small graben shown in Fig. 174 are clearly the result of tension. The gaping fissures offer undeniable evidence that the rocks have been stretched. The tensional forces operated in a direction somewhat north of west. The tension was caused, however, by a couple, in which the rocks to the northeast were moving southeasterly relative to the rocks to the southwest.

Intrusion of Magma

The intrusion of magma may cause folding. The clearest example of this is offered by laccoliths (p. 298). Not only are the overlying sediments bowed up into a dome, but the roof may be fractured and faulted. Such structural features, however, will be of rather limited size and distribution. The basins associated with lopoliths (p. 301) are likewise genetically associated with the intrusion of magma. During major orogenic periods considerable deformation may accompany the intrusion of magma (p. 323), but in many such cases the movement of the magma is the result of the orogeny and not the cause.

[9] Bucher, W. H., *The Deformation of the Earth's Crust*, pp. 119–123. Princeton: Princeton University Press, 1933.

Intrusion of Salt Domes

Uplifts and faulting associated with the emplacement of salt domes are described in Chapter 16. But these are also small structural features seldom more than a few miles in diameter.

Vertical Movements of Unspecified Origin

A study of the geologic map or tectonic map of the United States shows that broad domes and basins, hundreds of miles across, are conspicuous. Extensive studies have shown that many of these domes and basins were continuously, or intermittently, moving up or down for long periods of time. Specific examples of domes are the Cincinnati, Nashville, and Ozark uplifts. Specific examples of downwarps are the Michigan, Illinois, and Williston basins.

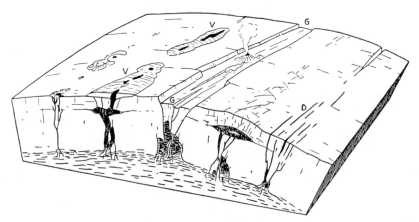

Fig. 195. Origin of graben. $G = $ graben; $D = $ dikes; $V = $ volcanics, with associated intrusives in solid black. (After H. Cloos.)

Many graben, both large and small, are associated with plateaus and domes, some of which are of continental proportions.[10] Because of the stretching of the rocks (Fig. 79), tensional forces develop, the rocks fail by rupture, and movement along the resulting fractures ensues (Fig. 195). The formation of the larger graben has often been associated with extensive volcanism, which is notably true of the graben of Africa, the Oslo graben, and the Rhine graben. The relation is generally not simple; that is, the master faults bounding the graben are not necessarily the fractures up through which the magma moves. In some instances, the most extensive volcanism is in the vicinity of, but beyond the limits of, the graben (Fig. 195).

---

[10] Cloos, Hans, "Hebung, Spaltung, Vulkanismus," *Geologische Rundschau*, Band 30, Zwischenheft 4A, pp. 406–527; cf. especially p. 434, 1939.

Fault-block mountains—both the tilted fault blocks and horsts—are similar in origin to graben. Although some may be due to tension that followed excessive compression during folding, most of them seem to be due to stretching induced by vertical movements. The domed area is broken by fractures, along which differential movement takes place. It was supposed in some of the older hypotheses that doming took place first and was later followed by collapse. It is apparent, however, that doming and faulting can go on simultaneously. If doming continues after a number of fractures have formed, the individual blocks will be uplifted differentially, and some blocks may subside.

NONTECTONIC PROCESSES

Introduction

By nontectonic processes are meant those processes that are not directly related to movements within the outer shell of the earth. In many cases the term surficial processes would be equally good because the deformation is the result of movements near the surface of the earth under the influence of gravity. Even in these instances, however, the deformation is usually an indirect result of movements within the earth.

Structural features related to sedimentation have been described on pages 70 to 78.

The structural features discussed in the present chapter may be classified under the following major categories: (1) those formed near the surface under the influence of gravity; (2) those related to chemical processes; and (3) those related to glaciation.

Structural Features Formed Near the Surface under the Influence of Gravity

Hillside creep. In many areas, especially those that have not been glaciated, it is not uncommon to find incompetent rocks, such as shale, dipping into the hillside. Careful study will show, however, that the dips may be very deceiving. In a zone several feet thick at the surface the

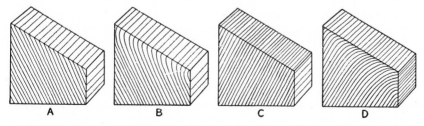

Fig. 196. Hillside creep, looking north. *A*. True attitude of strata before hillside creep. *B*. Same area as *A* after hillside creep. *C*. True attitude of strata before hillside creep. *D*. Same area as *C*, after hillside creep.

dip may be unlike the true dip at depth. Figure 196A represents a case where the true dip is 60° E., but because of down-hill creep the dip (Fig. 196B) is 60° W. Similarly, where the true dip is 60° W. (Fig. 196C), near the surface the dip is only 20° W. (Fig. 196D). In such areas it may be necessary to have exposures five or ten feet deep because data obtained at the surface may be very misleading.

Collapse structures. Collapse structures have been described by Goguel[11] and Harrison and Falcon.[12] In Fig. 197A a large block of limestone under the influence of gravity has slid out over the younger shales. It stimulates a thrust of tectonic origin, but the process itself is essentially landsliding. In Fig. 197B a block of limestone has folded back on

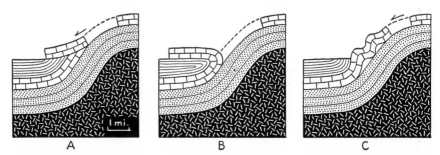

| A | B | C |

Fig. 197. Collapse structures. *A.* Landslide simulating klippe. *B.* Recumbent fold. *C.* Folds caused by gravity sliding. (After J. Goguel, J. V. Harrison, and N. L. Falcon.)

itself to simulate a recumbent fold formed under true tectonic conditions. In Fig. 197C a bed of limestone folded into a cascade as it slid down a hill.

It has been suggested that many large structural features, formerly considered tectonic, are similar in origin. Lugeon,[13] for example, has suggested that the sedimentary rocks of the Jura Mountains (Fig. 45) were folded as the whole sheet slid northward on a gently inclined surface, just as a thin layer of snow on a roof buckles into folds when it starts to slide, but is held firmly in place at its lower end. Similarly, many klippe, which were formerly considered to be erosional remnants of a

[11] Goguel, Jean, *Traité de Tectonique.* Paris: Masson et Cie, 383 pages, 1952; especially p. 213.

[12] Harrison, J. V. and N. L. Falcon, "Collapse Structures," *Geological Magazine,* Vol. LXXI, pp. 529–539, 1934.

[13] Lugeon, M., "Une hypothese sur l'origine du Jura," *Bulletin No. 73 des Laboratoires de Géologie, Minéralogie, Géophysique et de Musée Géologique de l'Université de Lausanne,* 1941.

Gignoux, M., "La Notion de Temps en Géologie et la Tectonique d' Écoulement par Gravité," *Eighteenth International Geological Congress,* Great Britain, 1948, Part XIII, pp. 90-96, 1952.

great thrust sheet, may represent large isolated blocks that slid down-
hill under the influence of gravity. Migliorini[14] says:

"The highly incompetent allocthonous formation covering extensive
areas of the Apennines . . . cannot have advanced as a nappe, and is
best accounted for by the successive landslip theory; that is, by a succession of orogenic landslips down the outer slopes of the individual

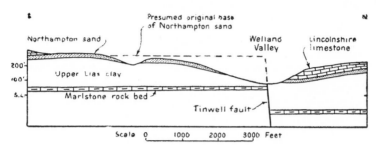

Fig. 198. Cambers. Welland Valley, England. (After S. E. Hollingsworth,
J. H. Taylor, and G. A. Kellaway.)

Apennine ranges, each landslip spreading sufficiently outwards to be
picked up and moved forward, together with any freshly deposited unconsolidated deposits, by similar landslips on the outer slope of the next
range to be uplifted."

A more detailed account, with a summary in English, is given by
Merla.[15]

Cambers. Cambers have been described from the Northampton area
of Great Britain.[16] As shown in Fig. 198 the Northampton sand dips
northward toward the Welland Valley. It will be noted, however, that
the "marlstone rock bed" is essentially horizontal, and hence the dip of
the Northampton sand is not tectonic. As erosion cut into the sediments
to form the Welland Valley, the Upper Lias clay flowed toward the valley
to be carried away. The Northampton sand was gradually let down.

Dip-and-fault structure. The same authors have shown that after a
camber has formed, the more competent bed may slide downhill, rupture,
and develop a "dip-and-fault" structure (Fig. 199A).[17]

[14] Migliorini, C. I., "Composite Wedges and Orogenic Landslips in the Apennines,"
Eighteenth International Geological Congress, Great Britain, 1948, Part XIII,
pp. 186–198, 1952.
[15] Merla, Giovanni, "Geologia dell'Appennino Settentrionale," *Bollettino della
Società Geologica Italiana*, Vol. LXX, pp. 95–382, 1952.
Maxwell, J. C., "Geology of the Northern Apennines, by Giovanni Merla; Com-
posite Wedges in Orogenesis, by Carlo I. Migliorini," *Bulletin American Association
Petroleum Geologists*, Vol. 37, pp. 2196-2202, 1953.
[16] Hollingsworth, S. E., J. H. Taylor, and G. A. Kellaway, "Large-Scale Superficial
Structures in the Northampton Ironstone Field," *Quarterly Journal of the Geological
Society of London*, Vol. C, pp. 1–44, 1944.
[17] Judson, Sheldon, "Large-Scale Superficial Structures—a Discussion," *Journal of
Geology*, Vol. LV, pp. 168–175, 1947.

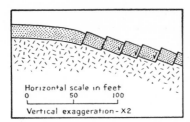 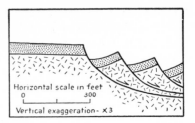

Fig. 199. Surficial faulting. *A.* "Dip-and-fault structure." *B.* Toreva-block landslide. (After S. Judson.)

Bulges. Figure 200 illustrates a "bulge" described by Hollingsworth, Taylor, and Kellaway. After erosion cut the valley occupied by Bytham Brook, the weak Upper Lias clay bulged upward. The resulting structure is an anticline, but it is not tectonic in origin.

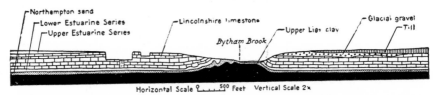

Fig. 200. Bulges Bytham Brook, England. (After S. E. Hollingsworth, J. A. Taylor, and G. A. Kellaway.)

Landslides. Landslides have been extensively described by Sharpe.[18] Figure 199B illustrates one of many kinds of landslides. The blocks are separated from one another by fractures which in every sense of the word are faults. But they are nontectonic in origin.

Differential compaction of sediments. Some folds, anticlinal and synclinal, are due to downward movements of rock masses directly under the influence of gravity. Although anticlines that result from the differential compaction of sediments over buried ridges have comparatively low dips, they form important traps for the accumulation of petroleum. The general principles are illustrated by Fig. 201. Diagram *A* represents a land surface carved on solid rocks; the hill is 100 feet high. Later, as shown in diagram *B*, sediments are deposited on this surface; these sediments are only 100 feet thick on the top of the hill, but are 200 feet thick over the surrounding lowlands. For purposes of illustration, these sediments have been shown as absolutely horizontal. Actually, of course, there would be some minor irregularities, and particularly on the flanks of the hill there would be some outward *initial dips.* If at some subsequent time the mud compacts 20 per cent over the top of the hill,

[18] Sharpe, C. F. S., *Landslides and Related Phenomena.* New York: Columbia University Press, 136 pages, 1938.

the highest sedimentary bed will sink 20 feet—that is, 20 per cent of 100 feet. Beyond the limits of the hill, the highest sedimentary bed sinks 20 per cent of 200 feet—that is, 40 feet. Consequently, the highest beds will dip away from the center of the buried hill (Fig. 201C.)

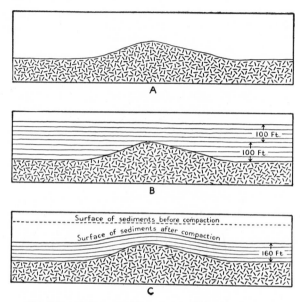

Fig. 201. Folds resulting from differential compaction of sediments. *A.* Ridge left by erosion. *B.* Same ridge covered by mud, but before compaction of mud. *C.* Same, but after compaction of mud.

Chemical Processes

Calcium sulphate is most commonly precipitated from evaporating water as anhydrite. Water is subsequently added to convert the anhydrite into gypsum, and the increase in volume is approximately 40 per cent. If the beds are flat lying and if all the expansion takes place upward, the beds thicken, but no folds develop. If, however, much of the expansion is horizontal, compressive forces are set up and folding ensues. The resulting folds are small, with a height of only a fraction of an inch, or, at the most, of a few feet. Moreover, gypsum is not an abundant rock.

If flat-lying beds of salt or some other rock are differentially dissolved, the overlying formation will collapse irregularly to form basins and domes. Such a type of structure is illustrated in Fig. 202, which is a structure contour map on the top of the Rustler formation of Permian age.[19] The salt in the underlying Salado and Castile formations, although

[19] Maley, V. C., and R. M. Huffington, "Cenozoic Fill and Evaporite Solution in the Delaware Basin, Texas and New Mexico," *Bulletin Geological Society America,* Vol. 64, pp. 539–546, 1953.

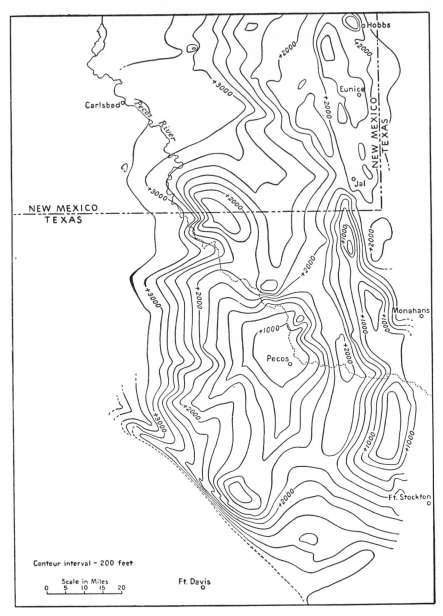

Fig. 202. Folds caused by differential solution of salt. Structure contours on top of Rustler formation of Permian age. Folds result from differential solution of underlying salt. (After Maley and Huffington.)

in several separate beds, originally had a total thickness of about 2,500 feet. In general, the domes shown by the top of the Rustler formation coincide with those places where the salt has been least dissolved, whereas the basins coincide with those places where the salt has been completely removed.

Glaciation

Glacial ice, pushing against the steep slope of a cuesta, may throw the strata, if they are poorly consolidated, into folds. Moreover, ice may override weak sediments and cause drag folds. Folds due to glacial action are well developed near the southern limits of the Pleistocene ice caps on Martha's Vineyard, an island off the southeastern coast of Massachusetts.

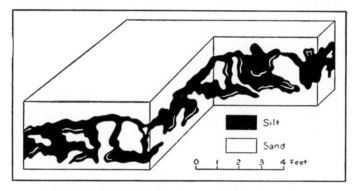

Fig. 203. Periglacial involutions. (After R. Sharp.)

Periglacial involutions have been described by Sharp.[20] In Illinois, some of the beds of glaciofluvial sand, silt, and clay are complexly deformed. Irregular masses of silt and clay intrude the sand (Fig. 203). Structural features of this type are confined to a zone from three to twelve feet beneath the surface. The deformation is partially the result of differential freezing and thawing, but is also the result of the formation and melting of masses of ground ice. These structural features probably formed when the ice front was 30 to 50 miles to the northeast during the late Middle Wisconsin.

Contemporaneous Deformation

Small folds and faults may form in soft sediments due to sliding down gentle slopes (Fig. 204).[21] The axes of the folds and the strike of the

[20] Sharp, Robert P., "Periglacial Involutions in Northeastern Illinois," *Journal of Geology,* Vol. L, pp. 113–133, 1942.

[21] Fairbridge, R. W., "Submarine Slumping and Location of Oil Bodies," *Bulletin American Association of Petroleum Geologists,* Vol. 30, pp. 84–92, 1946.

Fairbridge, R. W., "Possible Causes of Intraformational Disturbances in the Carboniferous Varve Rocks of Australia," *Journal and Proceedings of the Royal Society of New South Wales,* Vol. LXXXI, pp. 99–121, 1947.

thrusts will be at right angles to the direction in which the sediments slide. The axial planes of the folds and the thrust faults dip in the direction from which the slide comes. Movements of this type may occur on slopes as low as two and one-half degrees. In some cases it is probable that the disturbed layer was covered by younger sediments at the time of the deformation (Fig. 204A). Although all the beds were unconsolidated at the time, some were more competent than others. The overlying sediments slide without deforming, hence the folds in the incompetent bed are analogous to drag folds (Fig. 30). In other cases it is clear that the beds slid when they were the uppermost strata, covered only by water, because the overlying sediments rest on them unconformably (Fig. 204B).[22] After the sediments were deformed, mild subaqueous erosion truncated the folds.

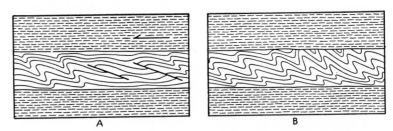

A   B

Fig. 204. Folds formed by contemporaneous deformation. *A*. The uppermost layer slid from right to left over the middle layer. *B*. The middle layer slid from right to left before the uppermost layer was deposited upon it unconformably.

Although in some areas the deformed layer may be only a foot to 15 feet thick, elsewhere it may be hundreds of feet thick.[23]

Beds of soft mud, sand, and ooze may slide because of a number of reasons. The slope on which deposition takes place may be inclined and, although the rocks are relatively stable for long periods of time, any disturbing factor may set them in motion. Slight tilting, excessive local deposition, or an earthquake may set masses of mud and ooze into motion. Local, subaqueous erosion may leave the beds with inadequate support. Large slides may even be related to contemporaneous faulting.[24]

It may be difficult to distinguish between features resulting from contemporaneous deformation and those due to later forces. If, as is

[22] Jones, O. T., "The Geology of the Colwyn Bay District: A Study of Submarine Slumping During the Salopian Period," *Quarterly Journal of the Geological Society (of London)*, Vol. XCV, pp. 335–382, 1940.

[23] Kuenen, P. H., "Slumping in the Carboniferous Rocks of Pembrokeshire," *Quarterly Journal of the Geological Society (of London)*, Vol. CIV, pp. 365–385, 1949.

Jones, O. T., *op. cit.*

[24] Fairbridge, R. W., "Gravitational Tectonics at Shorncliffe, S. E. Queensland," *Proceedings of the Royal Society of Queensland*, Vol. LIX, pp. 179–201, 1948.

sometimes observed, the folds are truncated by younger beds of the same sedimentary series, as in Fig. 204B, it is evident that the deformation was contemporaneous. The folds resulting from contemporaneous deformation are similar to drag folds. If the major structure is known, the orientation of the minor folds may be useful in deciding whether they are contemporaneous or secondary. If they are true drag folds, they should be related to the major structure in the manner indicated on p. 78; otherwise they are probably the result of contemporaneous deformation. Obviously, however, this criterion is unreliable, and it may lead to erroneous interpretations.

CHAPTER 15

Unconformities

INTRODUCTION

The structural geologist is concerned with unconformities for several reasons. Unconformities are definitely structural features, although their origin involves erosional and depositional as well as tectonic processes Moreover, unconformities may be confused with some kinds of faults. Most important of all, however, is the use of unconformities in dating orogenic and epeirogenic movements. Unconformities are also important to students of stratigraphy, sedimentation, and historical geology. Valuable deposits of petroleum and minerals are associated with unconformities.

An *unconformity* is a surface of erosion or nondeposition—usually the former—that separates younger strata from older rocks.[1] The development of an unconformity involves several stages. The first stage is the formation of the older rock. Most commonly this is followed by uplift and subaerial erosion. Finally, the younger strata are deposited.

Rocks of various origins may participate in unconformities; sedimentary rocks, volcanic rocks, plutonic rocks, or metamorphic rocks may be involved.

In Fig. 205 the unconformities are labeled *ab*. In some instances, as in Fig. 205A, the rocks both above and below the unconformity are sedimentary. After the lower limestone was deposited, the region was uplifted and eroded; then the upper sandstones and shales were deposited. In Fig. 205B, the rocks beneath the unconformity are limestone, those above the unconformity are volcanic. After the deposition of the limestone, there was uplift, erosion, and, finally, eruption of the volcanic rocks. In Fig. 205C, after the eruption of the lower volcanic rocks there was erosion—with or without a preceding uplift—and then eruption of the upper volcanic rocks. Figures 205D and 205E involve plutonic rocks. The plutonic rocks were intruded and then eroded, with or without a preceding uplift. Upon the erosion surface, younger sediments were deposited (Fig. 205D) or volcanics were erupted (Fig. 205E).

[1] For other discussions of unconformities see: Stewart, W. Alan, pp. 32–51 in LeRoy, L. W., *et al.*, *Subsurface Geologic Methods*, 2nd ed., 1156 pages, Golden, Colorado: Colorado School of Mines, 1950.

The relief on unconformities differs greatly. In some localities the older rocks were reduced to an extensive peneplane. In other localities, only a mature stage in the erosion cycle was reached before the younger rocks began to accumulate. The relief on the unconformity may amount to hundreds or even thousands of feet. The Cambrian sedimentary

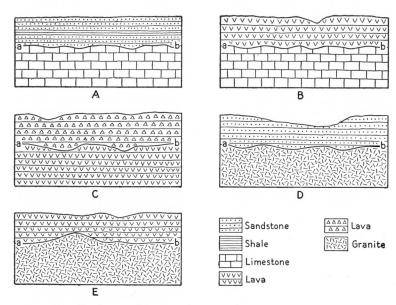

Fig. 205. Rocks participating in unconformities. Unconformities are labelled *ab*. *A*. Sedimentary rocks both above and below the unconformity. *B*. Volcanic rocks above, sedimentary rocks below. *C*. Volcanic rocks above and below. *D*. Sedimentary rocks above, plutonic rocks below. *E*. Volcanic rocks above, plutonic rocks below.

rocks of the Grand Canyon were deposited on a surface with a known maximum relief of 800 feet.[2] The Algonkian rocks of the Northwest Highlands of Scotland were deposited over hills at least 2,000 feet high.[3] The Carboniferous sedimentary rocks around Boston, Massachusetts, rest upon an unconformity with a relief of at least 2,100 feet.[4]

[2] Sharp, R. P., "Ep-Archean and Ep-Algonkian Erosion Surfaces, Grand Canyon, Arizona," *Bulletin Geological Society of America*, Vol. 51, pp. 1235–1270; cf. especially p. 1244, 1940.

[3] Peach, B. N., J. Horne, C. T. Clough, L. W. Hinxman, and J. J. H. Teall, *The Geological Structure of the North-west Highlands of Scotland*, Memoirs Geological Survey Great Britain, Glasgow, p. 4, 1907.

[4] Billings, M. P., F. B. Loomis, Jr., and G. W. Stewart, "Carboniferous Topography in the Vicinity of Boston, Massachusetts," *Bulletin Geological Society of America*, Vol. 50, pp. 1867–1884, 1939.

KINDS OF UNCONFORMITIES

There are various kinds of unconformities, the distinction depending upon the rocks involved and the tectonic history that is implied. The most important varieties are: angular unconformity, disconformity, local unconformity, and nonconformity.

As is illustrated by Fig. 206 and Plate XV, the rocks on opposite sides of an *angular unconformity* are not parallel. Figure 206A is a cross section, such as an exposure in a cliff; Figure 206B is a map of a different region. The first event recorded in Fig. 206A is deposition of sandstone and shale. These rocks were then deformed to assume dips of 70 degrees,

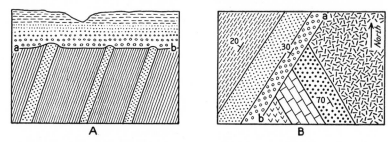

Fig. 206. Angular unconformity. *A.* Cross section. *B.* Map, not the same region as that shown in *A.*

either by folding or tilting of fault blocks. The ensuing erosion, probably accomplished by streams, but possibly marine, reduced the region to the surface *ab.* Eventually, erosion ceased and the younger conglomerate, sandstone, and shale were deposited. Although the rocks both above and below the unconformity represented in Fig. 206A are sedimentary, either one or both may be volcanic.

The precision with which the period of deformation can be dated depends upon the age of the rocks on either side of the unconformity. If the rocks beneath *ab* are upper Permian and the rocks above *ab* are lower Triassic, the deformation was late Permian or early Triassic. If, however, the rocks beneath the unconformity are upper Silurian and those above are lower Jurassic, the deformation could have occurred at any time between late Silurian and early Jurassic.

An excellent example of two angular unconformities based on drill records is shown in Fig. 207, a cross section of the Cymric oil field, California.[5] Unconformity *AA'* is between the Miocene and Pliocene. The Miocene was folded and faulted prior to the erosion that produced unconformity *AA'*. Then the Pliocene was deposited. Unconformity *BB'* is

[5] McMasters, J. H., "Cymric Oil Field, Kern County, California," *Structure of Typical American Oil Fields,* Vol. III, pp. 38–57. Tulsa: American Association Petroleum Geologists, 1948.

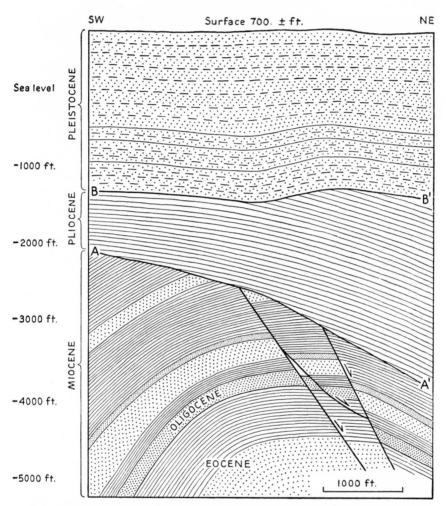

Fig. 207. Unconformities based on drill records. Cymric oil field, California. (After J. H. McMasters; permission of American Association Petroleum Geologists.)

between the Pliocene and Pleistocene. The Pliocene was gently folded prior to the erosion that produced unconformity *BB'*. The Pleistocene was then deposited and gently folded.

In a *disconformity*, the formations on opposite sides of the unconformity are parallel. A disconformity covers a large area and represents a considerable interval of time; the meaning of this somewhat vague statement will be more apparent after local unconformities have been discussed. Figures 205A, 205B, and 205C represent disconformities, and the history implied has been given above (page 242)

A *local unconformity* (Fig. 62) is similar to a disconformity, but, as the name implies, it is distinctly local in extent; the time involved is

PLATE XV. Angular Unconformity. Ouray, Colorado. Horizontal Devonian strata on vertical pre-Cambrian rocks. (Photo by K. F. Mather.)

short. In the deposition of continental sediments, such as gravels, sands, and clays, the streams may wander back and forth across the basin of deposition. At times of flood these streams may scour out channels scores of feet wide and many feet deep. As the flood subsides, or some days or even years later, the channel may be filled up again. Such an unconformity is local in extent and, in most instances, cannot be identified beyond the limits of the outcrop in which it is found. The time involved is short.

In a sense, a local unconformity is a disconformity of small extent representing a short interval of time. Under certain conditions it may be difficult to decide which term is the more appropriate.

Although the term *nonconformity* is used in various ways in the geological literature, it may be utilized most satisfactorily for unconformities in which the older rock is of plutonic origin (Figs. 205D and 205E).

RECOGNITION OF UNCONFORMITIES

Exposed in One Outcrop

Unconformities may be recognized in various ways, of which direct observation in a single outcrop is the most satisfactory. The outcrop may be small and only a few feet across; it may be an artificial opening, such as a quarry; or it may be the wall of a canyon, such as the Grand Canyon of the Colorado River.

If the unconformity is an angular one, the lack of parallelism of the beds on opposite sides of the contact will be readily apparent (Plate XV). This may be observed in a vertical section, such as a cliff (Fig. 206A), or on the surface of the outcrop (Fig. 206B). The lowest beds above the unconformity may consist of conglomerate with pebbles derived from the underlying formations. If the conglomerate is thin, it may be concentrated in small depressions eroded out of soft beds in the strata beneath the unconformity. But basal conglomerates are not necessarily present along angular unconformities. Faults and dikes may be truncated at the contact. The Grand Canyon of the Colorado, of course, displays two major unconformities in a striking way.[6]

Under favorable conditions, disconformities may be readily recognized in outcrops, road cuts, and quarries. If there is a sharp contrast in color between the rocks above and below the disconformity, if the disconformity is somewhat wavy, and especially if there is a thin conglomerate just above the disconformity, the nature of the contact is apparent. Regional relations must be considered (p. 245) in order to distinguish between a disconformity and a local unconformity. But disconformities

[6] Sharp, R. P., *op. cit.*

may be difficult to recognize, and in many cases paleon.tological evidence indicates considerable gaps in the geological record without any accompanying physical evidence.

Nonconformities must be distinguished from intrusive igneous contacts. The rocks above a nonconformity may contain fragments of the older igneous rock, either as readily recognized pebbles and boulders or as small fragments recognized only under the microscope. Some nonconformities are characterized by an arkose many feet thick, so that the plutonic rock seems to grade into the overlying strata. Along an intrusive contact, of course, dikes might be expected to penetrate the adjacent rocks; in some cases the intrusive is chilled against the older strata (see page 290).

A surface of erosion may be covered by a thick residual soil that grades into the underlying bed rock. Younger sediments deposited above this erosion surface may incorporate some of the residual soil, and a sharp contact may be lacking. Such a contact is called a *blended unconformity*.

Many unconformities are not exposed in an outcrop. This may be due to poor exposures, igneous intrusions, or faulting. In such cases other methods must be employed to detect the unconformity.

Areal Mapping

A geological map showing an angular unconformity is illustrated by Fig. 208A. A group of older rocks, *1, 2, 3*, and *4*, strikes into the base of a group of younger rocks, *5, 6, 7*, and *8*. Formation *5* is in contact with all the older formations along the line *CC'*, and the relations can be interpreted to mean an angular unconformity. But a fault between *5* and the older formations is equally plausible. The presence of pebbles of *1, 2, 3*, and *4* in formation *5* would indicate an unconformity, but even in this case the mapped contact *CC'* could be a fault. In the last analysis, therefore, it is necessary to see the contact of formation *5* with the older rocks. The areal mapping is suggestive, but not conclusive.

Areal mapping may bring out a disconformity in a similar way (Fig. 208B). Although, in any one exposure, the strata on opposite sides of a contact (*CC'*) may appear to be parallel to each other, the mapping may show that the younger beds truncate the older. But just as in the case described above, the truncation may be due to faulting; consequently, a solution is obtained only if the contact is visible.

A nonconformity may be suggested by areal studies. If the sedimentary rocks, such as formation *2* of Fig. 208C, contain pebbles of the plutonic rock, a nonconformity must exist. But the contact *CC'*, exposed at the surface, could be a fault, and the nonconformity itself is not necessarily exposed. If dikes of the igneous rock do not cut the sediments, or if inclusions of the sedimentary rocks are not found in the

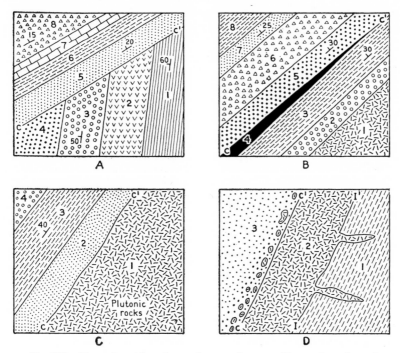

Fig. 208. Unconformities shown by areal maps. Formations in order of decreasing age: *1, 2, 3, 4, 5, 6, 7,* and *8. CC′* = unconformity. *A.* Angular unconformity. *B.* Disconformity. *C.* Nonconformity. *D.* Nonconformity (*CC′*) and intrusive contact (*II′*).

plutonic rock, a nonconformity rather than an intrusive contact is implied, but not proved. As in the case of the angular unconformity and disconformity, for a satisfactory solution of the problem it is highly desirable to see the contact.

Three angular unconformities are shown in Fig. 209.[7] The oldest unconformity is at the base of the Fort Union formation (*Tfu*), which clearly truncates the older rocks; the Fort Union formation rests on the Meeteetse formation (*Kme*) in the northern part of the area, and on the Lance formation (*Kl*) in the southern part. A second unconformity is at the base of the Wasatch formation (*Tw*); the faults that cut the Mesaverde (*Km*), Meeteetse (*Kme*), and Fort Union (*Tfu*) formations in the northern part of the map are truncated by the base of the Wasatch formation (*Tw*). The third and youngest unconformity is at the base of the Quaternary gravels (*Q*), which are in contact with the Fort Union and Wasatch formations.

[7] Hewett, D. F., "Geology and Oil and Coal Resources of the Oregon, Meeteetse, and Grass Creek Basin Quadrangles, Wyoming," *U. S. Geological Survey Prof. Paper 145*, Fig. 5, 1926.

Sharp Contrasts in Degree of Induration

A sharp contrast in the degree of induration indicates an unconformity. If unconsolidated sands and clays are associated with well-cemented sandstones and compact shales, it may be presumed that the unconsolidated material is unconformable on the consolidated rocks. Some caution must be exercised, however, because an unconsolidated rock may be locally indurated. Conversely, consolidated rocks may locally weather to loose sands and clays.

Sharp Contrasts in Grade of Metamorphism

If rocks with sharply contrasting metamorphism are found in the same region, it is probable that the less metamorphosed rocks were deposited unconformably upon the more metamorphosed rocks.

The grade of metamorphism[8] is commonly defined by the nature of the minerals resulting from recrystallization; a complete discussion of this subject is beyond the scope of this book. Under conditions of regional metamorphism, a shale becomes a slate or phyllite, with such minerals as sericite and chlorite. Biotite, garnet, staurolite, and sillimanite appear successively as zones of greater metamorphic intensity are approached. Most of these minerals persist into the higher zones; for example, a sillimanite schist commonly contains biotite and garnet. Staurolite is likely to disappear with the appearance of sillimanite. Thus if a sufficiently large area is studied, a single formation that was originally shale may be represented by the following different *metamorphic facies:* slate, biotite phyllite, biotite-garnet phyllite, biotite-garnet-staurolite schist, and biotite-garnet-sillimanite schist. Normally, a geological map will show that the change from one facies to another is gradual.[9]

If slate and sillimanite schist are found in adjacent outcrops, an unconformity probably exists, and the more metamorphosed rock is the older. This criterion, however, must be used with some caution. A large fault, in particular, may bring together different metamorphic facies of the same formation.

Sharp Contrasts in Intensity of Folding

If some formations in an area are highly folded, whereas others are gently inclined or horizontal, the less deformed rocks are probably unconformable above the more deformed rocks. Due regard, however, must be given to the relative competency of the formations involved. Whereas thick, massive sandstone may be thrown into a few broad, open folds, thin-bedded shales deformed at the same time may be crumpled into many small folds. Moreover, even the same formation may be much more

---

[8] Harker, Alfred, *Metamorphism*, 2d ed. London: Methuen and Co., 1939.
[9] Billings, M. P., "Stratigraphy and the Study of Metamorphic Rocks," *Bulletin Geological Society of America*, Vol. 61, pp. 435–448, 1950.

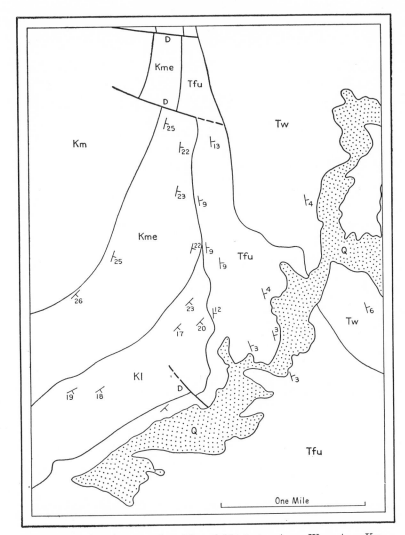

Fig. 209. Angular unconformities of Meeteetse Area, Wyoming. $Km =$ Mesaverde formation, $Kme =$ Meeteetse formation, $Kl =$ Lance formation, $Tfu =$ Fort Union formation, $Tw =$ Wasatch formation, $Q =$ Quaternary gravels. $D =$ Downthrown side of gravity faults. (After D. F. Hewett.)

folded in some tectonic zones than in others. It is apparent that variations in the degree of folding are not a very reliable criterion of an unconformity.

Relation to Plutonic Rocks

Two formations, such as *1* and *3* in Fig. 208D, may be separated from each other by granite (*2*) and may nowhere come into contact with each other. Formation *1* is intruded by the granite, but *3* is resting on the granite unconformably, and it contains pebbles of the granite. It is apparent, therefore, that *3* is above an unconformity and that *1* is beneath the unconformity.

Paleontological Record

The paleontologic record may indicate an unconformity. If a rock with Upper Triassic fossils is directly overlain by rocks with Lower Cretaceous fossils, even though the strata may appear to be conformable, a break representing all of Jurassic time is clearly indicated. In some instances the fossil record shows that a great hiatus is present in the midst of what is apparently a single homogeneous formation.

Additional Criteria

Additional criteria, many of which must be used with considerable discretion, are given by Krumbein, Pettijohn, and Stewart.[10]

CRITERIA FOR DISTINGUISHING FAULTS FROM UNCONFORMITIES

Reference has been made in several places to the danger of confusing faults with unconformities. Dip, diagonal, and transverse faults offer no difficulties. But if the bedding on one or both sides of the contact has the

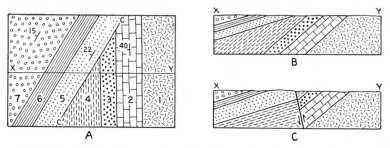

Fig. 210. Faults and unconformities. Formations in order of decreasing age are *1, 2, 3, 4, 5, 6*, and *7*. *A*. Map; contact *CC'* may be either an unconformity or fault. *B*. Cross section along line *XY; CC'* of Fig. 210A interpreted as an unconformity. *C*. Cross section along line *XY; CC'* of Fig. 210A interpreted as a fault.

same strike as the contact, as in Fig. 210A, either an unconformity or a fault may exist. Formation *5* may lie unconformably above formations *1, 2, 3,* and *4*, or the contact may be a fault, with either group of formations the older. Even if formations *1, 2, 3,* and *4* are known to be older, the contact can be either an unconformity or a fault. In Fig. 210B, a

[10] Krumbein, W. C., "Criteria for the Subsurface Recognition of Unconformities," *Bulletin American Association of Petroleum Geologists,* Vol. 26, pp. 36–62, 1942.

Pettijohn, F. J., *Sedimentary Rocks,* 526 pages. New York: Harper and Brothers, 526 pages, 1949, especially pp. 146–149.

Stewart, W. Alan, pages 32–51, in LeRoy, L. W., *Subsurface Geologic Methods,* 2d ed., 1156 pages. Golden, Colorado: Colorado School of Mines, 1950.

cross section along XY of Fig. 210A, the contact is interpreted as an unconformity, but in Fig. 210C it is interpreted as a fault.

Several methods of attack may prove fruitful if the contact cannot be observed. The contact is a fault if formations *5, 6,* and *7* are older than *1, 2, 3,* and *4* (Fig. 210C). Moreover, in a region of sufficient relief, it may be possible to ascertain the attitude of the contact CC' from its relation to topography. Under the simplest conditions, the dip of the unconformity would be essentially parallel to the dip of the beds in formation *5.* The greater the divergence of the dip of the contact from the dip of formation *5,* the greater the probability that the contact is a fault.

The presence of pebbles of formations *1, 2, 3,* or *4* in formation *5* would indicate an unconformity between the two formations, but even under such circumstances the contact CC' could be a fault.

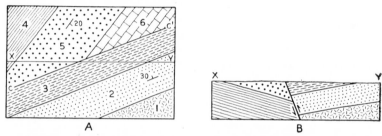

Fig. 211. Contact that is very probably a fault. Formations in order of decreasing age are *1, 2, 3, 4, 5,* and *6. A.* Geological map. *B.* Cross section along line XY of Fig. 211A.

If the younger beds strike or dip into the contact, a fault is indicated. This point is illustrated by Fig. 211A, where younger formations *5* and *6* strike into an older formation *3.*

In the final analysis, every effort should be made in the field to observe the actual contact. If it is an unconformity, small ridges of the older rock may project into the younger rocks, and a conglomerate or sandstone, with fragments of the older rock, may lie above the contact. Slickensides, gouge, and breccia would be absent from an unconformity, but would likely be present along a fault. Some faults, however, are sharp, knife-like contacts devoid of such features.

Additional complexity is introduced by the fact that faults may follow unconformities, particularly angular unconformities. In the Wasatch Plateau of Utah, for example, a hard, brittle, Eocene limestone was deposited with a strong angular unconformity on underlying weak shales. Subsequently the region was subjected to horizontal compression; the weak shales folded, but the brittle limestone slid along the unconformity.[11]

[11] Billings, M. P., "Thrusting Younger Rocks over Older," *American Journal of Science,* Vol. 25, pp. 140–165; especially pp. 153–155, 1933.

CHAPTER 16

Salt Domes

INTRODUCTION

Salt domes are of particular interest to the structural geologist. They constitute a superb example of the plastic movement of large bodies of rock, and their structural evolution is unusually fascinating. Moreover, very little information has been obtained from surface exposures. The data have been supplied by drill holes, geophysical methods, and a few mines. The growth of our knowledge of salt domes is an unparalleled example of co-operative enterprise, in which thousands of geologists—chiefly petroleum geologists—have participated.[1] Moreover, salt domes are of great economic importance, principally as a source of petroleum, sulphur, and salt.

A *salt dome* consists of a central core of rock salt and a surrounding dome of sedimentary strata. The core of many salt domes has pierced the adjacent sedimentary rocks, but this cannot be proved in all cases.

Salt domes have been found in a number of regions, notably the Texas-Louisiana-Mississippi area, the Colorado-Utah area,[2] Mexico, Spain, France,[3] Germany,[4] Russia, Iran, Arabia, Palestine, and India. In Texas and Louisiana over 150 salt domes are known.[5] Approximately one hundred salt domes were known in 1938 in the Emba district of Russia on the northeast coast of the Caspian Sea.[6]

[1] DeGolyer, E. L., *et al.*, *Geology of Salt Dome Oil Fields*, Chicago: American Association Petroleum Geologists, 1926.

Lalicker, C. G., *Principles of Petroleum Geology*. New York: Appleton-Century-Crofts, 377 pages, 1949; see Chapter 11.

[2] Harrison, T. S., "Colorado-Utah Salt Domes," *Bulletin American Association Petroleum Geologists*, Vol. 11, p. 111–113, 1927.

[3] Dupouy-Camet, J., "Triassic Diapiric Salt Structures, Southwestern Aquitaine Basin, France," *Bulletin American Association Petroleum Geologists*, Vol. 37, pp. 2348–2388, 1953.

[4] Roll, A., *"Die strukturelle Entwicklung und die Geschichte der Salzstockbildung in Hannoverschen Becken,"* pp. 69–89, in Bentz, A., editor, *Erdöl und Tektonik in Nordwest-Deutschland.* Hannover (Germany): Amt für Bodenforschung Hannover-Celle, 387 pp., 1949.

[5] Ver Wiebe, W. A., *North American Petroleum, with a Chapter on the Middle East*, p. 239. Wichita (Kansas), 1952.

[6] Ver Wiebe, *op. cit.*

Sanders, C. W., "Emba Salt Dome Region, U.S.S.R., and Some Comparisons with Some Other Salt Dome Regions," *Bulletin American Association Petroleum Geologists*, Vol 23, pp. 492–516, 1939.

SHAPE, SIZE, AND COMPOSITION

In considering the shape, size, and composition of salt domes, one should make a clear distinction between the anticlinal dome of sediments and the core, which is composed of rock salt overlain in many cases by a relatively thin cap rock. The core is thought to be a great pillar, with a greater vertical than horizontal extent.

Some American salt domes are expressed topographically, but many are not. The hills, which rise from a few feet to 40 feet above the surrounding lowlands, and, in exceptional instances, as much as 80 feet, cover an area a mile or so in diameter. Lakes occupy depressions above some of the domes. Oil seeps and salt springs were the means of discovering some salt domes.

The cores of American salt domes are essentially circular in plan, and they characteristically range in diameter from $\frac{1}{2}$ to 2 miles; some cores, however, are as much as 5 miles in diameter. The German salt domes are comparable in size.[7] In some of the Russian domes, on the northeast shore

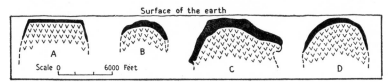

Fig. 212. Shape of the core of salt domes. Checks = rock salt; solid black = cap rock. *A.* Palangana, Texas. (After D. C. Barton.) *B.* Hoskins Mound, Texas. (After A. H. Marx.) *C.* High Island, Texas. (After M. T. Halbouty.) *D.* Brenham, Texas. (After S. O. Burfold.) Data from *Bulletin American Association Petroleum Geologists.*

of the Caspian Sea, the cores are 3.1 to 7.5 miles in diameter. The cores of the Rumanian salt domes are elliptical in plan, and the longer axis is parallel to the trend of the associated folds.[8]

In many salt domes the walls of the core dip steeply outward; the top may be flat (Fig. 212A) or domical (Figs. 212B and 212D). Some are symmetrical, the wall dipping at essentially the same angle on all sides; others are asymmetrical, the wall dipping steeper on some sides than on others; and in still others the wall on one side dips inward (Fig. 213A). In some salt domes in the United States, the core *overhangs* or "mushrooms" (Fig. 212C). In many cases the depth to which the salt extends is

[7] Stille, Hans, "The Upthrust of the Salt Masses of Germany," in *Geology of Salt Dome Oil Fields,* pp. 142–166. Chicago: American Association Petroleum Geologists, 1926. See also Roll, A., *op. cit.*

[8] Voitesti, I. P., "Geology of the Salt Domes in the Carpathian Region of Rumania, in *Geology of Salt Dome Oil Fields,* pp. 87–128. Chicago: American Association Petroleum Geologists, 1926.

Mason, S. L., "Rumanian Oil Fields," in *Geology of Salt Dome Oil Fields,* pp. 129–141. Chicago: *American Association of Petroleum Geologists,* 1926.

unknown because in the search for petroleum there is ordinarily little incentive to drill any great distance into the salt. But, as shown in Fig. 213, it has been demonstrated by drilling that some salt domes extend more than 11,000 feet below sea level. The probable shape of some salt domes is illustrated in Fig. 214. Seismic evidence (see Chapter 23) sug-

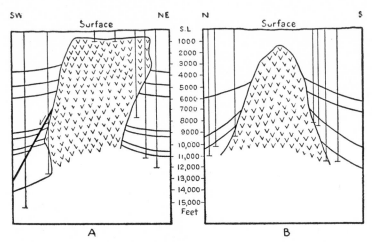

Fig. 213. Salt domes explored to great depth. *A.* Belle Isle salt dome, Louisiana. *B.* Iberia Falls salt dome, Louisiana. (Based on sections supplied by G. I. Atwater.)

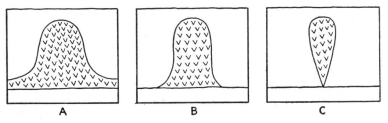

Fig. 214. Hypothetical shape of salt domes. (After Barton, *Bulletin American Association Petroleum Geologists.*)

gests that the bottom of some salt domes, shaped like those shown in Fig. 214A and 214B may be at depths of 16,000 to 26,000 feet.[9] The shape shown in Fig. 214C is hypothetical.

The core consists principally of rock salt (halite) overlain by cap rock. In the United States the salt is usually very homogeneous, with no trace of shale or other sedimentary rock. Argillaceous beds and potash-

---

[9] Swartz, C. A., "Seismograph Evidence on the Depth of Salt in Southern Mississippi," *Geophysics,* Vol. VIII, pp. 1–2, 1943.

Hoylman, H. W., "Seismograph Evidence on Depth of Salt Column, Moss Bluff Dome, Texas," *Geophysics,* Vol. XI, pp. 128–134, 1946.

rich beds are interbedded with the salt in the German salt domes. In general the structure of the salt in the American domes is not well known. Exceptions are those domes that have been mined for salt. Figure 215 is a reproduction of part of a detailed map of the salt core of the Grand Saline salt dome.[10] The map is on a level, made accessible by mining 700 feet below the surface of the earth (359 feet below sea level). The folds, because they plunge vertically, are superbly displayed on the roofs of the

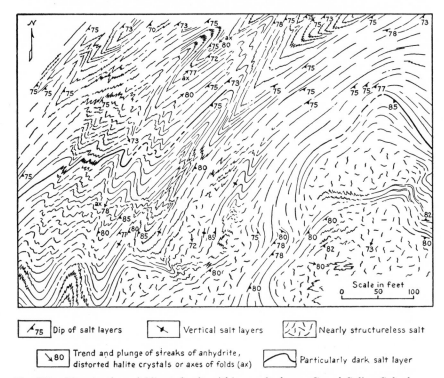

Fig. 215. Map to show folding of salt within a salt dome. Grand Saline Salt dome, Texas. (After R. Balk, *Bulletin American Association Petroleum Geologists.*)

workings, but on the walls the traces of the beds are parallel, vertical lines (compare Fig. 20C). The rocks in the cores of the German salt domes are also intricately folded.

The cap rock (Fig. 212) overlies the salt; absent from many salt domes, it reaches a maximum thickness of 1,100 feet on Sulphur dome in Louisiana.[11] The cap rock characteristically consists of limestone, gypsum, and anhydrite; the limestone is on top, the anhydrite on the bottom Commercial deposits of sulphur occur in the cap rock of a few domes.

[10] Balk, Robert, "Structure of the Grand Saline Salt Dome, Van Zandt County, Texas," *Bulletin American Association of Petroleum Geologists,* Vol. 33, pp. 1791–1829, 1949.

[11] Ver Wiebe, *op. cit.,* p. 240.

The sediments surrounding the core are uplifted into an anticlinal dome (Fig. 216). In *piercement domes* the sediments are sharply truncated by the rock salt in the core (Fig. 216A). In *nonpiercement domes* the bedding of sediments is parallel to the contact with the core (Fig. 216B). Some domes, however, may show both relationships; the core may truncate the older formations on its flanks, but not the younger strata near the roof.

The sedimentary rocks adjacent to the core have been dragged upward many thousands of feet. The exact amount may be calculated rather readily by comparing the depth of a bed near the core with its depth where it is undisturbed beyond the influence of the salt (Fig. 216A).

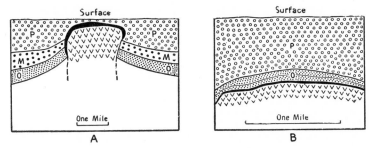

Fig. 216.   Piercement and non-piercement salt domes. Checks = rock salt; solid black = cap rock. Sedimentary rocks: O = Oligocene, M = Miocene, and P = Pliocene and Pleistocene. *A.* Barbers Hill dome, Texas. (After S. A. Judson and R. A. Stamey.) *B.* Sugarland salt dome, Texas. (After W. A. McCarter and P. H. O'Bannon.) Data from *Bulletin American Association Petroleum Geologists.*

A zone of gouge has been recorded from some of the American domes at the contact of the core and the surrounding sediments. Thick breccias locally surround the salt core of some of the Rumanian salt domes. The fragments, derived from the surrounding sediments, are embedded in a matrix of salt or, less commonly, gypsum.

The domed sediments overlying the cores of some salt domes are broken by gravity faults. These faults may be radial (Fig. 217A), but more commonly they belong to a more or less parallel system in which one or more graben are conspicuous (Fig. 217B). These gravity faults show clearly that the sediments in the dome have been under tension.

The depth of the core beneath the surface differs greatly, and salt domes are sometimes classified on this basis.[12] *Deep domes* are those in which the top of the core is 5,000 feet or more beneath the surface; in many so-called deep domes, the core has not been reached. *Intermediate-depth domes* are those in which the top of the core is 3,500 to 5,000 feet

[12] Sanders, C. W., *op. cit.*, p. 503.

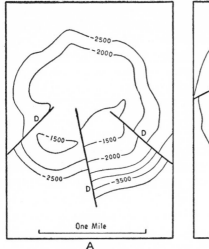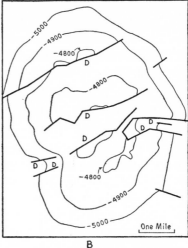

Fig. 217. Faulting on salt domes. Heavy black lines are faults, $D =$ downthrown side. *A.* Clay Creek salt dome, Texas; structure contours on top of cap rock; contour interval 500 feet. (After W. B. Ferguson and J. W. Minton.) *B.* Conroe oil field, Texas; structure contours on top of main Conroe sand; contour interval 100 feet. (After F. W. Michaux, Jr., and E. O. Buck.) Data from *Bulletin American Association Petroleum Geologists.*

beneath the surface. *Shallow domes* are those in which the top of the core is less than 3,500 feet beneath the surface.

In some of the Rumanian domes the rock salt is exposed at the surface of the earth, and in some of the Iranian domes the salt literally flows out on the surface to form spectacular "glaciers" composed of rock salt.[13]

ORIGIN OF SALT DOMES

Salt domes result from the plastic intrusion of halite (rock salt) into the surrounding sediments. The salt is derived from some underlying source bed, which in Texas and Louisiana may be of Upper Jurassic age.[14] In Germany, however, Permian salt beds form part of the normal stratigraphic sequence in the undisturbed sediments; all structural transitions are known from gently dipping beds through simple anticlinal domes to true salt domes.

The American salt domes have risen independently of tectonic forces. The motive force is the difference in density between the salt and the surrounding sediments. The salt, which is of lower specific gravity than the

---

[13] Harrison, J. V., "The Geology of Some Salt-Plugs in Laristan (Southern Iran)," *Quarterly Journal of the Geological Society of London,* Vol. LXXXVI, pp. 463–522, 1930.

[14] Ver Wiebe, *op. cit.,* p. 239.

sediments, has moved upwards somewhat in the same way that a fluid rises through an overlying heavier fluid. Nettleton[15] has investigated this subject experimentally, and he has obtained structures remarkably simulating salt domes (Fig. 218). According to his investigations, if a small anticlinal flexure exists on top of the original salt bed, upward movement starts here, and salt is drained away from the surrounding region. Eventually, the salt bed in the adjacent area may become so thin and constricted that further addition of salt is impossible. In fact, many salt domes may have been pinched from the source beds, and they may have a stream-lined shape with a rounded top and a sharp downward termination (Fig. 214C).

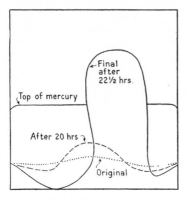

Fig. 218. Fluid mechanics of salt domes. At start a layer of paraffin lies beneath the dotted line, and mercury is above. (After L. L. Nettleton. Data from *Bulletin American Association Petroleum Geologists.*)

Barton has emphasized that, although the rock salt has moved upward relative to the surrounding sediments, it may have stayed at essentially the same position relative to sea level.[16] In other words, the surrounding sediments went down while the salt was remaining stationary; salt domes are the result of *downbuilding* rather than of *upthrusting*. Although this is probably essentially correct, such a distinction is mechanically unimportant.

In Rumania, horizontal compression has been an important factor in the development of salt domes. The salt, forced upward by orogenic pressure, has penetrated the sediments at the crests of the anticlines to form diapir folds (see also p. 59). Sanders has suggested that the American and Rumanian salt domes are two extreme types of a more or less transitional series.[17] Orogenic forces, which have played an important role in the formation of Rumanian salt domes, have also affected the German salt domes. The Russian domes around the Caspian Sea and the Iranian domes have been only slightly influenced by compressive forces.

The origin of the cap rock is a problem upon which there is no unanimity of agreement. According to one theory the cap rock is residual material left when salt is dissolved at the top of the rising dome, although

[15] Nettleton, L. L., "Fluid Mechanics of Salt Domes," *Bulletin American Association Petroleum Geologists,* Vol. 18, pp. 1175–1204, 1934; also *Gulf Coast Oil Fields,* pp. 79–108, Tulsa: American Association Petroleum Geologists, 1936.

[16] Barton, D. C., "Mechanics of Formation of Salt Domes with Special Reference to Gulf Coast Salt Domes of Texas and Louisiana," *Bulletin American Association Petroleum Geologists,* Vol. 17, pp. 1025–1083, 1933; also *Gulf Coast Oil Fields,* Tulsa: American Association Petroleum Geologists, pp. 20–78, 1936.

[17] Sanders, C. W., *op. cit.,* pp. 511–512.

the evolution is complex in detail.[18] Another theory supposes that the cap is sedimentary material deposited on top of the original salt bed; this material has been pushed ahead of the rising body of salt.

STRUCTURAL EVOLUTION OF SALT DOMES

A vast amount of precise information has accumulated on the structural evolution of salt domes, both in America and abroad. Some, and perhaps many, of the American salt domes have been rising throughout Tertiary time. The evidence is primarily stratigraphic. An angular unconformity, such as that illustrated in Fig. 219A, shows that considerable uplift occurred after the deposition of formation a, but before the deposition of formation b. The salt rose up through formation a, trun-

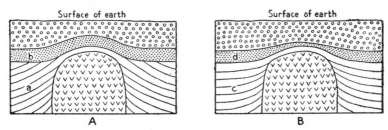

Fig. 219. Criteria for dating movements in salt domes. Checks = core of rock salt and cap rock. Rest are sedimentary rocks. *A.* Unconformity between formations a and b. *B.* Formation d thins over core of rock salt.

cating the bedding and doming up the sediments. Erosion followed, removing many of the younger beds in formation a. Formation b was subsequently deposited, and this was followed by renewed upward movement that slightly domed formation b.

In other instances a formation may become thinner over the top of the dome. This indicates, as illustrated in Fig. 219B, that the dome was actively rising throughout the deposition of formation d, but unconformities within formation d may be difficult to detect. It must be remembered that all the data are obtained from drill holes.

Topographically expressed salt domes have probably been active in relatively recent times. Moreover, if Pleistocene or recent gravels on the dome are uplifted relative to their position in the surrounding region, it is obvious that the salt has been active during the Quaternary.

ECONOMIC RESOURCES

A detailed discussion of the resources of salt domes is not appropriate in this book, but salt domes are of such great economic importance that

[18] Goldman, M. I., "Gypsum-Anhydrite Cap Rock of Sulphur Salt Dome," *Geological Society of America, Memoir 50,* 169 pages, 1951.

a brief discussion is desirable. Petroleum is trapped in the sediments that flank the core of rock salt, and in some instances it has been found in the cap rock. Large quantities of sulphur have been obtained from the cap rock of some salt domes. This sulphur has probably been derived from the anhydrite and gypsum normally present in the cap rock, but there is no agreement concerning the details of the process of formation. The rock salt in the core has also been exploited economically. Potash salts have been extensively mined in German salt domes, where the potash salts occur in strata that were deposited during the accumulation of the sediments.

CHAPTER 17

Extrusive Igneous Rocks

INTRODUCTION

Igneous rocks are the product of the consolidation of magma. *Extrusive igneous rocks* form when magma pours out on the surface of the earth as lava flows or is blown into the air and then settles on the surface to form beds of pyroclastic rocks. *Intrusive igneous rocks* form when magma consolidates beneath the surface of the earth.

This chapter is concerned with extrusive igneous rocks. In considering this subject, the exact limits of structural geology are particularly difficult to define. The petrography and chemistry of these rocks is primarily the concern of the petrologist.[1] The geomorphic forms are of interest to the physiographer.[2] All phases of the subject fall within the domain of the volcanologist.[3] The structural geologist is interested, however, because volcanic masses contribute to the architecture of the earth. In some instances, moreover, folds, joints, and faults are intimately related to volcanic processes. In this book, therefore, the emphasis will be placed upon the structures resulting from extrusive igneous activity, but nothing will be said about the mineralogy or chemistry. Some non-structural material must be introduced, however, in order to present the proper background.

Although a detailed discussion of texture belongs more appropriately in a text dealing with petrology, a few general terms are necessary in doing structural work. A *glass* is a rock that has cooled so rapidly that the atoms have not gathered together to form crystals. A *fine-grained rock* is one in which the individual crystals are less than 1 mm. in diameter. A *medium-grained rock* is one in which the crystals are 1 to 5 mm. in diameter, a *coarse-grained rock* is one in which the crystals are 5 mm. to 3 cm. in diameter, and a *very coarse-grained rock* is one in which the crystals exceed 3 cm. in diameter.

In many rocks crystals of two or more distinct sizes are present. A

---

[1] Turner, F. J., and J. Verhoogen, *Igneous and Metamorphic Petrology,* New York: McGraw-Hill Book Company, Inc., 602 pages, 1951.

[2] Cotton, C. A., *Volcanoes as Landscape Forms.* Christchurch, New Zealand: Whitcombe and Tombs, Ltd., 416 pages, 1944.

[3] Tyrrell, G. W., *Volcanoes.* London: Thornton Butterworth, 1931.

phenocryst is a grain that is conspicuously larger than the groundmass; in extrusive rocks they are likely to be 1 to 5 mm. long, but may be absent. A *porphyry* is a rock containing phenocrysts. In most extrusive rocks the groundmass is glassy or fine-grained, or a mixture of glass and tiny crystals.

Vesicles are cavities left after gases have escaped from the lava. *Pumice* is a variety of lava so full of non-connecting vesicles that it may float on water. The more siliceous lava (rhyolite, trachyte, and dacite) may show *flow structure*, that is, bands which differ somewhat from one another either in mineralogy, texture, or both. These bands are usually a fraction of an inch thick. Some mafic lavas (basalt and andesite), presumably because they consolidated under water, show *pillow structure* (p. 77).

The fundamental units resulting from extrusive igneous activity are lava flows and pyroclastic beds. A large number of these units are usually associated to constitute volcanoes, which result from central eruptions, and volcanic plateaus and plains, which generally result from fissure eruptions.

According to Sapper, during the last 400 years, much more volcanic material has been erupted explosively than has poured out as lava flows.[4]

LAVA FLOWS

Lava flows develop when magma wells out at the surface of the earth in a relatively quiet fashion, with little or no explosive activity. Lava flows are tabular igneous bodies, thin compared to their horizontal extent. The attitude corresponds in a general way to that of the surface upon which they are erupted; on flat plains, the lava flows are more or less horizontal, but, on the slopes of volcanoes, they may consolidate with a considerable inclination. Figure 220 shows the plan of a succession of lava flows at the top of Mauna Loa on the island of Hawaii.[5]

Although the surface of a lava flow may be smooth, it is generally covered by irregularities of different magnitudes.[6] *Pahoehoe lava* has a smooth, billowy or ropy surface (Plate XVI). *Aa lava* consists of irregular blocks that are covered with small spines. *Block lava* is composed of irregular blocks that lack spines. In general, pahoehoe and aa lavas are typical of basalts; aa is the result of greater viscosity caused by lower temperature and lower gas content. Block lava is typical of siliceous igneous rocks.

---

[4] Cotton, C. A., *op. cit.,* p. 44.

[5] Stearns, H. T., and G. A. MacDonald, "Geology and Ground-Water Resources of the Island of Hawaii," *Bulletin 9, Hawaii Division of Hydrography,* 363 pp., 1946.

[6] MacDonald, G. A., "Pahoehoe, Aa, and Block Lava," *American Journal of Science,* Vol. 25, pp. 169–248, 1953.

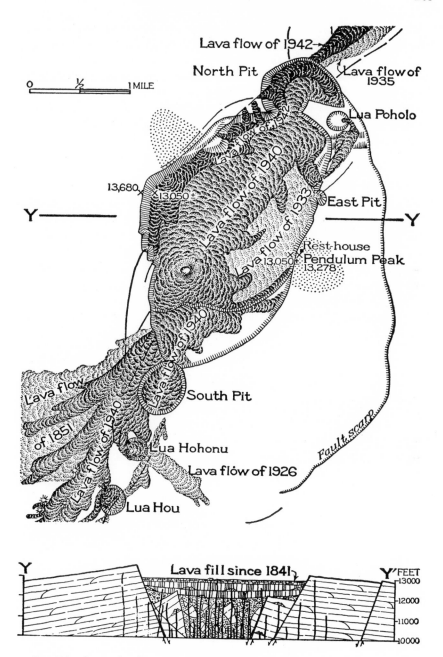

Fig. 220. Successive lava flows. Mokuaweoweo caldera on Mauna Loa, Island of Hawaii. (After H. T. Stearns and G. A. MacDonald; permission of Hawaiian Division of Hydrography.)

Tumuli (singular, *tumulus*), also called *Schollendome* and *lava blisters,* are low domical hills 20 to 60 feet long and 5 to 10 feet high. An open fracture, parallel to the long axis of the uplift, is not uncommon, and ropy masses of lava may issue from this crack. Some geologists believe that tumuli are due to the hydrostatic pressure of fluid lava beneath the crust of a gently dipping flow. Others believe that tumuli are caused by gigantic gas bubbles trapped beneath the crust of the lava.

Pressure ridges are long sharp ridges, many of which are broken by a central crack. In a flow in New Mexico, the shortest pressure ridge is

PLATE XVI. *Pahoehoe Lava. Cinder cone in background. New Mexico.* (Photo by R. L. Nichols.)

said to be 130 feet long, but some pressure ridges are more than 1,200 feet long; they are 10 to 25 feet high and as much as 100 feet wide.[7] Some pressure ridges are due to a compressive force imparted to the crust of a lava flow by the viscous drag of slowly moving subcrustal lava. Those cited from New Mexico are considered to be due to the collapse of the crust of a lava flow that was initially domical in cross section.

Squeeze-ups, small excrescences a few feet or tens of feet long on the surface of a flow, are due to the extrusion of viscous lava through an

[7] Nichols, R. L., "Pressure Ridges and Collapse Depressions on the McCartys Basalt Flow, New Mexico," *Transactions American Geophysical Union,* pt. 3, pp. 432–433, 1939.

Nichols, R. L., "McCartys Basalt Flow, Valencia County, New Mexico," *Bulletin Geological Society of America,* Vol. 57. pp. 1049–1086, 1946.

opening in the solidified crust. They may be bulbous or linear in form. *Driblet cones,* also called *spatter cones,* form if sufficient gas is present to cause rapid effervescence of the magma; they may be as much as 25 feet high and have steep walls. The successive layers of lava overlap one another in much the same way as does the accumulated wax on the sides of a partly burned candle. Lava flows that were very viscous at the time of eruption may possess concentric wave-like block ridges.[8]

Lava tunnels, as the name implies, are long caverns beneath the surface of a lava flow; in exceptional cases they may be 12 miles long.[9] They are caused by the withdrawal of magma from an otherwise solidified flow. Tunnels may be partially or completely filled with pyroclastic material or sediments that wash in through small fissures.

Depressions, circular or elliptical, are found on the surface of lava flows. Many depressions are due to the collapse of the roofs of lava tunnels. In a lava flow in New Mexico, the largest *collapse depression* is nearly a mile long and 300 feet wide, whereas the smallest is only a few feet across; one is 28 feet deep.[10]

A single flow may consist of several *flow units.*[11] Lava may flow in a series of spurts rather than at a constant velocity. A few hours or days after the advance guard of the lava has ceased to move and has consolidated, more liquid from the same flow may bury the part that has already stopped. This process may be repeated several times, and what is to all intents and purposes a single eruption, is actually composed of several flow units.

Individual flows differ greatly in size. Some are only a few feet thick; flows more than 300 feet thick are rare. The average thickness in the Columbia Plateaus of the northwestern United States is probably less than 50 feet; in India the average thickness of basaltic flows is less than 60 feet; in Iceland the average flow is 15 to 30 feet thick, and in Hawaii the basaltic flows average 10 to 30 feet in thickness, but a maximum of 900 feet has been recorded. The area may be a few acres or many square miles. In Iceland, single flows covering over 100 square miles are known, and one flow is said to cover 400 square miles.

PYROCLASTIC BEDS

Pyroclastic rocks, volcanic in origin, are composed of fragments that range in size from a fraction of an inch to many feet.[12] Some fragments

[8] Williams, H., "Newberry Volcano of Central Oregon," *Bulletin Geological Society of America,* Vol. 48, pp. 253–304, 1935.
[9] Stearns, H. T., "Volcanism in the Mud Lake Area, Idaho," *American Journal of Science,* 5th series, Vol. 11, pp. 353–363, 1926.
[10] Nichols, R. L., *op. cit.*
[11] Nichols, R. L., "Flow-Units in Basalt," *Journal of Geology,* Vol. 44, pp. 617–630, 1936.
[12] Wentworth, C. K., and H. Williams, "The Classification and Terminology of the Pyroclastic Rocks," *Bulletin National Research Council,* No. 89, pp. 19–53, 1932.

are composed entirely or partially of volcanic glass, thrown into the air as liquid, that hardened before it hit the ground or shortly thereafter. Some fragments are individual crystals, which were floating in the magma when the eruption began, or which were phenocrysts in the wall rock of the volcanic pipe. Some fragments are composed of older volcanic rocks, either glassy or fine-grained, that were ripped from the sides of the volcanic vent. Still other fragments have been derived from the country rock through which the magma erupted.

Uncemented pyroclastic detritus is classified, on the basis of size and origin, into dust, ash, lapilli, cinders, blocks, and bombs. *Volcanic dust* consists of uncemented pyroclastic fragments that are mostly less than 0.25 mm. in diameter. *Volcanic ash* consists of uncemented pyroclastic fragments that are mostly 0.25 to 4.0 mm. in diameter. *Lapilli* are uncemented pyroclastic fragments that are mostly 4 to 32 mm. in diameter; if the fragments are vesicular and glassy, they are called *cinders*. *Blocks* are fragments, usually angular and larger than 32 mm. in diameter, that were ejected in a solid state. *Bombs* are ejected as plastic magmatic material and have forms (in many instances that of a spindle) acquired during flight through the air. They are larger than 4 mm. in diameter. Material of similar shape and origin, but less than 4 mm. in diameter, is classified as *ash* or *dust*.

Indurated (cemented) pyroclastic material is classified into tuff, tuff-breccia, breccia, volcanic conglomerate, and agglomerate. *Tuff* is composed primarily of material less than 4 mm. in diameter; its fragmental character is usually readily recognized in the field and under the microscope. But a welded tuff on superficial examination is identical with lava. Microscopic study shows, however, that it contains many arcuate glass shards. Many welded tuffs are believed to be pyroclastic rocks that were deposited by *nuées ardentes* (p. 269), but were so hot that the fragments welded together.[13] Some welded tuffs may be collapsed pumice.[14] *Breccia*, more precisely called *volcanic breccia*, is composed chiefly of angular fragments larger than 4 mm. in diameter. If much of the matrix of such material is less than 4 mm. in diameter, the term *tuff-breccia* may be applied. Agglomerate is composed of rounded or subangular fragments, larger than 4 mm. in diameter, set in a finer matrix. The round or semiround shape of the fragments is not due to the action of running water; it may be original or it may result from constant attrition of the fragments. A *vent agglomerate* is the variety that is confined to a volcanic vent. *Volcanic conglomerate* is similar to breccia, but the fragments are rounded by the action of running water.

The material thrown high into the air during an eruption may stay

[13] Gilbert, C. M., "Welded Tuff in Eastern California," *Bulletin Geological Society of America*, Vol. 49, pp. 1829–1862, 1938.
[14] Iddings, J. P., "Geology of the Yellowstone National Park," *Monograph 32, U. S. Geological Survey*, 1899, pp. 404–406.

where it settles, thus forming rocks which, because of variations in the size of the fragments ejected at different times, are stratified. Sometimes *nueés ardentes*, which are masses of fragmental rock charged with interstitial gas, speed down the mountain slope as great avalanches. In 1902, such hot clouds killed 28,000 persons at the fot of Mt. Pelée, Martinique.[15] The rock deposited by such a cloud is an unstratified welded tuff or breccia. Sometimes, because of torrential rains, the pyroclastic material resting on the mountain slopes becomes saturated with water and moves as a *mud flow*. The consolidated rock is a typical breccia or tuff, which may be difficult to distinguish from one deposited by *nueés ardentes*. Some of the material erupted from a volcano either falls in standing water or, more commonly, is carried for considerable distances by running water. Under either of these circumstances it becomes stratified like sedimentary rocks. The finer-grained rocks are tuff, the coarser ones are volcanic conglomerate.

A body of pyroclastic material deposited during a single eruption or phase of an eruption tends to be tabular in shape; it is relatively thin compared to its lateral extent. A deposit of tuff blown directly from a volcano in one eruption may be only a few inches or a few feet thick, but it may cover hundreds or thousands of square miles. Such a bed may be a great aid in correlation. A bed of breccia that was deposited as a mud flow may have been confined to a valley; consequently, it would be very long compared to its width.

In Iceland [16] subglacial eruptions of basalt are not uncommon. Only the lower part of the glacier may melt, and if the water can get away, the upper surface of the glacier will sag to form depressions as much as several miles in diameter. In other cases a large lake forms because of the complete melting of part of the glacier. Sometimes the water escapes with catastrophic violence. Barth states that the daily discharge in some floods that lasted from two to seven days greatly exceeded that of the Amazon River. It is apparent that such floods can move large quantities of coarse volcanic debris.

FISSURE ERUPTIONS

In fissure eruptions the lava is extruded through a relatively narrow crack and flows out on the surface of the earth. In Iceland some fissures are tens of miles long.[17] The eruption of a whole succession of such flows produces a lava plateau or plain. Although pyroclastic rocks are rare, they may result from violent local explosions. Under favorable condi-

---

[15] La Croix, A., *La Montagne Pelée et ses Éruptions.* Paris: Masson et Cie, 1904.
[16] Barth, T. F. W., "Volcanic Geology, Hot Springs, and Geysers of Iceland." *Carnegie Institution of Washington,* Publication 587, 173 pp., 1950.
[17] Barth, *op. cit.,* p. 11.

tions, the dikes that served as feeders for the fissure eruptions are exposed by erosion.

Several of the great lava plateaus of the world have been constructed primarily by fissure eruptions. This is true of the Columbia Plateau of the northwestern United States, and of western India, South Africa, South America, and the North Atlantic volcanic field, remnants of which are found in Great Britain, Iceland, and Greenland. In each of the plateaus, which cover tens of thousands of square miles, the total thickness of the volcanics ranges from 3,000 to nearly 10,000 feet. Basalts constitute 90 to 95 per cent of the lavas participating in fissure eruptions.

GENERAL CHARACTER OF CENTRAL ERUPTIONS

The major forms that develop at the surface of the earth as a result of central eruptions, although really no more important than fissure eruptions, are more spectacular, partly because of their form and height, partly because of the violence that may attend their activity. These major forms may be classified as volcanoes, craters, and caldera.

VOLCANOES

General Features

Volcanoes are bodies of rock built up by the eruption of magma; they rise above their surroundings. Volcanoes may be classified in several different ways, depending upon the emphasis that the investigator wishes to make. A petrographic classification is based upon the lithology. A physiographic classification is based in part upon the stage of erosion. A structural classification is based primarily upon the internal structure of the volcano and, secondarily, upon the map pattern displayed by a number of volcanoes.

Classification Based on Internal Structure

On the basis of internal structure, volcanoes may be conveniently classified into pyroclastic cones, lava cones, composite cones, volcanic domes, large spines, and compound volcanoes.

The various kinds of cones may be considered first. Such volcanoes are conical in shape, the apex of the cone pointing upward (Fig. 221). A depression, either a crater or caldera (see p. 276), is commonly present at the top of the cone, unless erosion has been so extensive as to destroy it. The slopes of the cone are concave upward, and the steepest slopes, found at the top, are controlled by the angle of repose of the material when it was erupted. Internally, the cones consist of successive layers, either lava, pyroclastic material, or both; these layers dip outwardly more or less parallel to the slope of the cone.

Lava cones, more commonly called *shield volcanoes,* are built chiefly of lava that was very mobile at the time of eruption; they are broad cones with low angles of slope (Fig. 221A). Much of the lava erupts from small vents or fissures on the side of the cone. The Hawaiian Islands are superb examples of this type.[18]

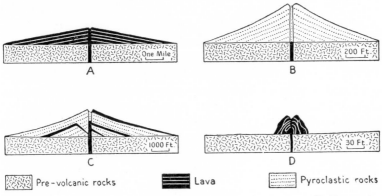

Fig. 221. Volcanic cones. *A.* Lava cone. *B.* Pyroclastic cone. *C.* Composite cone. *D.* Hornito.

Hornitos are relatively small, steep-sided lava cones constructed by the eruption of great plastic blobs of lava that were too cool to flow (Fig. 221D).

Pyroclastic cones, built chiefly of pyroclastic material, may possess very steep upper slopes (Fig. 221B); the variety that is composed chiefly of cinders is called a *cinder cone* (Plate XVII).

Composite cones, also called *strato-volcanoes,* are built of alternating layers of lava and pyroclastic material (Fig. 221C). Most of the lava erupts on the flanks of the cone rather than from the summit crater.

In the simplest type of volcanic cone, the pyroclastic rocks were blown out of the summit crater, from which some of the lava may issue as overflows. Some of the lava—and in many instances most of it—pours out from fractures on the sides of the mountain. *Adventive* or *parasitic* cones are subsidiary cones on the flanks of a larger volcano.

Volcanic cones differ greatly in size. Small cinder cones and hornitos may be only a few tens of feet high. On the other hand, some great giants tower five or ten thousand feet above the adjacent regions, and the base may be many miles in diameter. Some of the largest volcanoes in the San Francisco Mountains of Arizona rise 6,000 feet above the Colorado Pla-

[18] Stearns, H. T., "Geology of the Hawaiian Islands," *Bulletin 8, Hawaiian Division of Hydrography,* 106 pp., 1946.

PLATE XVII.   *Cinder Cones. Mauna Loa, Hawaii, 1926 eruption.* (Photo by United States Army Air Corps.)

teau and contain 33 cubic miles of rock.[19] Mt. Etna, in Sicily, rises 11,000 feet above sea level, and the base is 30 miles in diameter. The great volcanoes of the Hawaiian Islands rise 30,000 feet above the floor of the Pacific Ocean, attaining altitudes of 14,000 feet above the level of the sea.

Volcanic domes are steep-sided, bulbous bodies of lava that were so viscous at the time of extrusion that normal flows could not develop (Fig. 222). Many volcanic domes form inside a crater, but this is not always

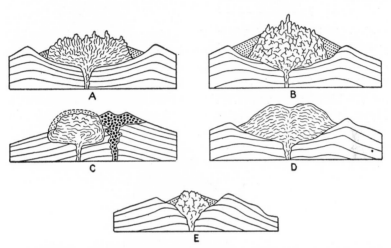

Fig. 222. Internal structure of volcanic domes. *A.* Fan-structure of flow planes; dots represent talus. *B.* Dome with crude concentric banding and irregular fissures. *C.* Dome on side of a cone. *D.* Dome formed by addition of layers on top of one another. *E.* Plug dome, irregularly fissured. (After H. Williams.)

true. The height of domes ranges from a few tens of feet to 2,500 feet. Many domes are difficult to study because the surface is covered by a jumble of irregular blocks caused by the rupture of the original dome; this rupture is partly due to thermal contraction of the lava, partly to stresses resulting from extrusion. Moreover, the steep sides of most domes are buried under talus.

Some domes grow primarily by expansion from within (Fig. 223). A few of these domes are characterized by concentric shells,[20] but such a structure apparently forms most readily if a slight cover of older rocks overlies the rising magma (Fig. 222C). Most such domes are intensely fissured and brecciated (Fig. 222B). During the rise of a dome, irregular dikes that are continuously injected into the outer shell may serve as feeders to small surface flows.

[19] Robinson, H. R., "The San Francisco Volcanic Field, Arizona," *U. S. Geological Survey, Professional Paper 76*, 1913.
[20] Reyer, E., *Theoretische Geologie*, Fig. 84. Stuttgart: E. Schweizerbart 'sche Verlagshandlung, 1888.

A common variety of volcanic dome displays a fan arrangement of the flow layers (Fig. 222A). Williams[21] suggests that such a structure is

due to the fact that the earliest lavas spread out from the vent at a low angle, forming a constricting ring that acted as a levee. The later flows, because they were restricted, rose at increasingly high angles.

Fig. 223. Dome formed by squeezing viscous material through a narrow opening. (After E. Reyer.)

Any pointed projecting eminence is a *spine;* spines associated with volcanic rocks may range in length from a fraction of an inch to many hundreds of feet. The classic example of a large spine is that of Mt. Pelée, in the West Indies (Fig. 224).[22] Two months after the disastrous eruption of May 8, 1902, a spine was first noted. Successive spines formed during

Fig. 224. Spine of Mt. Pelée, March 15, 1903. Height 1,145 feet. (After A. LaCroix.)

[21] Williams, H., "The History and Character of Volcanic Domes," *University of California, Department Geological Sciences Bulletin,* Vol. 21, pp. 51–146, 1932.
[22] La Croix, A., *op. cit.*

the summer, but each was destroyed by explosions. The most permanent of the spines, which began to rise in October, 1902, reached its greatest height on May 31, 1903, when it was over 1,000 feet high; the diameter was approximately 450 feet. Thereafter the spine gradually lost height.[23]

Compound volcanoes are those that consist of two or more of the types described above. Thus a composite volcano that has an associated volcanic dome, either in its crater or on its flanks, would be a compound volcano.

Classification Based on Grouping of Volcanoes

A *volcanic cluster* consists of a group of volcanoes without any apparent systematic arrangement. Figure 225 is an example of a volcanic clus-

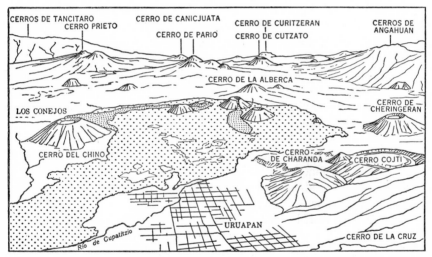

Fig. 225. Volcanic cluster. Cerros del Jabalí cone cluster looking west over Uruapan, Mexico. (After H. Williams, courtesy U. S. Geological Survey.)

ter in western Mexico.[24] A *volcanic chain* consists of a group of aligned volcanoes, the arrangement apparently controlled by a single fracture.

CRATERS, CALDERAS, AND RELATED FORMS

Craters

A *crater* is the normal depression at the top of a volcanic cone, and it is directly above the pipe that feeds the volcano. A crater, in its simplest

---

[23] For a later eruption of Mt. Pelée see Perret, F. A., "The Eruption of Mt. Pelée, 1929–1932," *Publication No. 458, Carnegie Institute of Washington*, 125 pp., 1937.

[24] Williams, H., "Volcanoes of the Parícutin Region, Mexico," *Bulletin 965, U. S. Geological Survey*, pp. 165–279, 1950.

form, is a flat-bottomed or pointed, inverted cone more or less circular in horizontal section. Immediately after an eruption, the diameter of the bottom of the crater (probably the same as the diameter of the conduit that fed the volcano) is seldom over 1,000 feet. Subsequent landslides from the walls, however, may partially fill the bottom of the crater. The walls of a crater are composed of interbedded lava and pyroclastic rocks, but the ratio of the two depends upon the type of volcano; some crater walls are composed exclusively of lava, others are composed exclusively of pyroclastic material. An unusually strong explosion may blow away part of the crater wall, thus exposing the layers of which the top of the cone is composed.

Craters are primarily due to explosions at the top of the pipe feeding the volcano. Fragmental rocks are blown into the air, and the largest material, landing within some hundreds of feet, builds a circular wall. Whenever magma rises in the pipe, it melts and dissolves whatever may be directly above it; it thus helps to maintain the depression.

Pit craters, typically exposed in the Hawaiian Islands, are circular depressions with steep walls. In the Kau district,[25] where pit craters range in diameter from 50 feet to nearly a mile, the depth of some is many hundreds of feet. Some pits are floored by solid lava; those that are occupied by a lake of lava are sometimes called *lava pits.*

Stearns believes that at some place along a crack, the magma works upward by stoping and fluxing to form a more or less cylindrical chamber occupied by magma. After the magma subsides, the roof of the chamber collapses, forming a circular pit. The pit may be widened later by landsliding and circular faulting.

Maars, also called *embryonic volcanoes* and *explosion pits,* are flat-floored explosion craters that are either devoid of cones or have very small cones. There is little or no associated magmatic material because the cones consist largely or entirely of fragments of the country rocks. They have been described from Swabia in Germany, and from Abyssinia.

Calderas

Following Williams, we may classify all large volcanic depressions as *calderas.*[26] More or less circular in form and miles in diameter, calderas are much larger than the pipe feeding the volcano. Calderas may be classified into three major types: *explosive calderas, collapse calderas,* and *erosion calderas.*

Explosive calderas are due to a violent explosion that blows out a huge mass of rock. A classic example is Bandai-San in Japan, which blew up

[25] Stearns. H. T., and W. O. Clark, "Geology and Water Resources of the Kau District, Hawaii," *U. S. Geological Survey Water-Supply Paper 616,* pp. 29–194, 1930.
[26] Williams, H., "Calderas and Their Origin," *University of California, Department of Geological Sciences, Bulletin,* pp. 239–346, 1941.

within a minute. The volcano had not erupted for more than a thousand years, but on the morning of July 15, 1888, 15 or 20 explosions occurred within little more than a minute. Although much rock was blown into the air, the last explosion, which was horizontal, initiated a great avalanche containing 1¼ cubic kilometers of rock. The summit and much of the northern side of the volcano were blown away, leaving a great amphitheatre 1½ square miles in area, with walls more than 1,200 feet high. No lava appeared, and the cataclysm was caused by a *phreatic explosion;* that is, ground water was converted to steam by volcanic heat until such a great pressure was generated that an explosion ensued.

Collapse calderas are most common. The essence of this mechanism is collapse of the superstructure of the volcano because of withdrawal of the underlying support. The details may differ; a single large cylindrical block may sink as a unit, or the collapse may be piecemeal, either during the eruption or immediately thereafter. The collapse may be due to one of several factors, or it may be due to a combination of factors.

The rapid eruption of great volumes of ash or pumice may lower the level of the magma in the main reservoir to such an extent that the whole superstructure of the volcano is left unsupported (Fig. 226). Collapse is apparently piecemeal (Fig. 226C); good examples of this type are Krakatau in Indonesia (East Indies), which violently erupted in 1888, and Crater Lake, Oregon. Collapse apparently followed the eruption of the pumice—probably within the hour. In the past, many such calderas have been considered to be of explosive origin, similar to Bandai-San. But if this were the case, the erupted material would consist of fragments of older

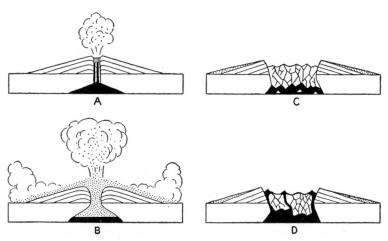

Fig. 226. Collapse caldera of the Krakatau type. *A.* Mild explosion of pumice. *B.* Violent explosions: part of pyroclastic material is thrown into air, part rushes down slopes as *nuées ardentes. C.* Collapse of the top of the cone. *D.* Renewed volcanic activity. (After H Williams.)

volcanics. But pumice is the chief visible product of such eruptions, indicating the inadequateness of the explosion hypothesis.

Of 76 known active and extinct volcanoes in the Aleutian Islands and Alaska Peninsula, at least 17 are caldera.[27] One of these is Katmai, which was in eruption in 1912.[28] Collapse and eruption were simultaneous; vast quantities of the original cone collapsed into the reservoir only to be hurled out after partial assimilation by the magma.

Figure 227 is a map and a structure section of Okmok caldera, Umnak Island, one of the Aleutian chain.[29] The caldera is 6 miles in diameter. Three stages in the evolution of the volcano are recognized. (1) Eruption of basaltic flows and tuffs that built up a composite cone that rose 7,000 to 10,000 feet above sea level. (2) A great eruption, during which the caldera formed; simultaneously, ash deposits were strewn over the volcano and far beyond. (3) Cinder cones, basalt flows, and lake beds partially filled the caldera. That this is still going on is indicated by a flow as recent as 1945.

The rapid outflow of lava from fissures far down on the slopes of a volcano may cause collapse. A volcano may be underlain by a reservoir several miles in diameter. If magma withdrawn from this reservoir by lateral fissures is not replenished, the roof is left unsupported. The *volcanic* sinks of Hawaii, exemplified by Kilauea, are of this type (Fig. 228).

Kuno says that of the 16 caldera in Japan, most are of the Krakatau type, and only a few are the result of subsidence along ring fractures.[30] Whereas pumice and welded tuff are associated with the former type, they are absent in the second type.

Erosion calderas are the result of the enlargement of craters or calderas by erosional processes.

VOLCANIC PIPES

The central conduit that supplies the magma (Fig. 221) can never be observed, of course, in active volcanoes; but after erosion has removed the superstructure of lava and pyroclastic rocks, the shape and filling of the *pipe* may be observed. Such filled pipes are called *vents, necks,* and

[27] Coats, Robert R., "Volcanic Activity in the Aleutian Arc," *Bulletin 974,* U. S. *Geological Survey,* pp. 35–49, 1950.

[28] Griggs, R. F., *The Valley of Ten Thousand Smokes,* National Geographic Society, 340 pp., 1922.

Fenner, C. N., "Earth Movements Accompanying the Katmai Eruption," *Journal of Geology,* Vol. 33, pp. 116–139, 193–233, 1925.

[29] Byers, F. M., Jr., *et al.,* "Volcano Investigations on Umnak Island, 1946": pp. 19–53 in Robinson, G. D., *et al.,* "Alaska Volcano Investigations, Report No. 2, Progress of Investigations in 1946," U. S. *Department of the Interior,* 105 pp., 1947.

[30] Kuno, H., "Formation of Caldera and Magmatic Evolution," *Transactions American Geophysical Union,* Vol. 34, pp. 267–280, 1953.

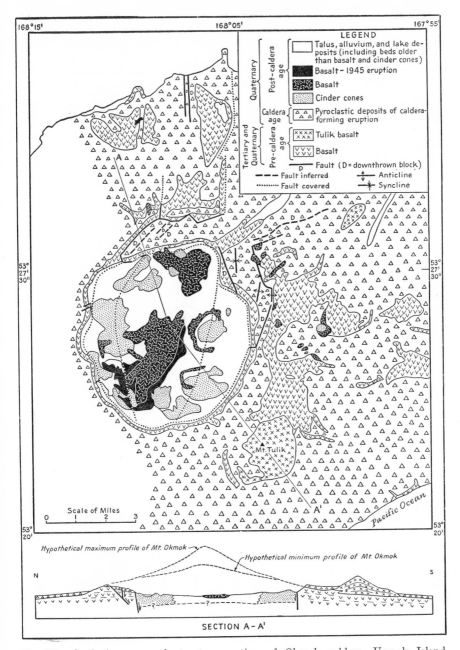

Fig. 227. Geologic map and structure section of Okmok caldera, Umnak Island, Aleutian Islands. (After F. M. Byers, Jr., *et al.*)

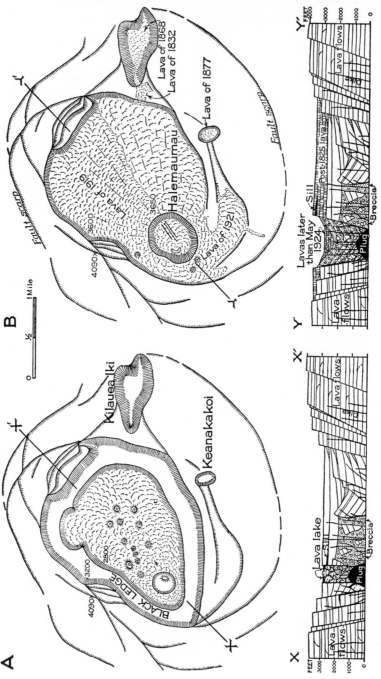

Fig. 228. Kilauea caldera. Approximate altitude in feet; ash beds omitted; structure beneath caldera is hypothetical. *A.* In 1825. *B.* In 1944. (After H. T. Stearns and G. A. MacDonald; permission of Hawaii Division of Hydrography.)

plugs (see p. 312).[31] They indicate that the pipe is relatively small and circular, seldom over a few hundred or thousand feet in diameter.

The mechanics of formation of such circular pipes are by no means clear. Some may be localized by the intersection of two fractures. Others, particularly where a number of central eruptions are aligned, may develop along a master fissure that is locally widened by melting, gas fluxing, stoping, or explosion. Some volcanoes may form directly over cupolas in magma reservoirs. Mining operations in South Africa have demonstrated that volcanic necks pass downward into dikes (Fig. 229).[32] Apparently the magma rose through a fissure, but, when it approached the surface, the gas began to come out of solution with such rapidity that a violent explosion occurred. This was localized at a point of weakness, and a circular hole (*diatreme*) was blown through the crust.

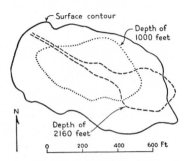

Fig. 229. Changing form of volcanic vent with depth, Kimberly Mine, South Africa. Plan of neck at different levels is shown. (After Wagner.)

RATE OF GROWTH

Little is known about the rate of growth of extinct volcanoes. Some information is available, however, for active volcanoes. The inner cone of Vesuvius grew 230 feet higher between 1913 and 1920.[33] The most spectacular modern example of the evolution of a volcano has been Parícutin (Plate XVIII), about 200 miles west of Mexico City.[34] The following brief account of its history has been taken from Williams.[35] The volcano formed in the midst of a cultivated field. Earthquakes which began on February 5, 1943, increased in number and intensity for two weeks. On February 20 a small fissure opened up about 4 p.m. and "smoke" or ash began to rise. By 6 p.m. low mounds of fine ash were accumulating and by 10 p.m. showers of incandescent rock were visible from a village 3 miles away. By 8 a.m. on February 21 the volcano was 30 feet high and

[31] For a description of conduits now exposed by erosion, see Williams, H., "Volcanoes of the Three Sisters Region, Oregon Cascades," *University of California, Department of Geological Sciences, Bulletin,* Vol. 27, pp. 37–84, 1944.

[32] Wagner, P. A., *The Diamond Fields of Southern Africa.* Johannesburg: The Transvaal Leader, 1914.

[33] Perret, F. A., "The Vesuvius Eruption of 1906," *Carnegie Institution of Washington, Publication No. 339,* 151 pp., 1924.

[34] Ordoñez, E., *El Volcan de Parícutin.* Mexico City: 1947, 181 pp. (Three parallel accounts in Spanish, English, and French.)

[35] Williams, H., "Volcanoes of the Parícutin Region, Mexico," *Bulletin 965, U. S. Geological Survey,* pp. 165–279, 1950 (especially pp. 222–228.)

by noon was 40 feet high. Up to this time only pyroclastic material had been ejected, but now lava also erupted. By February 26 the cone was about 500 feet high. A year later the cone had reached a height of 1,100 feet. In late 1946 it was 1,349 feet above its original base.[36] In August 1951, the highest point on the rim of the crater was 2,120 feet above the

PLATE XVIII. *Parícutin Volcano, Mexico.* (Photo by H. Williams.)

[36] Ordoñez, *op. cit.,* p. 179.

original base.[37] Whereas during its first year of activity the greatest ejection of pyroclastic material occurred, since then most of the magma has been erupted as lava. In fact, an irregular lava field about 3 miles in diameter has been constructed. Near the volcano the lava was about 600 feet thick, so that the cone rose only 750 feet above the surface of the lavas. All this lava was erupted from vents well down on the flanks, and none issued from the summit crater. In February, 1952, Parícutin became dormant or extinct.[38]

CRYPTOVOLCANIC AND RELATED STRUCTURES

Cryptovolcanic structures are, as the name implies, supposedly related to volcanism, but little or no direct evidence of volcanic rocks is visible. One type of cryptovolcanic structure consists of more or less circular depressions, 1 to 15 miles in diameter, and from 200 to 1,700 feet deep. Such caldera are located in nonvolcanic regions, and in most instances little or no volcanic material is found in the vicinity. The best known of these is the Ries Basin in southern Germany.[39]

The tectonic map of the United States shows 9 "cryptovolcanic structures or similar disturbances." [40] Some of these are topographically expressed by hills, others by basins. Ranging from 2 to 8½ miles in diameter, a central area has been uplifted 350 to 1,200 feet. There is characteristically a circular structural depression surrounding the central uplift. Faults, both radial and peripheral, are common.

Figure 230, a geologic map of the Wells Creek Basin in Tennessee,[41] is an example of American cryptovolcanic structure. The central domical uplift has carried the lower Ordovician limestones 1,000 feet above their normal position. In the surrounding syncline (s_1), the Mississippian formations are 300 feet below their normal position. An incomplete circular anticline (a_1) and an outer ring syncline (s_2) are still farther from the center. Peripheral, radial, and irregular faults are common.

One theory is that these structural features in the United States are due to an explosion caused by the sudden liberation of volcanic gases. Another theory is that these circular disturbances are the result of meteorite impact. If a meteor reached the surface of the earth a crater would be blown out. But at a depth of some hundreds of feet the rocks would first

[37] Fries, Carl, Jr., and C. Gutierrez, "Activity of Parícutin Volcano from July 1 to December 31, 1951," *Transactions American Geophysical Union*, Vol. 33, pp. 725–733, 1952.

[38] Kennedy, G. C., personal communication.

[39] Bentz, A., "Drehwaagmessungen im Ries bei Nördlingen, Geologische Einführung," *Zeitschrift für Geophysik*, Band 7, pp. 1–6, 1931.

[40] Bucher, W. H., "Cryptovolcanic Structures in the United States," *16th International Geological Congress*, pp. 1055–1084, 1936.

[41] W. H. Bucher, *loc. cit.*

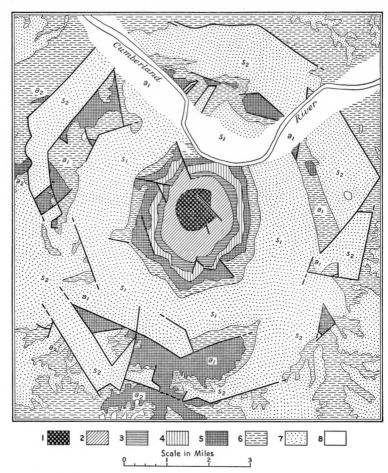

Fig. 230. Geological map of Wells Creek Basin, Tennessee. *1,* lower Ordovician; *2* and *3,* middle Ordovician; *4,* Silurian and Devonian; *5,* lower Mississippian; *6* and *7,* middle Mississippian; *8,* Quaternary; s_1, inner syncline; a_1, inner anticline; s_2, outer syncline; a_2, outer anticline. Heavy lines are faults. (After W. H. Bucher.)

be compressed elastically into a basin, and then the center would rebound to form a central dome.[42] The final form, therefore, would be a depression with a centrally uplifted area (Fig. 230).

[42] Boon, J. D., and C. C. Albritton, Jr., "Meteorite Scars in Ancient Rocks," *Field and Laboratory,* Vol. V, pp. 53–64, 1937.

CHAPTER 18

Plutons

INTRODUCTION

Intrusive igneous rocks form when magma consolidates beneath the surface of the earth. Rocks that mineralogically, texturally, and chemically resemble igneous rocks may result from the *metasomatic replacement* of older rocks. That is, older rocks may be gradually transformed by the introduction and removal of elements; the new rock may have all the characteristics of an igneous rock. Unfortunately, no satisfactory general term is in common use to include both the truly igneous rocks and the pseudo-igneous rocks. Therefore in this chapter, "igneous" will be used to include both types.

A *pluton* is a body of igneous rock or pseudo-igneous rock that has formed beneath the surface of the earth, either by consolidation from magma or by metasomatic replacement of an older rock. The "body of rock" may be a few feet long or hundreds of miles long. It might at first seem desirable to restrict the term pluton to those bodies that consolidated from magma. However, at the present time there is considerable disagreement concerning the formation of some of these bodies composed of igneous or pseudo-igneous rocks. Consequently, since a genetic term cannot be profitably used, it seems best to use pluton in a non-genetic sense.

It is by no means easy to define the limits of petrology and structural geology in this particular subject. The petrologist is primarily concerned with the mineralogy, chemistry, and origin of the rocks in these bodies.[1] The structural geologist is interested in their shape because they play an important rôle in the architecture of the crust of the earth. Moreover, he is concerned with the emplacement of these bodies and their relation to deformation. The internal structure of the rocks in plutons is significant because it offers evidence on the emplacement of the rocks and on later forces that have operated upon an already consolidated rock. Ideally the student of plutons should be both a petrologist and a structural geologist; a good field geologist and petrographer, he should possess a thorough

[1] Turner, F. J. and J. Verhoogen, *Igneous and Metamorphic Petrology.* New York: McGraw-Hill Book Company, Inc.. 602 pages, 1951.

knowledge of the physical chemistry of rocks. However, this book is concerned only with the structural phases of the problem.

Such a general term as pluton may at first seem of little value. But when the data are insufficient it is far better to call a body a *pluton* than to use a term with a definite meaning. All too often in the past, despite the fact that the field data were quite inadequate, a body of intrusive igneous rock has been called a *laccolith* or a *batholith*. A geologist can call a body a *pluton,* and then tell exactly what he knows about it.

A structural study of plutons involves a consideration of their internal structure, shape, and size, as well as the structural and chronological relations to the adjacent rocks.

TEXTURE AND INTERNAL STRUCTURE

The rock in a pluton is generally fine-grained to very coarse-grained (p. 263). In general the grain size is related to the size of the pluton or the proximity of the contact, but this is a generalization with many exceptions. Fine-grained rocks (crystals less than 1 mm. in diameter) are generally confined to small bodies a few feet across or to the contacts of larger bodies. Medium-grained rocks (crystals range from 1 to 5 mm.) are generally in bodies a few tens of feet across or are near the margins of larger bodies. Coarse-grained rocks (those in which the crystals range from 5 mm. to 3 cm.) are generally found in bodies that are at least several hundred feet wide. Coarse-grained igneous rocks that formed beneath the surface of the earth are generally called *plutonic rocks.* Very coarse-grained rocks, in which the minerals are 3 cm. or more in diameter, are generally called *pegmatites.* The coarse grain of pegmatites is apparently largely the result of the presence of volatiles during the crystallization rather than the result of slow cooling; consequently pegmatites may occur in small bodies.

Many of the rocks in plutons, whether they have consolidated from magma or are the result of metasomatism, are *massive,* showing no preferred orientation of the constituent minerals (Fig. 231A). Others are characterized by *foliation* resulting from the parallel arrangement of platy minerals (Fig. 231B). The perfection of the foliation differs greatly, being well marked in some instances and barely perceptible in others. *Primary foliation* forms during the crystallization of a magma; it is discussed further on page 326. *Secondary foliation* forms in an already consolidated rock (Chapter 20). *Inherited foliation* is a relic from older schistose rocks that have been metasomatically replaced. *Banded* or *layered rocks* are those that consist of alternate layers of different mineral composition. In Fig. 231C, the dark minerals, shown in solid black, are abundant in layers 1, 3, and 5, but are rare in layers 2 and 4. The layers range typically in thickness from an inch to several inches, but in

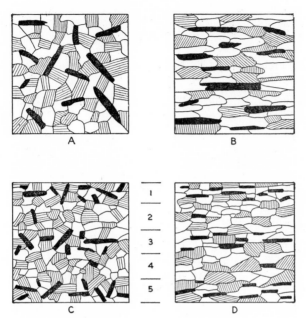

Fig. 231. Internal structure of intrusive igneous rocks.
Natural scale. Solid black represents platy dark minerals,
such as biotite; lined pattern represents feldspar; white
represents quartz. *A*. Massive rock. *B*. Foliated rock. *C*.
Banded or layered rock. *D*. Banded and foliated rock.
In *C* and *D* layers *1, 3,* and *5* are richer in dark minerals
than layers *2* and *4*.

exceptional cases the thickness may be greater or less than that. If the
minerals in such a layered rock are platy and lie parallel to one another,
the rock is foliated as well as banded (Fig. 231D).

Lineation is the result of the parallelism of some directional property
in the rock, such as the long axes of hornblende crystals (Fig. 232A).

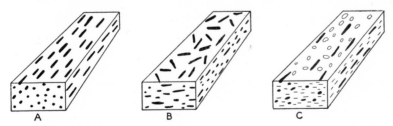

Fig. 232. Lineation. Solid black is a prismatic mineral, such as hornblende; dashes and circles represent a platy mineral, such as mica. *A*.
Lineation due to parallelism of crystals of a prismatic mineral; no platy
flow structure. *B*. Foliation due to orientation of crystals of a prismatic
mineral parallel to the top of the block; no lineation. *C*. Lineation due
to parallelism of crystals of a prismatic mineral, associated with a foliation
due to parallelism of a platy mineral.

PLATE XIX. *Dike and Plutonic Breccia. Beach Bluff, Massachusetts. The breccia consists of angular fragments of dark diorite in a light-colored granodiorite. The black dike appears to the left and is offset by small faults.* (Photo by K. F. Mather.)

Platy minerals or spherical grains may be strung out in lines to produce a lineation (Fig. 291C). A rock may have a lineation without foliation (Fig. 232A) or it may possess both foliation and lineation (Fig. 232C). Like foliation, lineation may be primary, secondary, or inherited. Primary lineation is discussed further on page 326.

Inclusions are fragments of older rock surrounded by igneous rock (Plate XIX). They may be angular, subangular, or round. A *xenolith* is an inclusion that has obviously been derived from some older formation genetically unrelated to the igneous rock itself, as, for example, a fragment of sandstone in granite. An *autolith,* sometimes called a *cognate xenolith,* is an inclusion of an older igneous rock that is genetically related to the rock in which it occurs. Thus an inclusion of diorite in granodiorite is called an autolith if it can be shown that both were derived from a common parent magma. Whether or not the two rocks have a common parentage is, however, primarily a problem of petrology.

A *segregation* is a round or irregular body, a few inches to many feet in diameter, and in some cases hundreds of feet across, that has been enriched in one or more of the minerals composing the igneous rock. Thus a hornblende granite may contain clots that have much more hornblende than the surrounding granite. These clots are segregations if they formed while the granite was consolidating, and if their formation was due to concentration of the atoms of which hornblende is composed. Petrographic methods may be necessary to distinguish a segregation from an inclusion, particularly if the latter has been modified by reaction with the magma.

Schlieren are somewhat wavy, streaky, irregular sheets, usually lacking sharp contacts with the surrounding igneous rocks. Schlieren may be either darker or lighter than the rock in which they occur. Some are disintegrating, altered inclusions, some may be segregations, and some may represent concentrations of residual fluids into layers in a rock that had otherwise crystallized.

AGE RELATIVE TO THE ADJACENT ROCKS

An intrusive igneous rock can be either older or younger than the adjacent formations. If the intrusive rock is older, the adjacent rocks must rest on it unconformably (Fig. 233A). The bedding in the sedimentary rocks above the unconformity is essentially parallel to the contact. Debris from the igneous rock, either in the form of pebbles or mineral fragments, may generally be found in the overlying formations. The igneous rock is coarse up to the contact, and faults and dikes (see p. 307) in the igneous rock may be truncated at the contact.

An *intrusive contact* is present wherever magma intrudes the surrounding rocks (Fig. 233B). Small dikes or sills (p. 294) of igneous rock may cut the adjacent formations, and inclusions of the latter **may** be found in the intrusive. The igneous rock may become finer-grained adjacent to the older rocks; it would give a *chilled contact*. The bedding in the adjacent formations may or may not be truncated by the contact. Conclusive data may be difficult to obtain along many contacts, but

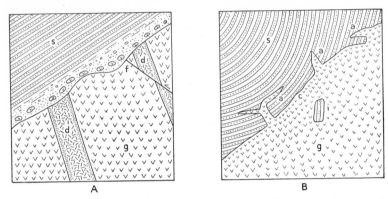

Fig. 233. Relative age of pluton and adjacent rocks. s = sandstone and shale; g = granite; d = dike of diorite; f = fault; i = inclusion; a = apophyses; c = chilled contact of granite. *A.* Unconformity. *B.* Intrusive contact.

assiduous search will usually reveal critical information. Along some contacts there may be a zone of metasomatically replaced rocks, which grade in one direction into sedimentary rocks and in the other direction into typical igneous-looking rocks. The zone of metasomatism may be a few feet wide, thousands of feet wide, or even cover many square miles.

STRUCTURAL RELATIONS TO THE SURROUNDING ROCKS

In many instances the older rocks adjacent to a pluton are characterized by bedding or schistosity. A body is said to be *concordant* if the contacts are parallel to the bedding or schistosity of the older rocks (Fig. 234A). A body is said to be *discordant* if the contacts cut across the bedding or schistosity of the older rocks (Fig. 234B). In many cases, of course, a contact may be concordant in some places, discordant in others. When one refers to the large plutons, the terms *concordant* and *discordant* may be used to a certain extent in a relative sense. For example, a pluton that is regionally concordant may locally transgress the structure of the older rocks.

The most satisfactory classification of plutons is based upon whether the contact is concordant or discordant, but shape and size are also factors. The concordant bodies include sills, laccoliths, lopoliths, and phacoliths. The discordant bodies include dikes, volcanic vents, batholiths, and stocks.

The structural relations to the surrounding rocks may be determined in various ways. The smaller bodies, a few feet or tens of feet across, may be observed directly in a single outcrop, and the concordant or discordant nature may be established directly (Fig. 234). For larger plutons,

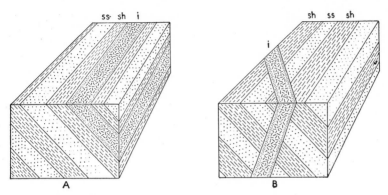

Fig. 234. Concordant and discordant intrusions: ss = sandstone, sh = shale, i = igneous rock of pluton. A. Concordant pluton. B. Discordant pluton.

more indirect methods are necessary. Figure 235A, for example, is a map of a pluton, 100 feet wide, trending northeast. At localities a and c, the bedding dips 40 degrees to the southeast. At locality b, the southeast contact of the pluton is exposed, and it dips 40 degrees to the southeast. At

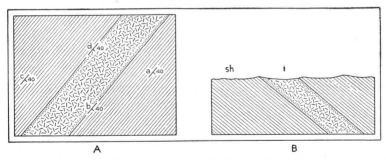

Fig. 235. Concordant pluton, the contacts of which are exposed: sh = shale, i = igneous rock of pluton. A. Geological map; letters are mentioned in text. B. Inferred cross section.

locality d, the northwest contact of the pluton is observed to dip 40 degrees to the southeast. It is apparent, therefore, that the body is concordant, as shown in Fig. 235B, at least within the zone of observation.

Figure 236A is a map of another region. As in the previous case, the bedding dips 40 degrees to the southeast. But the southeast contact at b

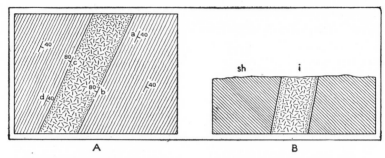

Fig. 236. Discordant pluton, the contacts of which are exposed: $sh =$ shale, $i =$ igneous rock of pluton. A. Geological map; letters are mentioned in text. B. Inferred cross section.

and the northwest contact at d dip 80 degrees to the northwest; the pluton must be discordant (Fig. 236B).

Several indirect methods are available to ascertain the attitude of contacts that are not exposed. One of these methods is based upon topography. In Fig. 237A, the strata dip 40 degrees to the southeast. The contacts of the pluton are not exposed, but the outcrops are good enough to permit location of the contact within a few feet. The contact bends downstream where it crosses a valley. If the altitudes of the southeastern

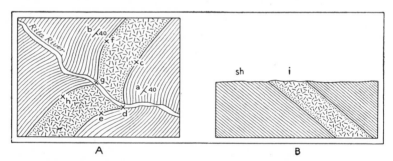

Fig. 237. Concordant pluton—attitude of contacts deduced from relations to topography: $sh =$ shale; $i =$ igneous rock of pluton. A. Geological map; letters referred to in text. B. Inferred cross section.

contact at c, d, and e are known, the dip of the contact may be calculated by the three-point method (pp. 68, 427). Similarly, the attitude of the northwestern contact may be determined if the altitude of points f, g, and h are known. If both contacts dip 40 degrees to the southeast, the pluton is concordant.

Another method utilizes whatever primary foliation may be present in the igneous rock. In Fig. 238A, the bedding dips 40 degrees to the southeast, but the actual contact of the pluton is nowhere exposed. The primary foliation near both contacts also dips 40 degrees to the southeast. Observations in many parts of the world show that the primary foliation is commonly parallel to the adjacent contacts. This subject is discussed more fully on p. 326. It is inferred, therefore, that the contact in this case dips 40 degrees to the southeast and that the pluton is concordant.

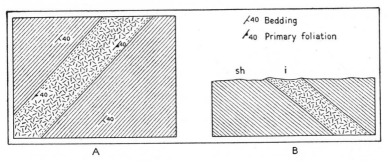

Fig. 238. Concordant pluton—attitude of contacts deduced from attitude of foliation: *sh* = shale; *i* = igneous rock of pluton. *A.* Geological map. *B.* Inferred cross section.

The attitude of a contact may be determined by artificial means such as tunnels, mines, or drill holes. Geophysical methods (Chapter 23) may also be used.

DETERMINING THE SHAPE AND SIZE OF PLUTONS

The shape and size of plutons are almost always a matter of conjecture. This is true of even the smaller bodies. An intrusion such as that illustrated in Fig. 235 is presumably tabular. The northeast-southwest dimensions can be ascertained if exposures are available. But the dimension down the dip is unknown—unless by some artificial means, such as drilling or mining—and the former extent up the dip is forever lost by erosion.

For the larger plutons, the ground plan is determined by areal mapping, which may show that the body is linear, circular, arcuate, or irregular. The attitude of the contact is determined by the methods discussed above—direct observation, relation to topography, or attitude of primary foliation. The application of these principles is discussed more fully in those sections describing the various kinds of plutons. The downward extent of the body is beyond the realm of observation, however, and is of necessity a matter of extrapolation. In regions of high relief, the contacts may be exposed throughout a vertical range of thousands of feet, or data throughout a considerable depth may be obtained wherever there has been mining or drilling.

CONCORDANT PLUTONS

Sills

Sills, sometimes called *sheets*, are tabular plutons that are parallel to the bedding or schistosity of the adjacent rocks (Fig. 239, Plate XX). The rock in the sill is younger than the rock on either side of it. Sills are horizontal, vertical, and inclined; the concept that a sill must be horizon-

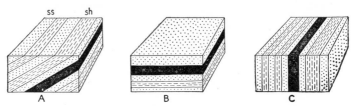

Fig. 239. Sills: *ss* = sandstone; *sh* = shale; *i* = igneous rock of sill. *A*. Dipping sill. *B*. Horizontal sill. *C*. Vertical sill.

tal is quite erroneous. Sills are relatively thin compared to their exten' parallel to the structure of the adjacent rocks.

Sills range in size from tiny sheets less than an inch thick to large bodies many hundreds of feet thick. The smaller sills can usually be

PLATE XX. *Sill. The gabbro sill is in the middle of the picture, with lower Cambrian sediments on either side of it dipping 50° W. (right). Nahant, Massachusetts.* (Photo by K. F. Mather.)

traced for only a few feet or scores of feet, but the larger sills cover thousands of square miles.

A *simple sill* results from a single injection of magma (Fig. 240A). A *multiple sill* results from two or more injections of the same kind of magma (Fig. 240B). Ideally, a simple sill is chilled only at the margins. A multiple sill, although possessing chilled margins, also possesses a

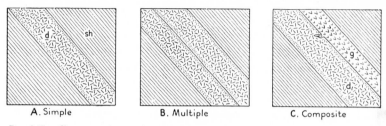

Fig. 240. Cross sections of sills: sh = shale; d = diorite; g = granite. *A.* Simple sill. *B.* Multiple sill. *C.* Composite sill.

medial zone of finer-grained rock, the position of which depends upon the relative thickness of the individual sills. The greater the number of separate injections comprising the multiple sill, the greater will be the number of chilled zones. If the injections followed one another in relatively rapid succession, the chilled zones may be obscure. A *composite sill* results from two or more injections of magma of differing composition.

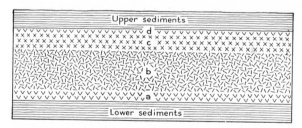

Fig. 241. Differentiated sill: a and d = rock with chemical composition of original magma; b = part of rock richer in dark minerals than a and d; c = part richer in light minerals than a and d.

Figure 240C illustrates a sill formed by separate injections of diorite and granite. A small offshoot of the granite cuts the diorite, indicating that the granite is younger than the diorite.

Differentiated sills (Fig. 241) are of particular interest to petrographers because of their bearing on the problem of magmatic differentiation.[2] Such sills are generally hundreds of feet thick, and they are

[2] Daly, R. A., *Igneous Rocks and the Depths of the Earth,* pp. 333–344, New York and London: McGraw-Hill Book Company, 1933.

Turner, F. J., and J. Verhoogen, *Igneous and Metamorphic Petrology,* pp. 155–161. New York and London: McGraw-Hill Book Company, 1951.

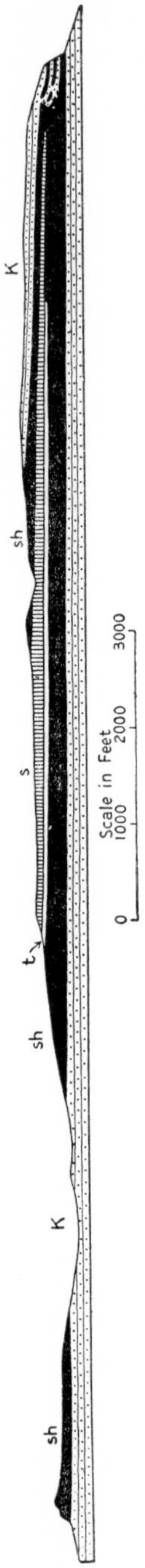

Fig. 242. Shonkin Sag intrusive of Montana. An example of differentiation in place. K = Cretaceous sediments; sh = shonkinite (syenite rich in dark minerals); t = transition rock; s = syenite. (After C. S. Hurlbut, Jr., and D. T. Griggs.)

initiated by the injection of a horizontal sheet of magma. The magma cools slowly and, under the influence of gravity, separates into layers of different composition. As crystallization proceeds, any minerals that are heavier than the magma tend to sink, whereas crystals lighter than the magma tend to rise. Rising gases play a role, the importance of which is as yet undetermined. In the ideal case, such as is illustrated in Fig. 241, a differentiated sill will have at both the top and the bottom relatively thin layers, a and d, of fine-grained rock, representing the rapidly cooled original magma. Above the bottom layer are heavier rocks, b, which contain minerals of relatively high specific gravity. Still higher is a layer of lighter rocks, c, containing minerals with relatively low specific gravity. The combined chemical composition of b and c should equal the combined composition of a and d. In the simplest case, the contacts between the four layers are gradational.

Many complications may exist in detail in differentiated sills. For example, one would suppose that if any density stratification occurred within layer b, the layers would be progressively heavier downward. A detailed study of a similar body at Shonkin Sag, Montana (Fig. 242),[3] showed that the heaviest rocks were many feet above the bottom of layer b. Moreover, the contacts of layer c were relatively sharp rather than gradational; this was due to movement of the partially-liquid magma after differentiation took place.

To distinguish a differentiated sill from a composite sill may be difficult. (1) Obviously, a sill in which the lighter rocks are at the bottom cannot be due to differentiation in place under the influence of gravity. (2) Differentiation in place is implied if the various layers are gradational into one another. But this is by no means an infallible criterion because under some conditions two intrusives of different ages show gradational rather than sharp contacts. A younger intrusive may react with an older rock to produce a transition zone that is many feet wide. (3) Although sharp contacts seem to imply successive injections, the liquid resulting from differentiation in place may move several scores of feet and produce sharp contacts.

[3] Hurlbut, C. S., Jr., and D. T. Griggs, "Igneous Rocks of the Highwood Mountains, Montana, Pt. 1, The Laccoliths," *Bulletin Geological Society of America*, Vol.

It is quite possible, of course, for a differentiated sill to be deformed in a later orogenic episode and even to assume a vertical or overturned attitude.

Sills resulting from metasomatic replacement may simulate simple, multiple, composite, and differentiated sills. However, in such bodies one would expect to find gradational contacts rather than sharp contacts; chilled contacts would not normally be present.

Lava flows as well as sills are tabular bodies of igneous rock that are parallel to the bedding of the overlying and underlying formations. It is essential, therefore, to establish criteria by means of which the two may be distinguished. These criteria are based primarily on the fact that sills are younger than the rocks above and below, whereas lava flows, although younger than the underlying rocks, are older than those above.

The essential differences between flows and sills are illustrated by Fig. 243. A sill (Fig. 243B) is characterized by a relatively smooth, fine-grained top, in which vesicles (gas bubbles) are rare. In particular, the overlying rocks may be penetrated by apophyses of the sill, and they may occur as inclusions in the sill.

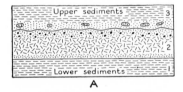 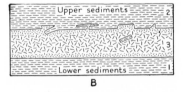

Fig. 243. Criteria for distinguishing sill from a flow. Diversely oriented dashes represent igneous rock; black dots are gas bubbles. *A.* Lava flow. *B.* Sill.

A lava flow (Fig. 243A), on the other hand, has a rolling, vesicular top. In particular, fragments of the lava may occur in the overlying rocks. Lava flows are likely to be cut by irregular dikes of sedimentary or pyroclastic material, representing debris washed into cracks in the lava. Moreover, if they are present, all the characteristics of lava flows described on pages 264 to 267 are diagnostic. In many instances the evidence may not be clear, and assiduous search may be necessary in order to find critical data.

50, pp. 1043–1111, 1939.

Barksdale, Julian D., "The Pegmatite Layer in the Shonkin Sag Laccolith, Montana," *American Journal of Science,* Vol. 250, pp. 705–720, 1952.

Laccoliths

A *laccolith*[4] is an intrusive body that has domed up the strata among which it has been inserted (Fig. 244). If the floor is relatively horizontal (Figs. 244 and 245A), the laccolith may be described as plano-convex, but if the floor is bowed down (uppermost laccolith of Fig. 245B), the laccolith may be described as doubly convex. Such a distinction, how-ever, is rarely possible because, as will be shown later, critical data concerning the nature of the floor are usually impossible to obtain. Lac-

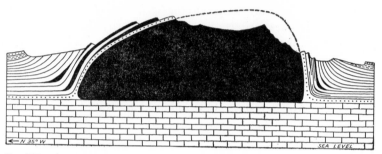

Fig. 244. Asymmetric laccolith. Solid black is igneous rock; other symbols represent sedimentary rocks. (After G. K. Gilbert.)

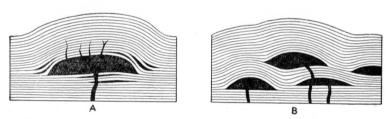

Fig. 245. Laccoliths. Solid black represents igneous rock; lined pattern represents sedimentary rocks. *A.* Ideal cross section of laccolith with ac-companying dikes and sills. *B.* Ideal cross section of grouped laccoliths. (After G. K. Gilbert.)

coliths are usually two to four miles in diameter, and the thickness is measured in thousands of feet.

It is apparent that all transitions may exist between laccoliths and sills. In a typical laccolith, the diameter is only a few times greater than the thickness. In a typical sill, the diameter is many times the thickness. The body may be termed a *laccolith* if the ratio of the diameter to the thickness is less than ten; if the ratio is greater than ten, the body should be called a *sill*. This is an arbitrary figure, but in all geological classifi-cations continuous series must be artificially assigned to compartments.

[4] Gilbert, G. K., "Report on the Geology of the Henry Mountains," *U. S. Geo-graphic and Geologic Survey of the Rocky Mountain Region,* 1880.
    Jaggar, T. A., Jr., "The Laccoliths of the Black Hills," *U. S. Geological Survey 21st Annual Report,* Pt. 3, pp. 163–303, 1901.

The typical laccolith has a floor, but this is usually based on inference rather than observation. Most laccoliths, especially in the western United States, are found in regions where the sedimentary rocks are essentially horizontal. Figure 246A is the map of an ideal laccolith. A central core of igneous rock is surrounded by outwardly dipping sedi-

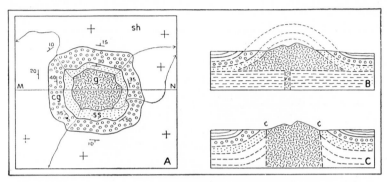

Fig. 246. Intrusive rock in the center of domed-up sediments: $g =$ granite porphyry; $ss =$ sandstone; $cg =$ conglomerate; $sh =$ shale; $c =$ contact of intrusive. The granite porphyry intrudes the sandstone. *A*. Geological map. *B*. Interpreted as a laccolith. *C*. Interpreted as a "bottomless" stock.

ments. For the body to be considered a laccolith two additional conditions must be met: the igneous rock must be younger than the overlying sediments, and the contacts must be concordant. The observed data are shown by solid lines in Fig. 246B, the inferred structure by broken lines. The floor is inferred.

The nature of the conduit way through which magma enters a laccolith is problematical. In Fig. 246B a small, vertical pipe is shown beneath the center of the laccolith. Gilbert concluded that the magma would spread laterally in all di-

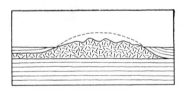

Fig. 247. Laccolith intruded from the side.

rections from the feeder; hence the feeder must be centrally located. Hunt,[5] in a restudy of the Henry Mountains, concluded that many of the laccoliths were fed from the side (Fig. 247). As shown by Fig. 248 the magma rose from depths through a centrally-located cross-cutting stock. On reaching favorable stratigraphic horizons the magma moved out laterally to form the laccoliths.

[5] Hunt, Charles B., "Guidebook to the Geology and Geography of the Henry Mountain Region," *Guidebook to the Geology of Utah, No. 1, Utah Geological Society*, 1946.
Hunt, Charles B., *et al.*, "Geologic Map of the Henry Mountains Region, Utah," *Oil and Gas Investigations, Map OM131*, U. S. Geological Survey, 1952.

An *asymmetric laccolith* is one in which the dip of the roof rocks differs considerably in different sectors (Fig. 244). An *interformational laccolith* is one injected along an unconformity. A *bysmalith* is a variety of laccolith, the roof of which has been uplifted along cylindrical faults. It is obvious, however, that in the field it would ordinarily be impossible to distinguish such a body from a "bottomless" intrusion.

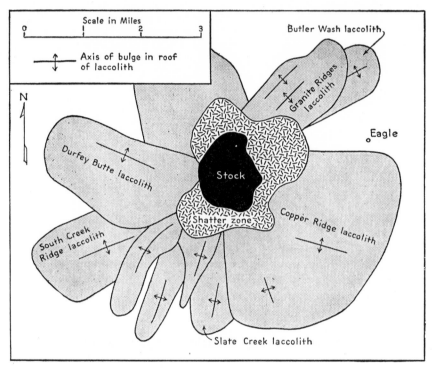

Fig. 248. Laccoliths fed from central stock. General plan of intrusion around Mt. Ellen stock, Henry Mountains, Utah. (After C. B. Hunt.)

Whether a laccolith or a sill develops when magma spreads along horizontal bedding planes depends upon several factors, of which the most important is the viscosity of the magma. Low viscosity will cause thin, wide-spread intrusions such as sills; high viscosity, because it prevents lateral spreading of the magma, causes laccoliths.[6]

The roof of the laccolith is lifted by the hydrostatic pressure of the magma. The overlying sedimentary rocks, compressed by the force of the magma, are elongated parallel to the bedding. The amount of the elongation depends, of course, upon the shape of the laccolith, but in some cases it is as great as 10 per cent and even more. Similarly, the thickness of

[6] Paige, S., "The Bearing of Progressive Increase of Viscosity during Intrusion on the Form of Laccoliths," *Journal of Geology*, Vol. 21, pp. 541–549, 1913.

the overlying sedimentary rocks is reduced. Tension cracks may form because of this "stretching" of the roof, and the roofs of some experimental laccoliths[7] are broken by radiating and concentric cracks. This is partly because the roof rocks have generally been destroyed by erosion; but even where the roof is preserved, such fractures are rare—apparently because the rocks were sufficiently plastic to yield without rupture.

Lopoliths

A *lopolith*[8] is a concordant intrusion associated with a structural basin (Fig. 249). In the simplest and ideal case, the sediments above and below the lopolith dip inward toward a common center. The diameter of

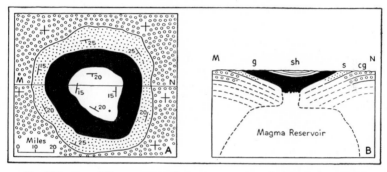

Fig. 249. Lopolith: $cg =$ conglomerate; $s =$ sandstone; $sh =$ shale; g $=$ gabbro of lopolith. Usual dip-strike symbols; $+ =$ flat strata. *A*. Geological map. *B*. Structure section.

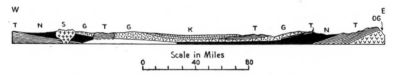

Fig. 250. Lopoliths of the Bushveld igneous complex of South Africa: $OG =$ older granite; $T =$ Transvaal system; $K =$ Karroo system; $N =$ norite of the lower lopolith; $G =$ newer granite of the upper lopolith; $S =$ younger syenites, unrelated to lopolith. (After A. L. Hall.)

a lopolith is commonly measured in tens or even hundreds of miles, and the thickness in thousands of feet. Superb examples are furnished by the Bushveld igneous complex of South Africa, where there are two lopoliths (Fig. 250), an upper one composed of granite and a lower one composed

[7] Howe, E., "Experiments Illustrating Intrusion and Erosion," *U. S. Geological Survey, 21st Annual Report*, Pt. 3, pp. 291–303, 1901.

MacCarthy, G. R., "Some Facts and Theories Concerning Laccoliths, *Journal of Geology*, Vol. 33, pp. 1–18, 1925.

[8] Grout, F. F., "The Lopolith; an Igneous Form Exemplified by the Duluth Gabbro." *American Journal of Science*, 4th series, Vol. 46, pp. 516–522, 1918.

of norite and related rocks.[9] If a lopolith is injected along an angular unconformity, the rocks above the intrusion will display the inward dip, but the underlying rocks will not, because they have been previously folded. The Duluth lopolith of Minnesota is such a body, but is incomplete because it is chiefly confined to the northwestern quadrant of the structural basin. At Sudbury, Ontario, a large intrusion, with which nickel ores are associated, is considered by many to be a lopolith.

The nature of the feeder of a lopolith is problematical. It may be a relatively narrow, centrally-located conduit, as is shown in Fig. 249B, or it may be much larger. No data pertinent to this subject are available. The basining is probably contemporaneous with the intrusion. The overlying rocks sag downward while large masses of magma are being withdrawn from the underlying magma reservoir (Fig. 249B). In fact, some geologists consider this contemporaneous basining an essential part of the definition of a lopolith. If a large, concordant sheet injected into flat sedimentary rocks were deformed into a basin, during some later orogenic period, these geologists would use the term *sill* rather than *lopolith*.

Lopoliths, like sills, can be simple, multiple, composite, or differentiated. Differentiation is characteristic of lopoliths. The Duluth lopolith is primarily gabbro, but a granite that is the product of gravitative differentiation has accumulated near the top. The differentiation of the norite lopolith of the Bushveld complex is simple in its larger features, but very complicated in detail.

Phacoliths

Phacoliths[10] are concordant intrusives confined to the crests of anticlines (Fig. 251B) or to the troughs of synclines. Phacoliths are not only

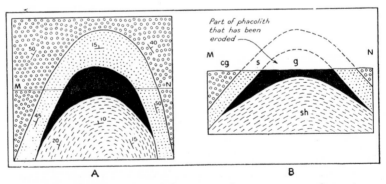

Fig. 251. Phacolith: sh = shale; s = sandstone; cg = conglomerate; g = granite. *A*. Map of granite phacolith in a northerly-plunging anticline. *B*. Cross section of the same phacolith.

[9] Hall, A. L., "The Bushveld Igneous Complex of the Central Transvaal," *Geological Survey of South Africa*, Memoir 28, 1932.

[10] Harker, A., *The Natural History of Igneous Rocks*, pp. 77–78. New York: The Macmillan Company, 1909.

crescentic in cross section, but also in plan because they are commonly associated with plunging folds. Figure 251A is a geological map of a northerly-plunging anticline intruded by a phacolith, shown in solid black. The thickness of phacoliths is measured in hundreds or, at the most, several thousands of feet. In plan, phacoliths are seldom more than a few thousand feet long, as measured around the crescent. Whereas sills, laccoliths, and lopoliths characteristically force their way into place, some geologists believe that phacoliths are passively intruded, the magma filling potential cavities that form during the folding. In an anticline, for example, the upper beds may pull away from the lower beds. It seems probable, however, that the magma must be under some pressure and that it actually makes space for itself.

Other Concordant Plutons

It is becoming increasingly apparent that large, more or less concordant plutons are integral parts of some orogenic belts. Although special names might be given to such bodies, depending upon their shape and size, it seems better to use the general term, *pluton*, rather than to coin new words.

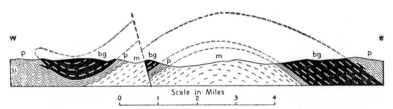

Fig. 252. Large concordant pluton, Mascoma quadrangle. New Hampshire. P = Paleozoic schists; m = granitic rocks of Mascoma group; bg = Bethlehem gneiss, which forms a large concordant pluton. (After C. A. Chapman.)

In western New Hampshire a large sheet of orthogneiss, the Mt. Clough pluton, is 100 miles long and several thousand feet thick (bg of Fig. 252).[11] It is probable that this body was intruded as a horizontal sheet and subsequently folded. Although most of the field geologists familiar with this body believe that it was injected as magma, C. A. Chapman[12] has suggested that it is a sediment that was metasomatically replaced.

Another type of pluton common in areas of considerable metamorphism have been called *mantled gneiss domes* by Eskola.[13] A mass of

[11] Chapman, C. A., "Geology of the Mascoma Quadrangle, New Hampshire," *Bulletin Geological Society of America*, Vol. 50, pp. 127–180, 1939.

[12] Chapman, C. A., "Structure and Petrology of the Sunapee Quadrangle, New Hampshire," *Bulletin Geological Society of America*, Vol. 63, pp. 381–426, 1952.

[13] Eskola, P., "The Problem of Mantled Gneiss Domes," *Quarterly Journal Geological Society of London*, Vol. civ, pp. 461–476, 1949.

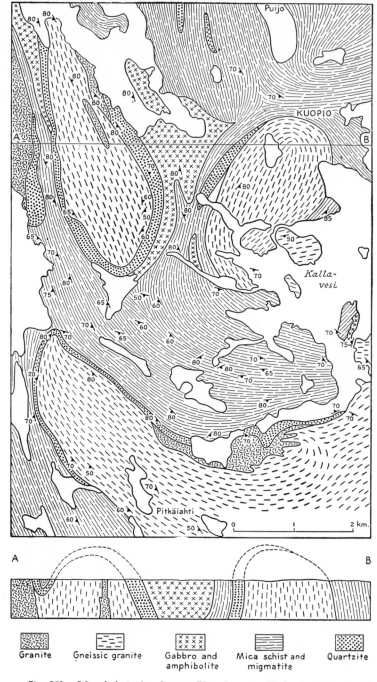

Fig. 253. Mantled gneiss domes. Kuopio area, Finland. Attitude of foliation shown by dip-strike symbols; see also p. 338. Gneissic granite is a foliated granite. (After P. Eskola and W. W. Wilkman.)

gneissic granite occupies the center of doubly plunging anticlines (Fig. 253). Metamorphosed sedimentary rocks surround the gneissic granite. The contact is parallel to the foliation in both the granite gneiss and the metamorphic rocks. The granite gneiss intrudes the metamorphic rocks. Eskola believes that such domes indicate two periods of orogeny, as shown in Fig. 254. Sediments and volcanics are deposited on an unknown basement (Fig. 254A). During the first period of orogeny (Fig. 254B) a body of granodiorite or quartz diorite is intruded contemporaneously with the folding. Younger sedimentary rocks are then deposited on the eroded surface of the older rocks (Fig. 254C). During the second orogeny (Fig. 254D) the older intrusive is partially transformed metasomati-

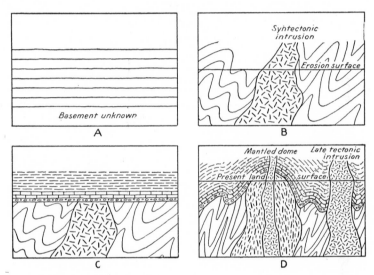

Fig. 254. Origin of mantled gneiss domes. *A.* First sedimentation. *B.* First orogeny. *C.* Second sedimentation. *D.* Second orogeny. (After P. Eskola.)

cally into a granite and rises to form the domical structure. New intrusions of younger granite may invade the area during the last stages of this second orogeny.

Geometrically similar domes are common in western New Hampshire.[14] One of these domes is shown in Fig. 252. A granite gneiss *m* underlies the older Paleozoic sediments *p*. One interpretation is that the granite gneiss was injected as a horizontal sheet and was later folded.

A pluton shaped like a great vertical cylinder is illustrated in Fig. 255.[15] In plan the granodiorite of the intrusion is oval in shape, except for

[14] Billings, Marland P., "Mechanics of Igneous Intrusion in New Hampshire," *American Journal of Science*, Vol. 243-A, pp. 40–68, 1945.

[15] Hietanen, Anna, "Metamorphic and Igneous Rocks of the Merrimac Area, Plumas National Forest, California," *Bulletin Geological Society of America*, Vol. 62, pp. 565–608, 1951.

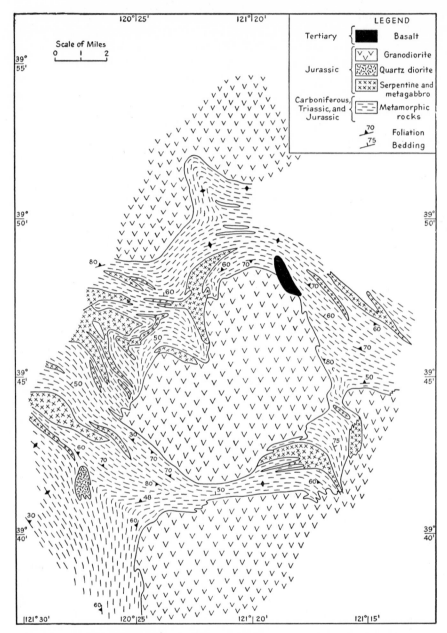

Fig. 255. Irregular cylindrical intrusion, composed of granodiorite. Geological map of Merrimac area, California. (After A. Hietanen.)

a pronounced dimple on the northwest margin. The metamorphosed sedimentary and volcanic rocks wrap around the intrusion concordantly with the contacts, which appear to dip very steeply. The granodiorite was emplaced partly by pushing the country rocks aside and partly by stoping and granitization (see page 321). As shown below, this body can be called a stock.

DISCORDANT PLUTONS

Dikes

Dikes are tabular bodies of igneous rock that cut across the structure of the older formations (Fig. 234B, Plate XIX). Tabular bodies of intrusive rock cutting massive, structureless rocks are also called dikes. Most dikes are formed by the injection of magma into a fracture; the walls may be pushed apart by the pressure exerted by the intruding magma, or the magma may quietly well up into fractures opened by tensional forces. Some bodies that appear to be dikes have been formed by metasomatic replacement.[16]

The terms *simple, multiple, composite,* and *differentiated* may be applied to dikes in the same sense that they are used for sills. A *simple dike* is the result of a single intrusion of magma. A *multiple dike* is the result of two or more intrusions of the same kind of magma. A *composite dike* is the product of the intrusion of two or more kinds of magma. A *differentiated dike* is one that was intruded as a homogeneous magma, but from which two or more varieties of rock have formed *in situ.*

Dikes may be very small, and dikes a fraction of an inch wide and a few inches long may be associated with larger igneous bodies. Most dikes are one to twenty feet wide, but wider and narrower dikes are not uncommon. The distance for which a dike may be followed depends in part upon the nature of the exposures. In Iceland, dikes 10 miles long are common, and some are 30 miles long; at least one is 65 miles long. In England, the Cleveland dike is 110, and perhaps 190, miles long.

The Medford dike near Boston, Massachusetts, is 500 feet wide in places. A differentiated dike at Brefven, Sweden, is 20 miles long and one mile wide. The Great Dike of Rhodesia is 300 miles long and 2 to 7 miles wide, but it may not be a true dike in the sense of being tabular.

A *dike set* consists of parallel dikes; where the dikes are very abundant, the term *dike swarm* may be applied (Fig. 256).[17] In some areas several sets may be present, and each set may be characterized by its

---

[16] Goodspeed, G. E., "Dilation and Replacement Dikes," *Journal of Geology,* Vol. 48, pp. 175–195, 1940.

[17] J. E. Richey, "Guide to the Geological Model of Ardnamurchan," *Memoirs of the Geological Survey of Scotland,* 1934.

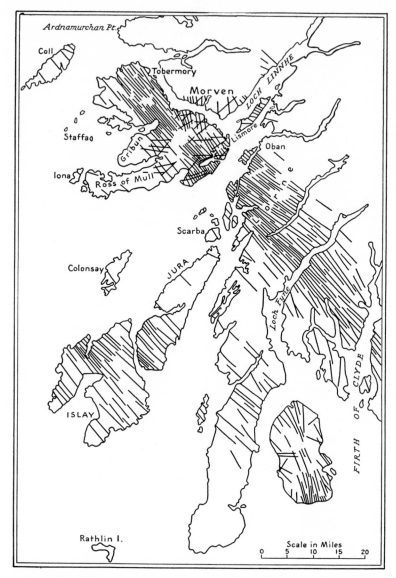

Fig. 256. Dike swarm. Tertiary dikes of the Southwest Highlands of Scotland. The map is diagrammatic in the sense that: (a) each line represents 10 to 15 dikes; (b) each dike is only a few feet wide, and not as wide as the scale implies; and (c) individual dikes cannot be traced for the long distances that the map implies. (After J. E. Richey, with permission of the Controller of Her Britannic Majesty's Stationery Office.)

own peculiar petrography, indicating that the various sets are of different ages.

The fractures occupied by dikes may originate in many ways. Some are older fractures, such as joints or faults that greatly antedate the intrusion. If the hydrostatic pressure of the magma is greater than the lithostatic pressure, the walls will be pushed apart elastically or plastically. On the other hand, the older fracture may be opened up by tensional forces, in which case the magma quietly wells up into the opening. In many cases the fracture is produced by the magma that fills the dike. The stresses at the edge of a wedge of magma are very great; consequently the fracture may propagate itself very rapidly. Magma in a reservoir may exert sufficiently strong pressure on its walls to form extension fractures (page 96), which are promptly occupied by the magma. Dike swarms are related to regional stresses. Anderson[18] believes that such dikes occupy fractures that form perpendicular to the least principal stress axis when the stress differences exceed a critical value.

Radiating dikes are found around volcanic centers. Most of the dikes —some of which can be followed for miles—radiate from the central volcanic region. In the Sunlight area of Wyoming (Fig. 257), the radiating

Scale in Miles

Fig. 257. Radiating dikes and cone sheets of the Sunlight area, Wyoming. Straight lines are dikes; heavier lines, with dip symbol, are cone sheets. (After W. H. Parsons.)

[18] Anderson, E. M., *The Dynamics of Faulting and Dyke Formation with Applications in Britain*, 2nd ed. Edinburgh: Oliver and Boyd, 1950.

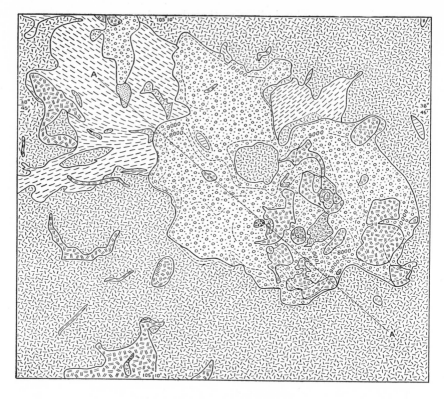

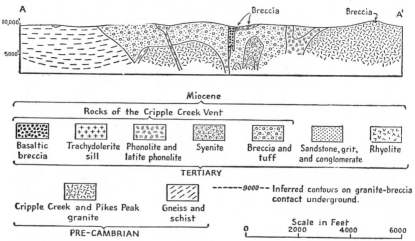

Fig. 258. Volcanic vent. Cripple Creek, Colorado. (After T. S. Lovering and E. N. Goddard.)

dikes extend 5 to 7 miles from the central area.[19] There are thousands of dikes averaging 4 feet in width, although some are 20 feet wide.

The original fractures, now filled by the dikes, are tensional in origin. In some cases, the magma in the conduit within the cone of the volcano exerts a horizontally directed compressive force on the surrounding rocks. The resulting extension fractures constitute a vertical, radiating system. In other instances, the fractures may be related to forces initiated by the magma reservoir underlying the volcano. The upward pressure exerted by the magma would cause vertical, radiating extension fractures.

Cone sheets are dikes that belong to a concentric, inward-dipping system (Fig. 259). None of the cone sheets extend all the way around the central area; in fact, a cone sheet can be followed for only a few

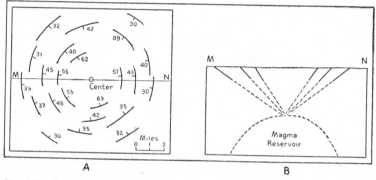

Fig. 259. Cone sheets. *A.* Map: direction and value of dip is indicated. *B.* Cross section along line *MN.*

miles at the most. The average dip is 45 degrees, but the outer cone sheets tend to dip more gently than the inner. If the Scottish cone sheets,[20] which are Tertiary in age, are projected downward, they meet at a focus approximately 3 miles beneath the present surface (Fig. 259B). Cone sheets, typically a few feet thick, may attain a thickness of 40 feet. In Mull, an island off the west coast of Scotland, they are concentric about two distinct centers. The cone sheets of the older center are cut by those associated with the younger center. Cone sheets are apparently not extensively developed in North America. Some have been mapped, however, from the Sunlight area of Wyoming (Fig. 257). The origin of cone sheets is discussed on page 315.

Few direct data are available concerning the direction of movement of magma in dikes. It is commonly assumed that the magma moved upward, and for many dikes this is undoubtedly correct. There is reason to

[19] Parsons, W. H., "Volcanic Centers of the Sunlight Area, Park County, Wyoming," *Journal of Geology,* Vol. 47, pp. 1–26, 1939.

[20] Richey, J. E., "The Tertiary Volcanic Districts," *British Regional Geology, Scotland,* Edinburgh, 1935.

believe, however, that the magma in the radiating dikes of the Sunlight area moved horizontally.

Apophyses (singular, *apophysis*) and *tongues* are dikes (in some instances rather irregular) that obviously have been derived from a nearby igneous body.

Volcanic Vents

Volcanic vents, also called *necks* and *plugs*, are the roots of volcanoes that have been eroded away. They are circular, subcircular, or even irregular in plan, and are a few score feet to a mile in diameter.[21] Some composite vents are even larger and have resulted from several successive eruptions. The contacts of volcanic vents with the surrounding country rock are typically steep; they are either vertical or inward-dipping, rarely outward-dipping.

Although it is unusually large, the vent at Cripple Creek, Colorado (Fig. 258) shows many of the features characteristic of vents.[22] The contacts are discordant, and the foliation of the pre-Cambrian schists is cut off by the material in the vent. The contacts generally slope inward. In this case the vent is composed of several separate funnels that narrow downward; this can be seen on the map by studying the structure contours that show the granite-breccia contact and by studying the structure section. Much of the rock in the vent is tuff and breccia. Lava is represented by rhyolite and phonolite. Medium-grained intrusive rocks are represented by syenite. The pre-Cambrian rocks were blown out in series of explosions, but the voids were promptly filled by tuff and breccia. Magma pushing up through the breccia consolidated to form the rhyolite, phonolite, and syenite. In other areas some vents are filled exclusively by tuff and breccia, others are filled exclusively by lava.

Ring-Dikes

Ring-dikes are oval or arcuate in plan (Fig. 260); the contacts are steep, either vertical or very steep. The average diameter of ring-dikes (Fig. 260A) is four and a half miles, but some have a diameter of only 1,000 feet, whereas others are 15 miles in diameter.[23] The average width (Fig. 260A) of ring-dikes is 1,600 feet; the maximum is 14,000 feet. Down-faulted volcanics are found inside some ring-dikes; they were erupted during the same igneous cycle as the ring-dike.

Figure 262 is a map of a region of ring-dikes a short distance west of

[21] Geikie, A., *The Ancient Volcanoes of Great Britain*, Vol. 1 and Vol. 2. New York: The Macmillan Company, 1897.

[22] Lovering, T. S., and E. N. Goddard, "Geology and Ore Deposits of the Front Range, Colorado," *U. S. Geological Survey, Professional Paper 223*, pp. 292–298, 1950.

[23] Billings, Marland P., "Ring-Dikes and Their Origin," *Transactions of the New York Academy of Sciences*, Series II, Vol. 5, pp. 131–144, 1943.

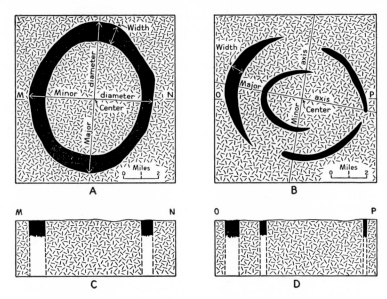

Fig. 260. Ring-dikes. Solid black represents igneous rock of ring-dikes. *A.* Circular (complete) ring-dike. *B.* Arcuate (incomplete) ring-dikes. *C.* Structure section along line *MN* of diagram *A.* *D.* Structure section along line *OP* of diagram *B.*

Oslo, Norway.[24] The ring-dikes and stocks (see page 319) are grouped about two centers, one in the north-central part of the map, the other in the southwestern part of the map. The one in the southwestern part of the map is known as the Glitrevann cauldron (see page 317). Outside the igneous complexes are the folded Paleozoic sedimentary rocks of Cambrian, Ordovician, and Silurian age. The manner in which the folds are truncated at the igneous contact is strikingly shown, especially in the northeast corner of the map. Inside the Glitrevann cauldron are several large areas of subsided volcanics, which are of Permian age and rest unconformably on the older Paleozoic rocks. On the south and southwest sides of the cauldron a discontinuous ring-dike of quartz syenite forms the boundary between the cauldron and the older Paleozoic rocks. Also on the southwest side a second ring-dike, composed of quartz porphyry, lies chiefly within 'he volcanics and is nearly 10 kilometers long. In the northern part of the cauldron is another ring-dike of quartz syenite, in places forming the boundary between the volcanics and the Ordovician rocks, but in many places lying within the volcanics. This ring-dike extends almost all the way around the cauldron, although it is rather irregular in the southern part of the area. Large bodies of quartz por-

[24] Oftedahl, Christoffer, "Cauldron Subsidences of the Oslo Region," *Report of the 18th International Geological Congress*, Great Britain, 1948, Part XIII, pp. 205–213, 1952.

phyry and coarse biotite granite occupy the center of the cauldron. A body of coarse biotite granite also cuts out the southeast part of the cauldron.

The body in the north-central part of the area consists of an outer ring-dike of monzonite, an inner ring-dike of quartz monzonite, and a large central stock of biotite granite.

This Norwegian example of ring-dikes differs in two respects from those described elsewhere. Wherever the volcanics and older Paleozoic rocks are adjacent to one another, the contact appears to be an unconformity that dips inward toward the center of the subsided area. In most areas described in New Hampshire and Scotland this contact is usually a ring-dike or a fault.

Anderson's theory for the formation of the fractures occupied by ring-dikes and cone-sheets is illustrated in Fig. 261.[25] Let us first assume that the hydrostatic pressure of the magma exceeds the lithostatic pressure of the surrounding rocks. The magma will be pushing on its walls. The trajectories of the greatest principal stress axes will radiate out from

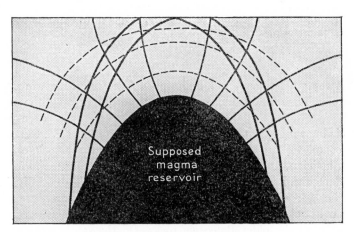

Fig. 261. Origin of ring-dikes. (After E. M. Anderson; see text for explanation.)

the magma reservoir; they are the lighter solid lines of Fig. 261. The trajectories of the least principal stress axes are shown by the broken lines. Tension fractures will form parallel to the lighter solid lines. These are the fractures that control the emplacement of cone sheets.

If the hydrostatic pressure of the magma is less than the lithostatic pressure in the surrounding rocks, the latter will push on the magma. Now the lighter solid lines are the trajectories of the least principal stress

[25] Anderson, E. M., in Bailey, E. B., *et al.*, "The Tertiary and Post-Tertiary Geology of Mull, Loch Aline, and Oban," *Memoir Geological Survey of Scotland,* 1924.

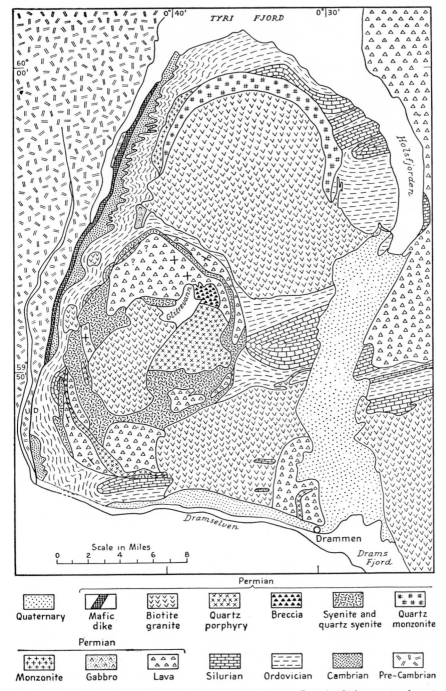

Fig. 262. Ring-dikes and stocks. Oslo region, Norway. Longitude is measured west from Oslo. Dip-strike symbols show attitude of volcanic rocks. D = downthrown side of gravity fault. (Based on maps by W. C. Brögger, J. Scheltig, and C. Oftedahl.)

axes, and the broken lines are trajectories of the greatest principal stress axes. Tension cracks would form parallel to the broken lines. Two sets of shear fractures might form (page 95), making angles of 30 degrees with these broken lines. One set of these shear fractures is shown in heavy solid lines. Anderson believes that these are the fractures that are most commonly utilized in the emplacement of ring-dikes.

When one of these fractures or sets of fractures becomes large enough, a block of country rock is isolated from the rest of the roof. It sinks

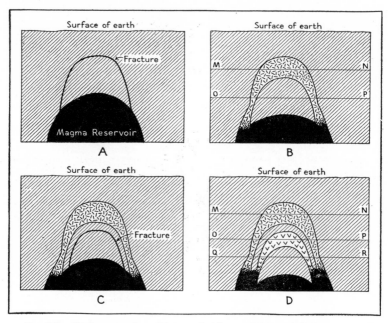

Fig. 263. Underground cauldron subsidence. Diagonal lining represents older country rock; diversely oriented short dashes represent one intrusion; checks represent a second intrusion. *A, B, C,* and *D* represent successive stages of intrusion. *MN, OP,* and *QR* are a few of the many levels to which erosion may cut.

because it is heavier than the magma in the reservoir (Fig. 263). While the central block subsides (Fig. 263B), magma rises from the reservoir to fill the potential void left between the stationary walls and the sinking block. If erosion subsequently cuts deeply enough, to a level such as *OP* in Fig. 263B, a circular or oval intrusion with steeply dipping contacts is exposed. If the central block subsides several times (Figs. 263C and 263D), a number of concentric ring-dikes will form. A remnant of the older country rock left between two ring-dikes is called a screen (Fig. 263D).

In New Hampshire many of the ring-dikes are essentially vertical. It seems unlikely that they could have formed in the manner outlined above. An alternate hypothesis is that the magma (Fig. 264) pushes on its roof like a punch. Vertical fractures form above the reservoir. Once the overlying block is isolated by fractures it sinks into the reservoir because it is heavier than the magma. The space occupied by the ring-dike is made largely by piecemeal stoping (page 321) along the fracture.

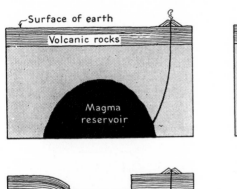
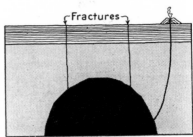

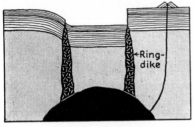

Fig. 264. Surface cauldron subsidence. Light stippling represents older country rock. Diversely oriented short white dashes represent intrusive rock of a ring-dike. Upper left: after eruption of volcanics. Upper right: fracture forms. Lower left: subsidence accompanied by some volcanism; drag that commonly occurs near ring-dikes has been omitted. Lower right: erosion to present topography.

The mechanism by which ring-dikes form is called *cauldron subsidence*. *Surface cauldron subsidence* results when the fractures extend all the way to the surface (Fig. 264). *Underground cauldron subsidence* results when the subsiding block does not reach the surface (Fig. 263).

BATHOLITHS AND STOCKS

The term *batholith* is most commonly used for any large body of plutonic rock with the characteristics described below. (1) The term is arbitrarily restricted to those bodies that occupy an area of more than 40 square miles. (2) They commonly enlarge downward; that is, the contacts dip outward and there is no visible floor; moreover, any floor is presumably at a depth of at least several miles (Figs. 265 and 267). (3) The roof may be irregular; *roof pendants* are downward projections of the

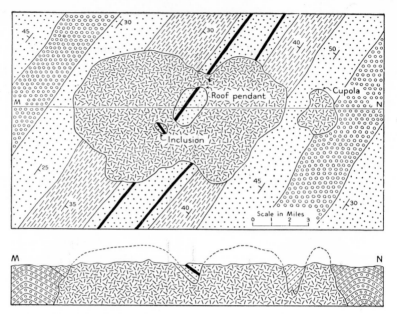

Fig. 265. Batholith, Circles, dots, parallel dashes, and solid black are sedimentary rocks. Diversely oriented dashes are granite. Map is above, structure section is below.

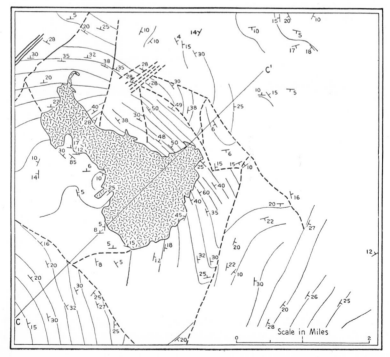

Fig. 266. Map of Marysville stock, Montana. Diversely oriented dashes are quartz diorite. Rest of area consists of sedimentary rocks. Dip-strike symbols refer to bedding. Light lines are structure contours; contour interval about 500 feet. Heavy broken lines are inferred faults. Heavy solid lines are observed faults. For cross section along line *CC'*, see Fig. 267. (After J. Barrell.)

roof; *cupolas* are isolated plutonic bodies that presumably connect down-ward with the main batholith. (4) Some batholiths are discordant bodies, cross-cutting the country rock both in plan and in section (Figs. 265, 266, and 267). Daly considers this an essential characteristic in order to call

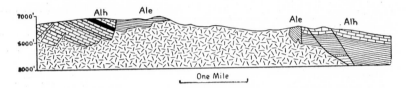

Fig. 267. Structure section of Marysville stock, Montana. Along line *CC'* of Fig. 266. Diversely oriented dashes are quartz diorite. *Ale* = Empire shale; *Alh* = Helena limestone. (After J. Barrell.)

a body a batholith.[26] (5) Most batholiths are composite, consisting of numerous varieties of plutonic rock that were emplaced at slightly dif-ferent times.

Stocks are similar to batholiths, but the surface area is less than 40 square miles.

TIME OF EMPLACEMENT

For many years geologists have known that the emplacement of plutons may be associated with orogenic movements. *Atectonic plutons* are those that are unrelated to orogenic movements and that are found in horizontal strata. *Pre-tectonic plutons* are those that are older than a period of folding; they may be genetically related to the orogeny, or they may be much older and may bear no genetic relation to the orogeny. *Syntectonic* or *synchronous plutons* are emplaced during the orogeny. *Post-tectonic* or *subsequent plutons* are later than the orogeny; they may be genetically related to the folding, or they may be much later and may bear no genetic relation to the folding. The situation is complicated, of course, if there has been more than one period of folding in the region. In such a case, an igneous body could be post-tectonic relative to the first orogeny, but pre-tectonic relative to the second. The ensuing discussion applies, therefore, to a region in which there has been only one period of folding.

Post-tectonic intrusions are undeformed, the associated dikes and sills are not folded, the rocks are not granulated, and they do not have a secondary foliation (p. 336). All ring-dike complexes are post-tectonic.

Syntectonic and pre-tectonic plutons are difficult to distinguish from each other. The rocks in each are likely to be *granulated;* that is, the in-

[26] Daly, R. A., *Igneous Rocks and the Depths of the Earth,* pp. 113–136. New York and London: McGraw-Hill Book Company, 1933.

dividual crystals are broken, strained, and rounded, with the result that the rock has a sugary texture. This is particularly true along the contacts, where most of the strain is concentrated. Apophyses of such intrusions may be folded. Syntectonic bodies generally have the form of great sheets or lenses, or perhaps even of "domes." Primary foliation is characteristic. Such bodies may cut across some of the older thrust faults, but may themselves be broken by later thrust faults.

Igneous rocks that lie unconformably beneath highly folded sedimentary rocks are obviously older than the deposition of the overlying sedimentary rocks; hence they are older than the orogeny. Such igneous rocks are pretectonic—at least relative to the orogeny that has been impressed upon the sedimentary rocks.

CHAPTER 19

Emplacement of Large Plutons

INTRODUCTION

One of the most controversial subjects in geology at the present time is the origin of plutonic rocks and the manner in which they have been emplaced. The word "emplaced" is used in a noncommittal sense to avoid any implication that might be implied by the word "intrusion." A few geologists might maintain that all large plutons, including batholiths, have been emplaced by the same mechanism and that there is only one way in which plutonic rocks may form. Most geologists would probably agree that plutonic rocks can be emplaced in several different ways. But here the agreement ends. Some believe that one mechanism is dominant, others believe that a second method is most important, and still others advocate a third method.[1]

Three mechanisms of emplacement may be considered: stoping, forceful injection, and metasomatic replacement (granitization).

MAGMATIC STOPING

The hypothesis of *magmatic stoping* assumes that a body of magma is working its way up into the crust of the earth.[2] *Piecemeal stoping*, one variety of the process, is illustrated in Fig. 268. The roof of the magma chamber is shattered, and blocks are surrounded by apophyses. Any block that is isolated by the magma will sink—provided, of course, that the specific gravity of the block is greater than that of the magma. The blocks may sink to great depth, where they may be reacted upon by the magma and assimilated. Thus the magma can gradually eat its way upward into the country rock. The size of the individual blocks is measured in feet, tens of feet, or even hundreds of feet. The shattering of the country rock may be due to thermal or mechanical causes. Inasmuch as the country rock is heated by the magma, it expands and cracks, especially if the heating is rapid. Mechanical shattering is probably even more im-

---

[1] Gilluly, James, *et al.*, "Origin of Granite," *Geological Society of America, Memoir 28*, 139 pages, 1948.

[2] Daly, R. A., *Igneous Rocks and the Depths of the Earth*, pp. 267–286. New York: McGraw-Hill Book Company, 1933.

portant because the roof rocks will be subjected to numerous forces, particularly tensional and torsional forces.

In favor of the hypothesis of piecemeal stoping, it is possible to cite examples of the process "caught in the act." Xenoliths and autoliths attest to the actuality of stoping, and at some contacts it is possible to observe apophyses of igneous rock enveloping the country rock (Fig. 268; Plate XIX).

On the other hand, xenoliths are surprisingly rare in many batholiths and stocks. Moreover, the specific gravity of the rocks involved must be favorable. In general, the specific gravity of magma is 7 to 10 per cent less than that of the corresponding solid rock. Thus a magma could stope its way into a rock of the same chemical composition. But the specific gravity of gabbro or diorite magma is as high as that of crystalline granite; in such a case piecemeal stoping could not be very effective. Furthermore, many sedimentary rocks have a lower specific gravity than magma.

Surface of earth

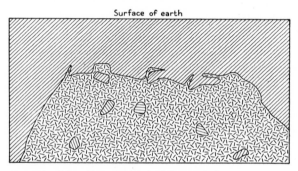

Fig. 268. Magmatic stoping. Diagonal lines are older rocks. Diversely oriented dashes are plutonic rock.

Cauldron subsidence differs from piecemeal stoping only in the size of the blocks involved. Whereas in piecemeal stoping the sinking blocks are measured in feet, the blocks involved in cauldron subsidence are measured in miles. The term *ring-fracture stoping* may be used synonymously with *cauldron subsidence*. Underground cauldron subsidence (p. 317) may produce either a ring-dike or a stock, depending upon the amount the central block subsides and upon the depth of erosion. In Fig. 263D, for example, if erosion penetrates to the level *QR*, two ring-dikes will be exposed. If, however, erosion penetrates only to *MN*, a circular intrusive with all the characteristics of a stock will be exposed. The mechanism of cauldron subsidence explains the rarity of small inclusions in many batholiths and stocks. Moreover, this hypothesis is in accord with the smooth walls so typical of batholiths and stocks; piecemeal stoping should produce jagged, irregular walls. Specific gravities, however, would play the same role as in piecemeal stoping, and a subsiding block must be heavier than the magma in the reservoir.

The alkalic batholiths and stocks of New Hampshire and Norway are composite complexes made up of ring-dikes and stocks, and they have therefore attained their position in the outer shell of the earth by ring-fracture stoping. Available data indicate that such ring-dike complexes are rather exceptional in orogenic belts. Underground cauldron subsidences may have been important in other batholiths, but the individual subsidences may have been of such magnitude that only stocks rather than ring-dikes are exposed.

FORCEFUL INJECTION

General Considerations

The hypothesis of forceful injection, like the stoping hypothesis, assumes that magma is available. The magma pushes the older rocks aside or upward. Vertically rising magma would behave much like a rising salt dome. The rocks into which the magma rises are in many cases much more deformed and much more competent than the sedimentary rocks through which salt domes move. Hence the resulting structure would undoubtedly be more complex than around a salt dome. The movement of the magma may be entirely under the influence of gravity—that is, a magma that is lighter than the surrounding rocks tends to move upward. In other instances the magma may be pushed around by orogenic forces.

That magma may be emplaced by forceful injection is clearly demonstrated by laccoliths. Similarly, in most dikes, sills, and lopoliths the walls move apart because the hydrostatic pressure exerted by the magma exceeds the lithostatic pressure on the rocks. The manner in which the structure wraps around some stocks shows that they have been forcefully injected. An example was given in Fig. 255. Other examples have been described by Billings.[3]

An example of doming related to forceful injection has been described by Noble[4] and is illustrated by Fig. 269. The white areas are pre-Cambrian schists, whereas the stippled areas are Paleozoic sedimentary rocks that rest with pronounced angular unconformity (see page 244) on the pre-Cambrian. The black areas are intrusive bodies of Tertiary age; these intrusive bodies make up a ccmplex composed of a large number of

[3] Billings, Marland P., "Mechanics of Intrusion in New Hampshire," *American Journal of Science,* Vol. 243-A, pp. 40–68, 1945.

[4] Noble, James A., "Evaluation of the Criteria for the Forcible Intrusion of Magma," *Journal of Geology,* Vol. 60, pp. 34–57, 1952.

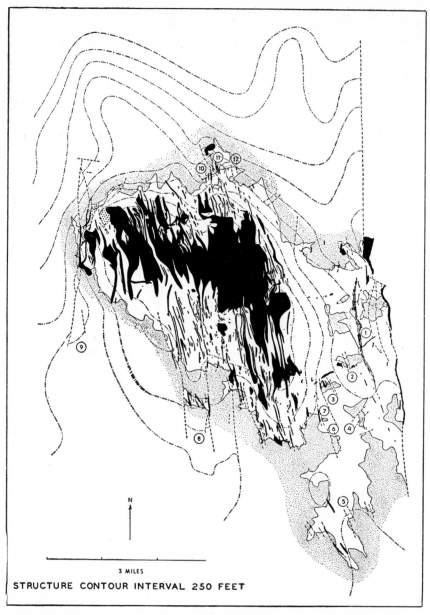

STRUCTURE CONTOUR INTERVAL 250 FEET

3 MILES

Fig. 269. Doming by forceful intrusion. Black Hills of South Dakota. Black = rhyolite of Tertiary age. Stippled area = base of the Paleozoic strata (only the base of the Paleozoic is stippled; the white area outside the stippled area is Paleozoic and Mesozoic). White inside of the stippled area = pre-Cambrian. Dash-dot lines = structure contours on base of Paleozoic; contour interval 250 feet; greatest uplift is in center of area. Numbers in circles refer to small horsts uplifted between paired faults (short dashes). (After **J. A. Noble**; permission of University of Chicago Press.)

separate steeply dipping dikes. The dash-dot lines are structure contours on the base of the Paleozoic formations. The highest part of the dome shown by the structure contours coincides with the area of greatest intrusion. Noble concludes that the intrusions are the cause of the doming. Although part of the space now occupied by the intrusions was made by pushing the schists aside, much of it was made by pushing slabs of schist upward between "paired faults." Noble further concludes that the Sierra Nevada batholith was intruded in much the same way. A somewhat similar conclusion is discussed on page 328.

Granite Tectonics

Introduction. The concept of forceful injection was especially emphasized by Hans Cloos. He further showed that in many instances the foliation, lineation, joints, dikes, and faults associated with a pluton are systematically related to the intrusion of the magma. This field of geology has been called *granite tectonics,* which is a satisfactory term as long as it is understood that "granite" is used in the broad sense to include all plutonic rocks and that the concepts may even be applied to fine-grained rocks. The best general description of the method is given by Balk.[5]

If the magma attains its destination before crystallization begins, it will be massive and will possess neither foliation nor lineation. Some of the schlieren and inclusions, however, may be oriented in the manner discussed below.

If the magma is crystallizing as it moves, and especially if the movement continues until after the rock is completely consolidated, a series of structural features develop. Even after the magma in the outer and upper parts of the intrusion has frozen, the liquid or semiliquid material below may continue to rise, subjecting the consolidated parts of the intrusion to systematic stresses. For convenience, the structures may be considered under the following headings: (1) structures of the flow stage and (2) structures of the solid stage.

Structures of the flow stage. Moving liquids are characterized by either turbulent flow or lamellar flow. In *turbulent flow,* the movement of the individual particles is irregular and unsystematic, and the particles are not confined to any one layer in the liquid. In *lamellar flow,* on the other hand, the individual particles move in parallel sheets which slide over one another like the cards in a sheared playing pack. The flow is lamellar in such a viscous substance as magma beneath the surface of the earth. The sheets tend to be parallel to nearby contacts, and at such localities the differential speed of the various layers will be much greater than in the interior of the body of the magma.

Platy flow structure, also referred to as *planar flow structure* or *planar*

[5] Balk, Robert, "Structural Behavior of Igneous Rocks," *Geological Society of America, Memoir 5,* 1937.

structure, forms during the flow stage. Platy material in a magma characterized by lamellar flow tends to become oriented with the largest face
parallel to the liquid layers. Consequently, platy inclusions, such as slabs
of shale, sandstone, or schist, become oriented parallel to one another.
Schlieren and platy minerals, such as biotite, align themselves in the
same way. Feldspar crystals, if well-formed, will tend to lie with the
largest faces parallel to the layers. Prismatic minerals—those shaped like
a short pencil—also become oriented so that the long axis lies in the
flow layers. If inclusions, schlieren, and platy minerals are all present,
they will ordinarily be parallel to one another, as shown by Fig. 270.

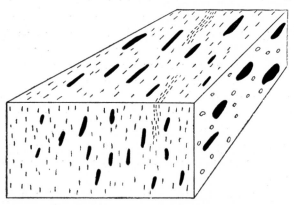

Fig. 270. Platy flow structure in an intrusive rock.
Shown by parallel arrangement of platy inclusions (solid
black), platy minerals (short dashes, except on side of
block, where they appear circular), and schlieren (closely
spaced dashes).

Primary foliation (page 286) is that variety of platy flow structure that
is due to the parallelism of platy minerals. Platy flow structure is thus
a more inclusive term because it refers to the parallelism of slab-like inclusions and schlieren as well as to the parallelism of platy minerals.

Linear flow structure, which is that variety of lineation formed in
moving liquids, is also formed during the flow stage (Fig. 232). The long
axes of prismatic minerals may be oriented parallel to one another (Fig.
232A). This is particularly true of a mineral such as hornblende, the
longest dimension of which is ordinarily parallel to the c-crystallographic
axis. Feldspar is also longer parallel to the c-crystallographic axis than it
is in any other direction.

The manner of measuring the attitude of lineation and of recording
it on a map is described on p. 355.

The long axes of spindle-shaped inclusions may also be parallel to
one another, thus showing the lineation. In some cases, although the in-

dividual inclusions are more or less spherical, they may be strung out in lines, like the beads on a string.

The significance of the lineation depends upon the shape of the pluton. There would be no lineation if all parts of a rising body of magma were moving at the same velocity. If, however, lamellar flow were caused by friction of the walls, any elongate minerals would probably be rotated to assume an orientation parallel to the direction of flow. But if the magma were expanding upward, in a manner analogous to the extrusive dome shown in Fig. 223, the elongation, and hence the lineation, would form an arch. Conversely, if magma were being forced into a progressively smaller opening, the lineation would be parallel to the direction of flow.[5a]

Structures of the solid stage. After the outer shell of the intrusion has completely consolidated, the interior may still be liquid or partially liquid. Continued movement of this interior will subject the consolidated shell to stresses that are systematically related to the structures formed in the flow stage. But the solid rock fails by rupture. In the early stages of the intrusion, the contact of the magma with the wall rock was not only a lithologic boundary, but also a dynamic boundary. Liquid magma was

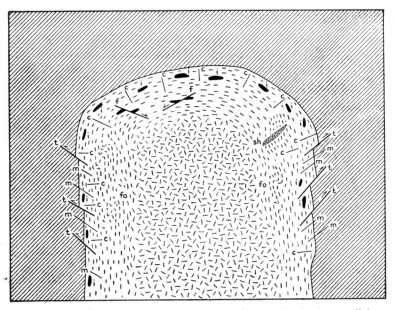

Fig. 271. Cross section of a hypothetical pluton. Section is parallel to strike of the linear flow structure. Short dashes are platy minerals; $i =$ inclusion; $fo =$ flexure; $sh =$ shear filled with pegmatite or coarse granite; $c =$ cross joint; $m =$ marginal fissure; $t =$ marginal thrust; $f =$ flat-lying gravity fault.

[5a] Mackin, J. H., "Some Structural Features of the Intrusions in the Iron Springs District," *Guidebook to the Geology of Utah, No. 2*, Utah Geological Society, 62 pages, 1947.

moving past solid rock. As the wall rock became heated and the outer shell of the intrusion consolidated, the contact became less important as a dynamic boundary. The wall rock began to participate in the movements; consequently, many of the fractures of the solid stage extend out into the country rock.

The fractures may be either joints or faults. Some of them may contain minerals similar to those in the igneous rocks. This is often taken as evidence that the fractures formed while some of the underlying magma was still liquid and consequently that the fracturing was related to the intrusion. Much later fractures, unrelated to the intrusion, would theoretically be devoid of such minerals. Some of the fractures are filled by dikes.

A detailed study of a pluton consequently involves the mapping of the joints, faults, and dikes as well as the structures of the flow stage. A detailed discussion of the fracture systems is given in Balk.[6] Some of the structural features associated with a vertically intruded pluton are shown in Fig. 271.

Figure 272 is a structure section across the Sierra Nevada batholith.[7] On both the west and east are metamorphosed sedimentary rocks. The rest of the section is occupied by granitic rocks. The planar structures define two great arches, the western one forming the western partial pluton, the other defining the eastern partial pluton. Although absent along the line of this cross section, elsewhere a septum of metamorphic

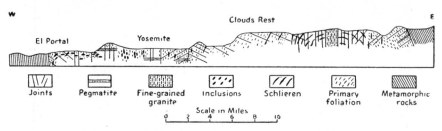

Fig. 272. Cross section of Sierra Nevada batholith. (After E. Cloos.)

rocks is present between the two partial plutons. The eastern partial pluton is made up of three units. In the interior is a fine-grained granite, the foliation of which truncates the structure of the intermediate unit on either side of it. The structure shown by schlieren of the intermediate unit in turn truncates the foliation of the outside unit. The eastern partial pluton is thus composed of three separate intrusions of magma. Associated with each of the two partial plutons is a joint fan. These are tension fractures that formed at right angles to the direction of stretching on the

---

[6] Balk, Robert, *op. cit.*

[7] Cloos, Ernst, "Der Sierra Nevada-Pluton in Californien," *Neues Jahrbuch für Mineralogie*, etc., Beil. Bd. 76, Abt. B, pp. 355–450, 1936.

rising magma. Although this cross section does not show the relations of
the two sets of fans to one another, other cross sections show that the
joints belonging to the eastern partial pluton cut the rocks of the western
partial pluton. The joints associated with the western partial pluton do
not cut the rocks of the eastern partial pluton. These facts are interpreted
to mean that the western partial pluton is older than the eastern partial
pluton.

Cloos lists several arguments against magmatic stoping but in favor
of forceful intrusion. One of the most cogent arguments are the arches
shown by the foliation and inclusions. These indicate an upward rising
magma in which the inclusions were also moving upward. If stoping had
been important, the inclusions would have moved downward.

Distinction between primary and secondary structures. A clear distinction between primary and secondary structures is essential for a correct
interpretation of the tectonics of plutons. The distinction becomes particularly difficult if primary structures are utilized for later secondary
movements.

Several criteria may be particularly useful in demonstrating that a
planar structure—particularly a foliation—is primary. In regions unaffected by orogenic movements, any foliation in an igneous rock must be

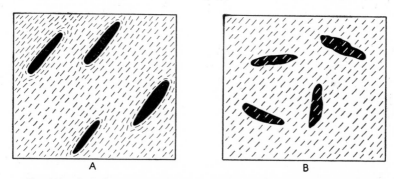

Fig. 273. Relation of inclusions to foliation. Solid black = platy inclusions; black and white short dashes = foliation due to platy minerals.
A. Platy inclusions parallel to primary foliation. *B.* Platy inclusions, diversely oriented, cut by a secondary foliation.

primary because the forces essential for the development of secondary
structures never existed. A second line of evidence is based on the attitude
of inclusions. A foliation to which the inclusions are parallel (Fig. 273A)
is probably primary. If a secondary foliation were imposed upon a rock
with diversely oriented inclusions (Fig. 273B), the long axes of the inclusions would be unrelated to the foliation. In the example illustrated by
Fig. 273A, the flat inclusions must have been oriented while the host rock
was still molten; obviously, they would lie parallel to the foliation of the

igneous rocks because the platy minerals and the slab-like inclusions are oriented by the same forces.

Two exceptions to the use of these criteria may be mentioned. In one case, platy inclusions might be oriented during the flow stage, but a foliation might fail to develop in the intrusive rock. During a later orogenic movement, a secondary foliation superimposed on the igneous rock might coincide with the oriented inclusions. In this example, the orientation of the inclusions would be primary, but the foliation would be secondary. In a second case, the "stretching" during the formation of a secondary foliation could be so great that inclusions, regardless of their original orientation, might be elongated to such an extent that they become parallel to one another and to the secondary foliation.

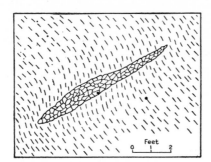

Fig. 274. Shear filled with pegmatite. Short dashes represent primary platy flow structure that is a primary foliation. Granular pattern is pegmatite or coarse granite.

A third line of evidence that the foliation is primary is illustrated in Fig. 274. The foliation is flexed, but along the axis of the flexure a dike-like body, rich in the lighter colored minerals, grades into the main body of the rock; the material in the dike was derived from the liquid that was still uncrystallized in the rock.

In regions unaffected by orogeny, lineation in igneous rocks must be primary. The orientation of hornblende needles in a dike, sill, or laccolith injected into flat sediments is primary (Fig. 275).[8] In orogenic belts, on the other hand, a clear distinction between primary and secondary lineation may be very difficult. If the lineation is obviously due to the granulation and dragging out of older minerals, it is presumably secondary. On the other hand, if the minerals in the igneous rock appear to be unstrained and ungranulated, the lineation may be primary; but the recrystallization of a highly granulated rock is a possibility that would have to be considered. Structural petrology (Chapter 22) may in some instances offer a solution to the problem. In general, no hard and fast rules can be established, and each case must be considered by itself.

METASOMATIC REPLACEMENT (GRANITIZATION)

Many geologists in recent years have accepted the idea that large plutons, including batholiths, have formed by metasomatic replacement,[9] sometimes referred to as granitization.

[8] Rouse, J. T., "The Structure, Inclusions, and Alteration of the Deer Creek Intrusive, Wyoming," *American Journal of Science*, Vol. 26, pp. 139–146, 1933.

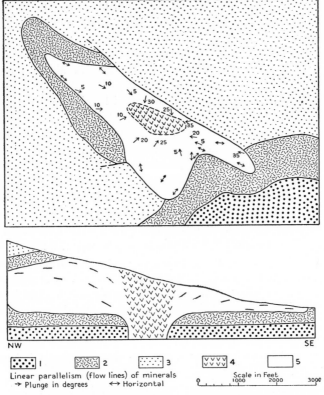

Linear parallelism (flow lines) of minerals
→ Plunge in degrees   ↔ Horizontal

Scale in Feet

Fig. 275. Deer Creek laccolith. Map is above, northwest-southeast cross section is below. 1 = early basic breccia, 2 = early basalt flows, 3 = late basic breccia, 4 = decayed quartz diorite porphyry, 5 = quartz diorite porphyry. (After J. T. Rouse.)

Although the term granitization is used with many different connotations, the best definition, modified from that given by Grout[10] is: *Granitization* includes a group of processes by which a solid rock is made more like granite than it was before, in minerals, or in texture and structure, or in both.

To convert a pure quartz sandstone into granite (in this case used in the narrow petrographic sense to mean a rock rich in potash feldspar and quartz, with lesser amounts of plagioclase feldspar and dark minerals) it

[9] Read, H. H., "A Commentary on Place in Plutonism," *Quarterly Journal of the Geological Society of London,* Vol. CIV, pp. 155–206, 1948.

Read, H. H., "A Contemplation of Time in Plutonism," *Quarterly Journal of the Geological Society of London,* Vol. CV, pp. 101–156, 1949.

[10] Grout, Frank F., "Formation of Igneous-Looking Rocks by Metasomatism: a Critical Review and Suggested Research," *Bulletin Geological Society of America,* Vol. 52, pp. 1525–1576, 1941.

would be necessary to add potash, alumina, and soda, as well as lesser amounts of lime, iron, and magnesia. If there were no change in volume, considerable silica would have to be removed.

To convert a slate into granite without any important change in volume, it would be necessary to remove iron, magnesia, alumina, and water, but add silica, soda, and perhaps potash.

Exactly how the elements are transported has been a matter of argument. Traditionally, geologists believed that these elements would be transported by solutions. However, in recent years some geologists have proposed that the ions diffuse through the rocks in a dry state.

The criteria for recognizing replacement granites that have not moved from the place where they originated are as follows: (1) The contact between the plutonic rock and the country rock is normally gradational. The transition zone may be only a few feet wide, but more commonly it is thousands of feet or miles wide. (2) The same structural pattern found in the country rocks continues into the plutonic rock. Thus if the country rock is characterized by gently plunging open folds, a similar structure may be shown by a weak to pronounced foliation in the plutonic rock. Even more striking are those cases where certain less readily replaceable beds can be traced for long distances into the plutonic rock. (3) Microscopic study of porphyritic rocks that have originated by replacement may show that the groundmass has the same texture as the surrounding sedimentary rocks. (4) There are also numerous petrographic and chemical criteria, but they are beyond the scope of this book.

The metasomatic replacement may take place during a period of deformation, in which case we may speak of *syntectonic granitization* (also *synkinematic* or *synorogenic granitization*). If the replacement occurs without any contemporaneous deformation, we may speak of *static granitization*.

Figure 276 is a cross section of an area in northwest Yunnan, China, showing granites formed by static granitization.[11] Gently inclined Mesozoic red beds have been replaced by "granodiorite porphyry." The evidence cited by Misch in favor of granitization is as follows. (1) As shown

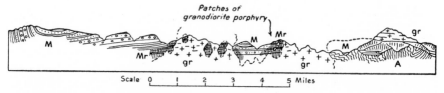

Patches of
granodiorite porphyry

Fig. 276. Static granitization. Northwest Yunnan, China. $A =$ Algonkian schists; $M =$ Mesozoic sedimentary rocks; $Mr =$ Mesozoic sedimentary rocks more or less recrystallized; $gr =$ "granodiorite porphyry." (After P. Misch.)

[11] Misch, Peter, "Metasomatic Granitization of Batholithic Dimensions," *American Journal of Science*, Vol. 247, pp. 209–245, 372–406, and 673–705, 1949.

by Fig. 276, the contact sharply truncates the gently dipping sediments. (2) The same flat structure is preserved within the "granodiorite porphyry." (3) The groundmass between the "phenocrysts" preserves the texture of the original sediments. (4) Small isolated patches of "granodiorite" found within the sediments are clearly the result of replacement.

A small-scale example of replacement in South Park, Colorado, is illustrated in Fig. 277.[12] A group of interbedded metamorphic rocks "fade" into a granite. Some of the metamorphic minerals that are most common in certain beds are most abundant in the granite along the strike of those beds.

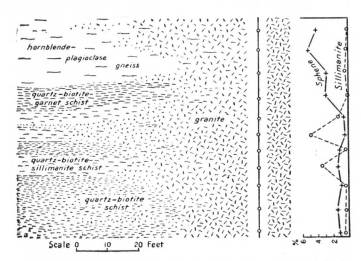

Fig. 277. Static granitization. Map of small area in South Park, Colorado. Graph on right shows percentage of sillimanite and sphene in specimens collected from localities represented by open circles on the north-south line. (After R. H. Jahns.)

Syntectonic granitization is illustrated by the Nanga Parbat region in the northwest Himalaya (Fig. 278). The central part of the map is occupied by granite gneiss. A particularly pertinent part of the area is in the southeast corner of the map, where phyllites grade northward along the strike into schists, these in turn grade into banded gneisses, and these in turn into the granite gneiss. The transformation involved the introduction of potash and silica.

CONCLUSIONS

Several mechanisms for the emplacement of plutonic rocks have been presented above. We should like to know, of course, the relative impor-

[12] Jahns, R. H., in Gilluly, J., *et al.*, "Origin of Granite," *Geological Society of America,* Memoir 28, pp. 91–96, 1948.

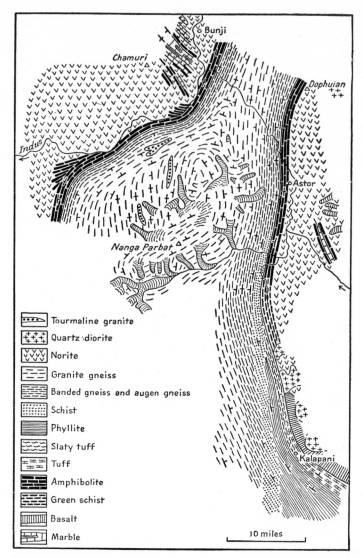

Fig. 278. Syntectonic granitization. Nanga Parbat area, Himalaya Mountains. Concentric lines are glaciers. (After P. Misch.)

tance of these several mechanisms. In trying to reach an answer we might follow two different lines of attack. One is to assume that all plutonic rocks are emplaced in the same way. In such a case two of the proposed mechanisms discussed above would be incorrect. The other approach is to assume that all the mechanisms have some merit and to try to integrate them into a single general hypothesis.

It is difficult to escape the conclusion that many igneous rocks have been forcefully injected. This point was discussed on page 323. That some stocks and batholiths have been emplaced by cauldron subsidence seems well established in some areas, notably New England, Norway, and Scotland. On the other hand, cross-cutting contacts are not in themselves sufficient evidence for stoping; they can be equally well explained by metasomatic replacement. Sharp, chilled contacts are difficult to explain by replacement. Finally, most geologists will agree that some plutonic rocks have formed by metasomatic replacement; the argument concerns the extent to which this has taken place.

Although it is apparent that plutonic rocks may be emplaced in a variety of ways, it is still possible that the ultimate origin is the same. Those favoring granitization suggest that in many cases the mush resulting from the replacement may be able to move, perhaps for miles, and intrude the country rock. This mush, composed of crystals and interstitial liquid, would differ mechanically in no important respect from a partially crystallized magma.

On the other hand, all plutonic rocks may be related to magma. Whether the magma originated by fractional crystallization or by the melting of older plutonic rocks is here irrelevant. The metasomatically replaced rocks would merely be contact zones related to such magma Eskola,[13] for example, believes that the motivating agent in granitization is magma. He believes that the granite is forcefully injected as small bodies and gradually replaces the older rocks.

The task of the structural geologist is to determine how the plutonic rock was emplaced. He is not immediately concerned with the origin of the magma or the source of solutions that might cause replacement. He is, of course, interested in this problem, but he should not let any ruling theory influence his field observations. Although it may be difficult to get an answer, the statement of the problem is relatively easy. Either the plutonic rock formed in place or it came in its entirety from some extraneous source. If it came from some extraneous source, the problem of emplacement is the same regardless of the ultimate origin of the invading mass. The problem is complicated by the possibility of a metasomatically developed plutonic rock moving a short distance. It may thus simulate truly magmatic rocks by intruding its surroundings and by breaking off inclusions.

It is essential, therefore, that the structural geologist do the following things: (1) make a detailed study of the structure and texture of the plutonic rock; (2) make a detailed study of the contacts of the plutonic rock and the country rock; (3) make a detailed study of the structure of the older country rock; and (4) utilize petrologic and chemical data in all ways possible.

[13] Eskola, Pentti, "The Nature of Metasomatism in the Processes of Granitization," *Report of the 18th International Geological Congress,* Part III, pp. 5–13, 1950.

CHAPTER 20

Cleavage and Schistosity

INTRODUCTION

Foliation is the property of rocks whereby they break along approximately parallel surfaces.[1] In some rocks this is a primary feature, inherited from the time of their formation. Many sedimentary rocks, particularly those that are fine-grained, tend to part parallel to the stratification, and thus they possess what is often called *bedding fissility*. Bedding fissility is probably caused by platy and elongate grains more or less parallel to the stratification.[2] The primary foliation of plutonic rocks has already been discussed (pages 326 to 329). The present chapter is concerned exclusively with foliation that is of secondary origin, and which develops some time—often millions of years—after the original formation of the rock. Such foliation may develop in rocks of either sedimentary or igneous origin, and the product is a metamorphic rock.

Cleavage, sometimes called *rock cleavage*[3] in order to distinguish it from *mineral cleavage*, is the property of rocks whereby they break along parallel surfaces of secondary origin (Plate XXI). Much rock cleavage is inclined to the bedding, but in some instances it may be parallel to the bedding. *Schistosity* is a term applied to the variety of rock cleavage found in rocks that are sufficiently recrystallized to be called *schist* or *gneiss*. Thus the secondary foliation of a slate would be called *cleavage*, but a similar structure in a mica schist would be termed *schistosity*. Obviously, there are transitional rocks in which either term might be appropriately used.

A *schist* is a metamorphic rock that possesses schistosity, but which is not characterized by layers of differing mineral composition. A *gneiss* is a metamorphic or igneous rock characterized by alternating bands, usually a few millimeters or centimeters thick, of differing mineral composition. These bands are rich in light minerals in many cases; others are rich in dark minerals. The layers may or may not possess foliation. *Para-*

[1] Mead, W. J., "Folding, Rock Flowage, and Foliate Structures," *Journal of Geology*, Vol. 48, pp. 1007–1021, 1940.

[2] Ingram, R. L., "Fissility of Mudrocks," *Bulletin Geological Society of America*, Vol. 64, pp. 869–878. 1953.

[3] Leith, C. K., "Rock Cleavage," *U. S. Geological Survey Bull. 239*, 1905.

schists and *paragneisses* are, respectively, schists and gneisses of sedimentary origin. *Orthoschists* and *orthogneisses* are, respectively, schists and gneisses of igneous origin. *Metasediments, metavolcanics,* and *meta-igneous* rocks are metamorphic rocks derived, respectively, from sedimentary, volcanic, and igneous rocks.

The attitude of cleavage and schistosity is measured in the same way

PLATE XXI. *Cleavage. Bedding dips 60 degrees to the left. Slaty cleavage in argillaceous beds dips 85 degrees to the right. Fracture cleavage in arenaceous beds dips 60 degrees to the right. Analysis of relation of cleavage to bedding indicates that beds are right-side-up, and that synclinal axis lies to the left.* (Photo by United States Geological Survey.)

as is the attitude of bedding. The strike is the direction of a horizontal line in the plane of cleavage; the dip, which is the angle between the cleavage and a horizontal plane, is measured at right angles to the strike.

Special symbols are employed to represent foliation on geological maps. Because the symbols are not standardized, it is necessary to look at the legend accompanying the map in order to understand the meaning of the symbols. Symbols recommended by the Map Symbol Committee of the U. S. Geological Survey are shown in Fig. 279. Symbols *a, b,* and *c* may be used for foliation in general. A long line gives the strike, and a

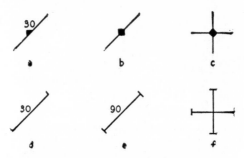

Fig. 279. Symbols for foliation. Upper line shows symbols for foliation in general. Lower line shows symbols for cleavage. *a.* Strike and dip of foliation. *b.* Strike of vertical foliation. *c.* Horizontal foliation. *d.* Strike and dip of vertical cleavage. *e.* Strike of vertical cleavage. *f.* Horizontal cleavage. (After map symbols of U. S. Geol. Survey.)

triangle, either open or solid black, shows the direction of dip; the value of the dip is given by a numeral. Symbol *a* indicates that the foliation strikes N. 45° E. and dips 30° NW. Symbol *b* indicates that the foliation strikes N. 45° E. and is vertical. Symbol *c* indicates horizontal foliation. Symbols *d, e,* and *f* may be used for those variations of foliation that are more appropriately called cleavage.

DESCRIPTIVE TERMINOLOGY FOR CLEAVAGE AND SCHISTOSITY

Introduction

Some of the terminology commonly applied to cleavage has certain genetic implications with which all geologists do not agree. Consequently, in so far as possible, the nomenclature should be descriptive rather than genetic. Nevertheless, the terms should be those established by long custom. This first section is, therefore, essentially descriptive. In a later section the genetic problems involved are discussed.

Slaty Cleavage or Schistosity

Slaty cleavage and schistosity are caused by the parallel arrangement of platy minerals, such as the micas or chlorites, or by the parallel arrangement of ellipsoidal grains of such minerals as quartz and feldspar (Fig. 280A). Elongate minerals, such as hornblende, may impart a cleavage to the rock if the long axes lie in the same plane but are not parallel to one another. Theoretically, a rock possessing slaty cleavage can be split into an indefinite number of thin sheets parallel to the cleavage. The term *slaty cleavage* is used if the rock is one of the less intensely metamorphosed rocks, such as slate, whereas *schistosity* is employed if the

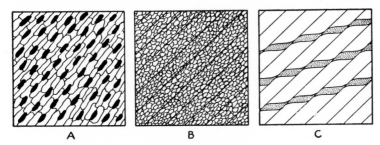

Fig. 280. Kinds of cleavage or schistosity. *A*. Slaty cleavage or schistosity. *B*. Fracture cleavage. *C*. Slip cleavage.

rock is recrystallized into minerals that are readily recognized by the naked eye. Cleavage and schistosity may or may not be parallel to bedding.

Fracture Cleavage

Fracture cleavage is essentially closely spaced jointing. The minerals in the rock are not parallel to the cleavage (Fig. 280B). The distance between the individual planes of cleavage can be measured and is commonly a matter of millimeters or centimeters. If the distance between the fractures exceeds a few centimeters, the term "jointing" is more appropriately used.

Slip Cleavage

Cleavage along which there has been some displacement is called slip cleavage (Fig. 280C). Bedding or an older cleavage or schistosity is commonly displaced one to several millimeters. The platy minerals, such as micas or chlorites, may be dragged into positions that are nearly parallel to the slip cleavage. In a sense this type of cleavage consists of closely-spaced faults.

Bedding Cleavage

Cleavage or schistosity that is parallel to the bedding is commonly referred to as bedding cleavage or bedding schistosity. It is commonly similar to slaty cleavage in that it is caused by parallel platy minerals.

ORIGIN OF CLEAVAGE

Slaty Cleavage or Schistosity

Much slaty cleavage or schistosity, but by no means all, is flow cleavage. *Flow cleavage* is a genetic term meaning that the cleavage is the result of rock flowage (plastic deformation). The rock is shortened at right angles to the cleavage but lengthened parallel to the cleavage. The most compelling argument in favor of this hypothesis is the fact that original spherical masses in the rock are deformed into ellipsoids, the shortest axes of which are perpendicular to the cleavage (Fig. 281A). More specifically, the original spherical masses are pebbles in conglomerates, quartz grains in sandstones, and in some rare cases, oölites in limestones. In the deformed rock they are oblate spheroids or, more commonly, ellipsoids. The long and intermediate axes are parallel to the cleavage, whereas the short axis is perpendicular to the cleavage. Of course, in many cases it may be impossible to prove conclusively that the deformed pebble or grain was originally spherical. But this can be done in some cases, very striking examples of which are the deformed oölites from Maryland and Pennsylvania.[4]

It is even possible under some circumstances to calculate the amount of shortening of the rock perpendicular to the cleavage and the amount of lengthening parallel to the cleavage. The volume of a sphere is

$$V_s = \tfrac{4}{3}\pi r^3 \tag{1}$$

where V_s is the volume and r is the radius of the sphere.

The volume of an ellipsoid is

$$V_e = \tfrac{4}{3}\pi \cdot a \cdot b \cdot c \tag{2}$$

where V_e is the volume of the ellipsoid, a is the half-length of the greatest axis, b is the half-length of the intermediate axis, and c is the half-length of the least axis.

If a sphere is deformed into a ellipsoid without any change in volume, then

$$V_s = V_e$$

or

$$\tfrac{4}{3}\pi r^3 = \tfrac{4}{3}\pi \cdot a \cdot b \cdot c$$

[4] Cloos, Ernst, "Oölite Deformation in the South Mountain Fold, Maryland," *Bulletin Geological Society of America*, Vol. 58, pp. 843–918, 1947.

or
$$r = \sqrt[3]{a \cdot b \cdot c} \tag{3}$$

where r is the radius of the original sphere from which the ellipsoid was derived.

In a hypothetical example let us assume that the following facts are established in a region of deformed conglomerates: (1) the short axes of the pebbles are perpendicular to the cleavage, whereas the other two axes lie in the plane of the cleavage; (2) all the long axes of the pebbles are parallel to one another, although this fact need not concern us at this time (however, see Chapter 21); (3) comparison with the same formation in areas where it is less deformed indicates that the pebbles were originally spherical; (4) although the pebbles are of different sizes, the ratios of the lengths of the axes to one another are similar. The axes of one representative pebble are 2, 4, and 6 centimeters. The half-axes are then 1, 2, and 3 centimeters. Using equation (3), r is 1.8 centimeters; the diameter was 3.6 centimeters. This means that the original sphere was shortened 1.6 centimeters perpendicular to the cleavage, but was lengthened 0.4 centimeters parallel to the intermediate axis and 2.4 centimeters parallel to the long axis. The rock mass as a whole must have deformed in a similar manner, although under some circumstances the matrix of a conglomerate may deform plastically even more than the pebbles. In any case, the formation of the cleavage is obviously associated with rock flowage and the term flow cleavage is entirely appropriate.

Although the cleavage of this type forms perpendicular to the least strain axis—that is, at right angles to the greatest principal stress axis— it is still necessary to explain the exact mechanism whereby the mineral grains become oriented. One factor is the rotation of platy and ellipsoidal grains. The greater the deformation, the more such grains will tend to lie perpendicular to least strain axis. A second factor is the flattening of grains. A spherical quartz grain, for example, will be flattened, partly by granulation, partly by recrystallization. Minerals with glide planes will change shape by gliding. Thirdly, any new platy minerals will crystallize with their flat faces perpendicular to the greatest principal stress axis.

However, some schistosity is a shear phenomenon, developing parallel to one of the shear fractures of the strain ellipsoid; that is, the cleavage forms at an angle of about 30 degrees to the least principal strain axis. Slip cleavage, as shown below, is also a shear phenomenon. Because of the displacements parallel to the cleavage, some of the platy minerals may be dragged into parallelism with the slip cleavage. Moreover, some new platy minerals may crystallize parallel to the planes of slip cleavage. In this way, the slip cleavage may gradually become a schistosity. Such relations have been described in eastern Vermont where a slip cleavage becomes a schistosity in the direction of more intense deformation.[5]

[5] White, Walter S., "Cleavage in East-Central Vermont," *Transactions American Geophysical Union*, Vol. 30, pp. 587–594, 1949.

Rotated minerals, as described on page 380, are also indicative of considerable displacement parallel to the cleavage, but whether this means that the cleavage was initially a shear phenomenon, or is merely a flow cleavage parallel to which there was later shearing is not clear.

Many geologists believe that all slaty cleavage is a shear phenomenon. According to this theory the rock is cut by a vast number of shear planes along which there is slight differential movement. It is also assumed that any platy minerals will tend to be rotated so that they are parallel to the

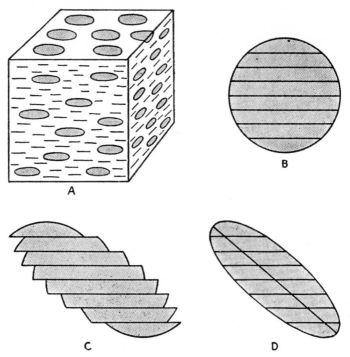

Fig. 281. Evidence against shear theory for origin of cleavage. A. Characteristics of slaty cleavage; short dashes are platy minerals, stippled areas are ellipsoidal grains. B. Circle cut by shear planes. C. Circle sheared to jagged ellipse. D. Same as C, but with shear planes so close that ellipse is smooth.

shear planes, and that any new platy minerals will form so that their flat faces are parallel to the shear planes. But a strong argument against this hypothesis is based on the orientation of deformed pebbles in schistose rocks. It will be recalled that the long and intermediate axes lie in the plane of the cleavage (Fig. 281A). If the slaty cleavage were a shear phenomenon, the longest axis of the deformed pebbles would be inclined to the cleavage. This becomes apparent from a study of Fig. 281. Figure 281B is a spherical pebble cut by cleavage planes prior to any movement. If, however, differential movement takes place along the cleavage planes, like cards slipping over one another, the sphere would be deformed into the jagged ellipsoid shown in Fig. 281C. But if the shear planes are very close together, the sphere would be deformed into the smooth ellipsoid represented by Fig. 281D. The significant point is that the long axis of the pebble would be inclined to the cleavage. It is apparent that this hypothesis does not explain the common parallelism between the long and intermediate axes of deformed pebbles and the associated cleavage.

We can therefore conclude that, although some slaty cleavage or schistosity is a shear phenomenon that formed parallel to one of the shear planes of the strain ellipsoid, much of it is a flow cleavage that formed perpendicular to the greatest stress axis. It is for this reason that it seems desirable to use slaty cleavage and schistosity in a purely descriptive sense, whereas flow cleavage can be used in a genetic sense.

Fracture Cleavage

Fracture cleavage (Fig. 280B) is a shear phenomenon that obeys the laws of shear fractures; consequently, fracture cleavage is inclined to the greatest principal stress axis at an angle of about 30°. In Fig. 282 the fracture cleavage is parallel to the planes represented by FF' and F"F'''. Ordinarily only one set of fracture cleavage planes forms. We are thus using fracture cleavage in both a descriptive and a genetic sense.

Slip Cleavage

Slip cleavage (Fig. 280C), also sometimes referred to as shear cleavage, is also a shear phenomenon and forms parallel to the shear fractures of the strain ellipsoid. But in this case small, visible displacements take place parallel to the cleavage. Thus this term is also used in both a descriptive and a genetic sense.

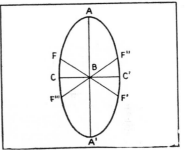

Fig. 282. Relation of cleavage to strain ellipsoid. Flow cleavage forms at right angles to the least strain axis (CC') of the strain ellipsoid; it includes the greatest strain axis (AA') and the intermediate strain axis (B), which is perpendicular to the plane of the paper. Fracture cleavage develops essentially parallel to the planes represented by FF' and $F"F'''$.

Bedding Cleavage

In some metamorphic rocks the cleavage is parallel to the bedding, and hence it may be called *bedding cleavage* or *bedding schistosity*. Cleavage parallel to the bedding may be due to: (1) isoclinal folding; (2) mimetic recrystallization; (3) flow parallel to bedding; and (4) load metamorphism.

(1) The bedding on the limbs of an isoclinal fold is parallel to the axial plane. Because the slaty cleavage is parallel to the axial plane

(Fig. 284) as shown on page 346, it will also be parallel to the bedding on the limbs. But on the nose of such folds the slaty cleavage cuts across the bedding at a considerable angle.

(2) In many localities, however, the schistosity follows the bedding and wraps around the noses of the folds. Such schistosity may be *mimetic;* during the recrystallization of the rock, the new platy minerals grew with their long dimensions parallel to the bedding fissility in the rocks. Little or no plastic deformation need accompany such recrystallization.

(3) In some localities characterized by bedding cleavage, originally spherical pebbles have been flattened so that the shortest axis is perpendicular to the bedding; conversely, the rocks must be elongated parallel to the bedding. In places, this type of deformation may be the result of stretching of the bedding on the limits of folds. In such cases the rock is shortened perpendicular to the bedding, and flow cleavage develops parallel to the bedding.

(4) Bedding cleavage has sometimes been ascribed to *load metamorphism.*[6] According to this hypothesis, the weight of an overlying thick column of rocks exerts vertically directed pressure on flat strata. Such a load, however, would produce a confining pressure that is essentially hydrostatic, and the proposed mechanism does not seem competent to explain bedding cleavage.

The field geologist must be exceedingly cautious in concluding that bedding and schistosity are parallel. Under some conditions of metamor-

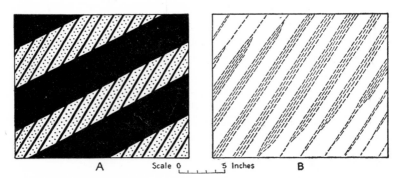

Fig. 283. Cleavage banding and segregation banding. *A.* Cleavage banding. Solid black represents shale; dots represent sandstone. Bedding dips 25 degrees to left; cleavage dips 60 degrees to left. The more plastic shale has been injected along cleavage in the sandstone to produce a rhythmic alternation of shale and sandstone that simulates bedding. *B.* Segregation banding. Short dashes represent bands rich in dark minerals. White areas are rich in light mineral. Bedding dips 25 degrees to the left.

[6] Daly, R. A., "Metamorphism and Its Phases," *Bulletin of Geological Society of America,* Vol. 28, pp. 375–418, 1917.

phism, where shales and sandstones are interbedded, the more plastic shale may be squeezed into inclined planes of cleavage that cut the sandstones. The resulting structure is *cleavage banding* (Fig. 283A). The individual bands of shale are characteristically a fraction of an inch thick. In other rocks, notably those that have been thoroughly recrystallized under conditions of high metamorphic intensity, the light and dark minerals may segregate into alternate bands parallel to the schistosity (Fig. 283B); the individual bands are a fraction of an inch to an inch thick.[7] This may be called *segregation banding.* The original rock may have been homogeneous, but during recrystallization the various elements moving in solution tended to accumulate in different bands. Segregation banding thus differs from the plastic injection characteristic of cleavage banding.

In such cases the ordinary criteria for recognizing bedding—compositional and textural differences—cannot be applied. If, however, the layers that differ in composition are many inches or feet thick, they presumably represent bedding. In the final analysis, however, each case must be decided on its own merits.

RELATION OF CLEAVAGE AND SCHISTOSITY TO MAJOR STRUCTURE

Introduction

Empirical observation in the field has shown that in many localities the cleavage bears a consistent relationship to the major structure. The systematic pattern shown by folds and cleavage is of the utmost importance to the structural geologist attempting to solve complicated field problems. The constancy of this relationship is, after all, not unexpected. Inasmuch as folds and cleavage generally develop contemporaneously under the same forces, a definite correlation is to be expected. Even in those areas where the folds and cleavage are not contemporaneous, if they developed under similar forces they would be related to one another. In some regions, of course, the tectonic history was more complicated; if the various structural features under consideration developed successively under forces acting in different directions, no simple relationship would occur.

The simpler case, in which folds and cleavage developed under the same force, or under successive applications of forces acting along the same lines, will be treated first; the more complicated situation will be discussed later.

[7] Turner, F. J., "The Development of Pseudo-Stratification by Metamorphic Differentiation in the Schists of Otago, New Zealand," *American Journal of Science,* Vol. 239, pp. 1–16, 1941.

Slaty Cleavage

Experience has shown that in many areas where slaty cleavage is diagonal to the bedding it is more or less parallel to the axial planes of the folds. In some cases the slaty cleavage is confined to the incompetent beds between the competent beds, in others a regional cleavage is present throughout a thick series of argillaceous strata. Cleavage that is parallel to the axial planes of the folds is of great use in solving structural problems. Its utility is a function of the geometrical relations and is independent of any theory of origin.

The methods may first be considered from the point of view of the relations in cross sections and in natural vertical faces that are perpendicular to the strike of the bedding. From Fig. 284 certain generalizations

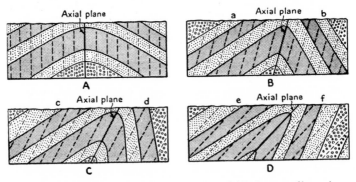

Fig. 284. Relation of slaty cleavage to folds in two dimensions. Cleavage represented by broken lines. Smaller letters are referred to in text. Rigorous parallelism of cleavage to axial plane is diagrammatic. *A.* Symmetrical fold. *B.* Asymmetrical fold. *C.* Asymmetrical fold with one steep limb. *D.* Overturned fold.

are apparent. (1) If the cleavage is vertical, it follows that the axial planes of the folds are vertical, and all the beds are right-side-up (Fig. 284A). (2) If the cleavage dips in the same direction as the bedding but more steeply (*a, c,* and *e* of Fig. 284), the beds are right-side-up, and the synclinal axis is in the direction in which the beds dip. (3) If the cleavage and bedding dip in opposite directions (*b* of Fig. 284B), the beds are right-side-up, and the synclinal axis is in the direction in which the beds dip. (4) If the bedding is vertical, the synclinal axis is in the opposite direction of that in which the cleavage dips (*d* in Fig. 284C). (5) If the cleavage dips more gently than the bedding, the beds are overturned; moreover, the synclinal axis is in the opposite direction of that in which the bedding and cleavage dip (*f* in Fig. 284D). (6) If the cleavage is horizontal, it follows that the axial planes are horizontal; in such a case the cleavage-bedding relations cannot be used to tell which beds are right-side-up and which are overturned.

In summary, the beds are right-side-up unless the cleavage dips in the same direction as the bedding and at a gentler angle; the synclinal axis is in the opposite direction from that in which the bedding and cleavage dip. If the beds are vertical, the synclinal axis is in the opposite direction from that in which the cleavage dips.

A few examples of the use of these principles are illustrated in Fig. 285. These are assumed to be isolated exposures of vertical faces that strike more or less at right angles to the strike of the bedding. In Fig. 285A the bedding and cleavage dip in the same direction, but the cleavage dips more steeply. Hence the beds are right-side-up and the syncline is to the west. In Fig. 285B, the bedding is vertical, but the cleavage dips

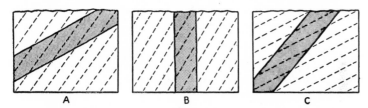

Fig. 285. Use of slaty cleavage to solve structure in two dimensions. Cleavage represented by broken lines. *A.* Syncline is to left. *B.* Syncline is to right. *C.* Syncline is to right.

to the west. Therefore, the top of the beds is to the east and the synclinal axis is toward the east. In Fig. 285C the cleavage and bedding both dip to the west, but the cleavage dips less steeply. It follows that the beds are overturned and the synclinal axis is toward the east.

From the illustrations given in Fig. 285, it is apparent that there is no evidence of the distance to the synclinal and anticlinal axes. This can be done only by a careful study of all the outcrops in the area. Suppose one outcrop shows that there is a synclinal axis to the east, but an outcrop 100 feet to the east shows that there is a synclinal axis to the west. The synclinal axis lies somewhere between the two outcrops; it can be located more precisely only if some additional information, such as stratigraphic evidence, is available.

Actually, of course, the cleavage-bedding relationship should be considered in three dimensions. From such studies it is possible to determine the direction in which the folds plunge. Still assuming that the slaty cleavage is parallel to the axial planes of the folds, the following relations are geometrically inevitable. If the axes of the folds are horizontal, the strike of the cleavage and bedding are parallel (Fig. 286A).

If the folds plunge, the strike of the cleavage is diagonal to the strike of the bedding (Fig. 286). The observer faces in the direction of the younger beds. He then imagines a line drawn on the ground perpendicular to the strike of the bedding. The direction in which he would measure the *acute angle* between this perpendicular and the strike of the cleavage is the direction in which the fold plunges. Suppose this method were applied to Fig. 286B. On the west limb of the syncline he would face eastnortheast. The acute angle between the perpendicular to the strike of the bedding and the strike of the cleavage is to the left (north). Hence the fold plunges north. If the observer were on the east limb, he would face

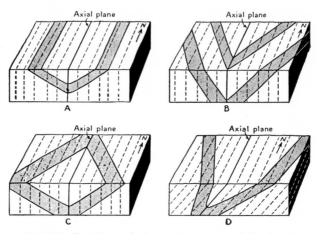

Fig. 286. Relation of slaty cleavage to folds in three dimensions. Cleavage represented by broken lines. Rigorous parallelism of cleavage to axial plane is diagrammatic; in many anticlines the cleavage diverges downward. *A*. Symmetrical non-plunging fold. *B*. Symmetrical fold plunging north. *C*. Symmetrical fold plunging south. *D*. Overturned fold plunging north.

westnorthwest. Now the acute angle lies to the right (north). Hence the fold plunges to the right (north). A similar analysis may be applied to Fig. 286C and 286D.

A few examples of problems that might be encountered in the field are illustrated in Fig. 287. The normal procedure is to examine first the vertical exposure perpendicular to the strike of the bedding. This is in order to determine the direction in which the synclinal and anticlinal axes are

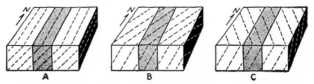

Fig. 287. Use of slaty cleavage to solve structure in three dimensions. Cleavage represented by broken lines. *A*. Syncline to right, does not plunge. *B*. Syncline to right, plunges north. *C*. Syncline to right, plunges south.

located. Then the horizontal surfaces are studied to determine the direction in which the folds plunge.

Examination of the vertical faces in Fig. 287 shows that in all three cases, inasmuch as the bedding is vertical and the cleavage dips to the west, the synclinal axes are to the east. The horizontal surface in Fig. 287A shows that the strike of the bedding is the same as the strike of the cleavage. Therefore the plunge of the fold is horizontal. From the vertical face in Fig. 287B we have already determined that the younger beds lie to the east. Hence the observer, standing on the outcrop, faces east. The acute angle between a line perpendicular to the strike of the bedding and the strike of the cleavage lies to the left (north). Hence the fold plunges north. On the outcrop represented by Fig. 287C the observer also faces east, but the acute angle lies to the right (south). Hence the fold plunges south.

It is even possible to measure the value of the plunge. As shown in Fig. 288, the plunge of the folds is the same as the attitude of the trace of the bedding on the cleavage. In Fig. 288 the trace of the bedding on the cleavage plunges about 25 degrees south. It follows that the fold plunges about 25 degrees south.

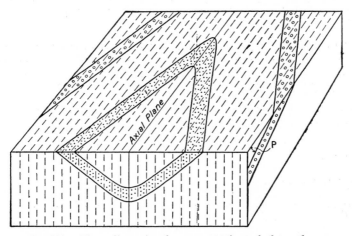

Fig. 288. Three-dimensional representation of slaty cleavage. Cleavage represented by broken lines. Value of plunge of fold is equal to *P*, which is measured on the cleavage; it is the angle between the trace of the bedding and a horizontal line.

The direction and value of the plunge can also be determined in another way. The attitude of the intersection of two planes, such as the bedding and the cleavage, can be determined by descriptive geometry (pages 459 to 463) or by the stereographic projection (pages 482 to 488). Hence, if we measure the attitude of bedding and cleavage, the direction and value of the plunge of the fold can be calculated.

Fracture Cleavage

Inasmuch as fracture cleavage is a shear phenomenon, its relation to the deforming forces will differ from that of flow cleavage. Fracture cleavage is characteristically developed in incompetent beds that lie between competent beds. Empirical observation shows that fracture cleavage in a fold has the relations shown in Fig. 289A. The cleavage is inclined to the bedding, and the acute angle, between the bedding and cleavage points in the direction in which the beds shear past one another. In a syncline each younger bed shears upward relative to the older bed beneath it (Fig. 77). In Fig. 289B the diagonal lining represents fracture cleavage. At locality *a* the relation of the fracture cleavage to the bedding shows that

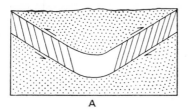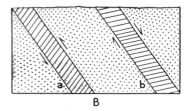

A   B

Fig. 289. Fracture cleavage. *A.* On the limbs of a fold. *B.* In isolated outcrops. Relations at *a* indicate a syncline to the right; relations at *b* indicate a syncline to the left.

the bed to the right has sheared upward relative to the bed to the left. Hence the synclinal axis is to the right, and the beds are right-side-up. At locality *b*, however, the bed to the left has sheared upward. Therefore the synclinal axis in this case is to the left and the beds are overturned.

Inasmuch as the intersection of fracture cleavage and bedding is parallel to the axes of the folds, the trace of the bedding on the fracture cleavage may be used to determine the direction and plunge of the axes of the folds.

Repeated Deformation

In the preceding discussion it has been assumed that the cleavage was contemporaneous with the folding or, if later, that it was caused by similar forces. On the other hand, it is conceivable that the forces producing the cleavage may be later and different from those causing the folding. In Fig. 290, the folds formed by simple horizontal compression, *H* and *H'*, are essentially symmetrical. The flow cleavage, which dips to the north, was formed by a later couple, *S* and *S'*; consequently, the flow cleavage is not parallel to the axial planes of the folds. In such a case, use of the methods outlined above to determine the major structure would not necessarily give the correct solution. At *b*, one would correctly deduce that a synclinal axis lay to the right. But at *a*, one would deduce that a synclinal axis lay to the left; that is, of course, incorrect.

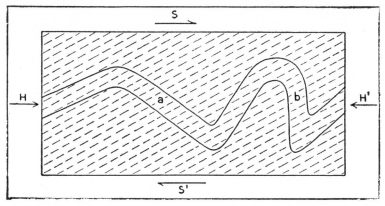

Fig. 290. Slaty cleavage that is not parallel to axial planes of folds. The folds resulted from simple compression, represented by H and H', and the axial planes are essentially vertical. The slaty cleavage, represented by the broken lines, was formed by a couple represented by S and S'.

Summary

Inasmuch as there are several kinds of cleavage, and their usefulness in interpreting major structure has limitations, it is obvious that discretion is necessary in field investigations. In some areas the nature of the cleavage may be readily apparent; in others, an intensive study may be necessary. As Mead [8] has said: "No hard and fast specifications can be written for the identification of foliate structures. The problem perhaps falls more into the category of an art than a science. Experience and familiarity with a wide variety of occurrences is of value."

[8] Mead, W. J., *op. cit.*, p. 1018.

CHAPTER 21

Lineation

NATURE OF LINEATION

Lineation, also called *linear parallelism* and *linear structure*, is the result of the parallelism of some directional property in the rock (Fig. 232A). For example, a rock in which the long axes of hornblende crystals are essentially parallel would possess a lineation. All transitions exist between rocks that possess no lineation and rocks with excellent lineation. In one rock the long axes of 90 per cent of the hornblende crystals might lie within a few degrees of each other; such a striking linear parallelism would be recognized immediately. In another rock, however, the long axes of the hornblende crystals might be rather evenly oriented in all possible directions within the rock; in such a case no lineation would exist.

As pointed out in Chapter 18, igneous rocks may possess a *primary lineation*—that is, a lineation due to the flow of the magma. Although the lineation of metamorphic rocks may be inherited from the original rock, more commonly it is a secondary feature developed during deformation. In this chapter we are concerned only with *secondary lineation*, and for the sake of brevity throughout the rest of this chapter, it will be referred to simply as lineation.

Lineation can occur with or without foliation (Fig. 232). A rock without cleavage or schistosity may, nevertheless, possess lineation. More commonly, however, lineation is associated with foliation, and the linear feature is parallel to the plane of cleavage or schistosity (Fig. 232C).

There are many kinds of lineation. Elongated or "stretched" pebbles or boulders are one of the most spectacular types (Fig. 291A). In Chapter 20 it was pointed out that these pebbles are irregular ellipsoids, but in that chapter we were primarily concerned with the fact that the shortest axis was perpendicular to the slaty cleavage. We are now concerned with the fact that the longest axes of all the pebbles are also parallel to one another; it follows, of course, that the intermediate axes of all the pebbles are parallel to one another. This statement is true, of course, only if the original pebbles were more or less spherical. If the original pebbles were very irregular in shape and diversely oriented, there would be some exceptions to the generalization. If the original pebbles were essentially spherical, it is possible to calculate the amount of the plastic deformation. In some parts of the area, for example, a conglomerate may have escaped intense deformation so that the shape of the original pebbles may be known. In the example cited on page 341, where the three axes of a pebble were 2, 4, and 6 centimeters long, the original pebble had a diameter of 3.6 centimeters. Thus the elongation parallel to the long axis is 2.4 centimeters, or 67 per cent. The elongation parallel to the intermediate axis is 0.4 centimeter or 11 per cent.

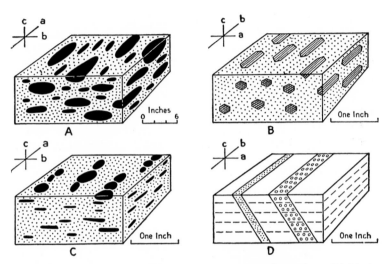

Fig. 291. Lineation. *A*. Elongated pebbles are shown in solid black. Each pebble is an irregular ellipsoid, the longest axis of which is parallel to *a*, the shortest axis is parallel to *c*, and the intermediate axis is parallel to *b*. *B*. Elongate crystals of hornblende, the long axes of which are parallel to *b* in the diagram. *C*. Lineation caused by circular plates of mica, shown in solid black, strung out like beads on a string. *D*. Cleavage is represented by top of block and by planes shown by broken lines. Bedding is shown by dots and open circles. Trace of bedding on cleavage gives a lineation.

Lineation is more commonly expressed by the minerals constituting the rock. As noted above, hornblende crystals, which have one long dimension, with the result that individual crystals are more or less needle shaped, may display an excellent lineation (Fig. 291B). In some instances, biotite occurs as elliptical plates, the long axes of which are parallel. In still other instances, an original, more or less spherical mineral may be granulated into numerous fragments which become strung out into an ellipsoidal group.

The schistosity or cleavage may be thrown into small corrugations or crinkles, with a wave length and an amplitude that are measured in millimeters (Fig. 305C). In such a case the lineation results from the parallel arrangement of the crests of minute drag folds formed by the sliding of different layers over one another.

The intersection of bedding and cleavage produces a lineation, because the intersection of two planes is a line. If the rock breaks parallel to the cleavage, the trace of the bedding appears as parallel streaks on the cleavage. In Fig. 291D, the top of the block is parallel to the cleavage; the trace of the bedding on the cleavage is parallel to b. On the other hand, if the rock breaks parallel to the bedding, the trace of the cleavage appears as minute fractures on the bedding.

Slickensides (Fig. 134A) are a type of lineation. In some cases the scratches may be very obvious and clearly indicate the direction of movement. At other places a streaking caused by concentration of dark minerals along certain lines may be caused by sliding of layers past one another.

Boudinage,[1] or "sausage structure," is illustrated in Fig. 292. In cross section a competent bed thickens and thins in such a way as to simulate a string of sausages. Parallel to the bedding the individual units look like sausages lying side by side. The line of junction of the individual units

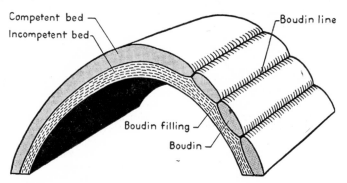

Fig. 292. Boudinage. In this case the boudin line is parallel to fold axis, but this is not necessarily true.

may be called the *boudin line* and is a lineation. In highly metamorphosed rocks the junction of two of the *boudins* may be occupied by quartz, feldspar, or some other mineral. Boudinage is clearly the result of stretching at right angles to the boudin line; it is analogous to the necking of a rod of metal under tension (Fig. 80). The more brittle bed is that one that shows the boudinage. Whereas the more ductile adjacent beds could yield plastically, the brittle bed first necked and then broke along a tension fracture.

Quartz *rods* are found in some areas of metamorphosed rocks.[2] In their

---

[1] Cloos, Ernst, "Boudinage," *Transactions American Geophysical Union,* Vol. 28, pp. 626–632, 1947.

[2] Wilson, Gilbert, "Mullion and Rodding Structures in the Moine Series of Scotland," *Proceedings of the Geologists Association,* Vol. 64, Part 2, pp. 118–151, 1953.

extreme development they are long cylindrical rods of quartz. A complete study of their evolution shows that in their simplest form they are small concordant veins of quartz (Fig. 293A) that may have been derived from silica secreted from the country rock. However, as the individual veins become more irregular and discontinuous, they assume forms not unlike those of boudins, but far more irregular (Fig. 293B); many are rod-like.

Mullion structure consists of a series of parallel columns. Each column may be several inches in diameter and several feet long. Each column is composed of folded metamorphic rocks.

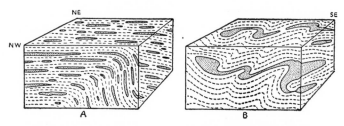

Fig. 293. Quartz rods. Quartz shown by dots, bedding by broken lines. *A.* Quartz lenses parallel to bedding. *B.* More irregular quartz lenses parallel to bedding. (Based on diagrams by G. Wilson.)

The fold axes are considered to be a lineation by some geologists. This, of course, is correct in the sense that the fold axes are lines. On the other hand, it is probably inadvisable to extend the term lineation to include every linear feature with which geology has to deal.

Cloos[3] has discussed the various kinds of lineation, and his publication is especially valuable because of the excellent annotated bibliography.

RECORDING ATTITUDE OF LINEATION

The attitude of the lineation is defined by the strike of its horizontal projection and by its plunge. Figure 32, although designed primarily to illustrate the method of measuring the attitude of the axis of a fold, may be used equally well to illustrate the measurement of lineation. The lineation is *FD*; the horizontal projection (*AD*) of the lineation trends northwest, and this is said to be the strike of the lineation. The angle *P* is the plunge of the lineation.

On geological maps the attitude of the lineation is generally represented by an arrow (Fig. 294). The trend of the arrow is parallel to the strike of the lineation. The arrow points in the direction of plunge, and an Arabic numeral gives the value of the plunge. Thus symbol *a* of Fig.

[3] Cloos, Ernst, "Lineation, a Critical Review and Annotated Bibliography," *Geological Society of America, Memoir 18,* 1946. Supplement, *Review of Literature,* 1942–52, 1953.

294 indicates a lineation that plunges 22 degrees in a direction N. 90° W. A special symbol such as *b*, with arrowheads at both ends, is employed for horizontal lineation. Symbol *b* means that the strike of a horizontal lineation is N. 45° E. Symbol *c* is used for vertical lineation.

Because lineation usually lies in the plane of the foliation, the two symbols are generally combined. Symbol *d* of Fig. 294 indicates a schistosity that strikes N. 45° E. and dips 30° NW.; lying in the plane of the schistosity is a lineation, the horizontal projection of which strikes

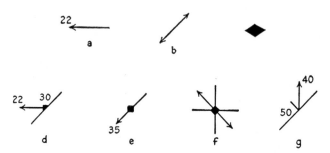

Fig. 294. Map symbols for lineation. *a.* Lineation plunging 22° W. *b.* Horizontal lineation striking NE. *c.* Vertical lineation. *d.* Foliation striking N. 45° E., dipping 30° NW.; lineation plunging 22° W. *e.* Vertical foliation striking N. 45° E., lineation plunging 35° SW. *f.* Horizontal foliation, with horizontal lineation striking N. 45° W. *g.* Bedding striking N. 45° E., dipping 50° NW.; lineation plunging 40° N.

N. 90° W.; the plunge is 22° W. Symbol *e* indicates a vertical schistosity that strikes N. 45° E., and on which a lineation plunges 35° SW. Symbol *f* indicates a horizontal foliation with a horizontal lineation that strikes N. 45° W. Symbol *g* indicates bedding that strikes N. 45° E. and dips 50° NW. On this is a lineation that strikes N. and plunges 40° N.

In the field, a careful record should be made concerning the kind of lineation, as all types of lineation are not formed in the same way. Ideally, this information should be shown on the map.

RELATION TO MAJOR STRUCTURE AND ORIGIN

Introduction

The orientation of the lineation relative to the major structure and the origin depend, of course, on the kind of lineation. In general, the lineation is systematically related to the major folds, but this is not necessarily the case if the lineation is the result of stresses independent of those that produced the folding.

Deformed Pebbles, Oölites, and Mineral Grains

The attitude of deformed pebbles, oölites, and grains of such minerals as quartz are generally related in some systematic way to the associated folds. But the relations may differ in different areas and in different parts of the same fold.

The attitude of the deformed oölites in Maryland and Pennsylvania are illustrated in Fig. 295A. The fold axes are essentially horizontal, whereas the axial planes of the folds and the slaty cleavage dip to the southeast. The long axes (l) and intermediate axes (i) of the ellipsoidal oölites lie in the plane of the slaty cleavage. The long axis of each oölite

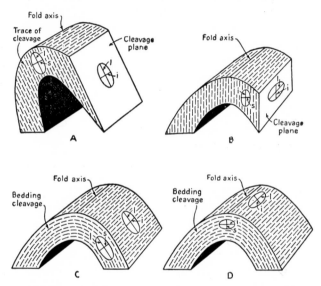

Fig. 295. Various orientations of long axes of deformed spheres. *A.* In axial plane cleavage and perpendicular to fold axis. *B.* In axial plane cleavage and parallel to fold axis. *C.* In bedding plane cleavage and perpendicular to fold axis. *D.* In bedding plane cleavage and parallel to fold axes.

plunges southeast essentially down the dip of the cleavage. It is apparent that in this case, because of a couple acting along northwest-southeast lines (Fig. 75B), the thick pile of sediments was elongating upward toward the northwest, partly by folding but especially by rock flowage.

Near Newport, Rhode Island, the Carboniferous sediments contain some very coarse-grained conglomerates. Many of the boulders are from one to three feet long. The fold axes plunge gently south. The long axes of the deformed boulders also plunge gently south (Fig. 295B). The intermediate axes are essentially vertical, parallel to the axial plane of the major fold; the short axes are almost horizontal, striking east-west, and are thus perpendicular to the axial plane of the major fold. Under east-west compression the sediments were thrown into folds striking north-south; the easiest relief was north-south, and thus the sediments elongated in that direction.

In much of eastern Vermont[4] the long and intermediate axes of the pebbles on the limbs of folds lie parallel to a bedding cleavage (Fig. 295C). The fold axes are essentially horizontal, and the long axes of the pebbles plunge directly down the dip. This type of deformation is the result of stretching of the limbs of the folds, accompanied, of course, by considerable thinning of the beds. Near the crests of the folds, however, the long axes of the pebbles are parallel to the fold axes (Fig. 295D). Here the easiest relief was parallel to the fold axes. In western New Hampshire the long axes of stretched pebbles are oriented this way.

Elongate Minerals

Lineation shown by elongate minerals, such as hornblende needles or flat oval flakes of mica, likewise show various orientations. In these cases, however, the mineral was not plastically deformed into its present shape, but grew in that direction because it was the easiest direction of growth.

Intersection of Bedding and Cleavage

A lineation that is the result of the intersection of bedding and an axial plane slaty cleavage is parallel to the fold axis. A consideration of the geometry of folds shows that this must be the case (Fig. 288). Simi-

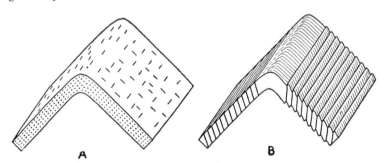

Fig. 296. Different kinds of lineation on folds. *A.* Two lineations, one parallel to axis of fold and other at right angles. *B.* Left-hand limb shows lineation due to intersection of fracture cleavage with bedding. Right-hand limb shows lineation due to intersection of slip cleavage with bedding; displacement on the cleavage causes either tiny faults or small crinkles.

larly the intersection of bedding and of fracture cleavage that is related to the folding is parallel to the fold axes (Fig. 296B). The same is true of the intersection of fracture cleavage with slaty cleavage that is parallel to the axial planes of the folds.

---

[4] Thompson, J. B., personal communication.

Crinkles

If a bedding cleavage is thrown into small crinkles, the axes of the crinkles are likely to be parallel to the major fold axes. This is because the crinkles are essentially drag folds. After an axial plane cleavage has been produced, further compression may cause slippage along this cleavage toward the major fold axes. The axes of any crinkles will likewise be parallel to the major fold axes. In many cases, however, the rocks may be so tightly compressed that the differential movements parallel to the bedding or cleavage are unrelated to the major fold axes; consequently the crinkles may be oriented in most any direction. In some areas it is not uncommon to find several sets of differently oriented crinkles. They were produced in succession as the rocks slipped in different directions parallel to the cleavage or bedding.

Slickensides and Mineral Streaks

Normally, as shown on page 89, the beds on the flank of folds slip past one another perpendicular to the fold axes. Consequently any slickensides on the bedding planes are perpendicular to the fold axes. Similarly, any mineral streaking (streaming) that is the result of differential movement (Fig. 291C) is likely to be perpendicular to the fold axes. Figure 296A shows two types of lineation. That parallel to the fold axis is a minute crinkling. That down the dip of the bedding is a mineral streaking caused by slippage of the beds past one another.

Boudinage, Rodding, and Mullion Structure

If boudinage is the result of stretching of a competent bed on the limbs of a fold, the boudin line will be parallel to the fold axis (Fig. 292). But if the boudinage is caused by stretching parallel to the fold axes, the boudin line will be perpendicular to the fold axis. The quartz rodding in Scotland is parallel to the fold axes. This is because some of the rods are the detached noses of folds. It is also because quartz layers are broken up into rods, the long axes of which are parallel to the fold axes.

Incongruous Orientations

It is obvious from the preceding discussion that even within a small body of rock some of the linear features may be parallel to the fold axes, whereas others may be perpendicular. Moreover, it is worthwhile emphasizing again that the lineation is congruous with the major structure only if it forms simultaneously with the major structure or is produced under similar conditions of stress. But if the lineation is distinctly younger or older than the folding or thrusting, it may be incongruous to the major structure. Even during a single period of deformation the rocks may be so badly squeezed that masses of rocks deform plastically quite independently of the major structure. The lineations may then be very unsystematic. Detailed study may show that an apparently erratic lineation is systematic.[5]

REFERENCE AXES

Many papers on lineation use a system of reference axes. Unfortunately there is some confusion as to just how the reference axes should be established. The reference axes could be defined by what is seen in the rock or by the movements that are believed to have produced the observed structures.

Imagine a pack of cards in which the individual cards are systematically sliding over one another (Fig. 297A). The direction of movement may be defined as a, the direction in the plane of the cards at right angles to the direction of movement as b, and the direction perpendicular to the plane of the cards as c. The axes of any folds that form under such a stress system will be parallel to b (Fig. 297B).

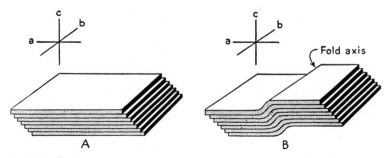

Fig. 297. Reference axes for lineation. A. Sheets sliding over one another in a direction. B. Axis of fold forms parallel to b.

But the field geologist does not know the direction of movement. He must infer it from what he sees in the rocks. From Fig. 297B it might be suggested that the fold axes be defined as b, in which case a lies at right angles to b in the plane of cleavage, and c is the perpendicular to the cleavage. In fact, this is what has been advocated.[6] But unfortunately there are instances in which the fold axes are parallel to the direction of movement. A second difficulty involves the whole concept of "direction of movement." In the case of the sliding cards it is clear what is meant. But in an area of folding the concept is not so obvious. Consider, for example, the right-hand fold in Fig. 192. The top bed at the extreme right-hand end of the diagram has moved horizontally from right to left. But the

[5] Lowe, K. E., "A Graphic Solution for Certain Problems of Linear Structure," *American Mineralogist,* Vol. 31, pp. 425–434, 1946.

[6] Cloos, Ernst, "Lineation, a Critical Review and Annotated Bibliography," *Geological Society of America, Memoir 18,* 1946.

same bed on the crest of the anticline has moved diagonally upward from right to left. Thus in such rocks, there is no one "direction of movement." Moreover, on the limbs of the folds the direction of movement is parallel to the dip of the beds because the beds slip past one another in this direction. Finally, the concept of the "direction of movement" is based on the erroneous idea that the slaty cleavage is necessarily parallel to one of the shear planes of the strain ellipsoid.

In conclusion, reference axes a, b, and c may be used under appropriate conditions to refer to the direction of movement when the deformation is analogous to the sliding of cards over one another, but otherwise they have no significance.

RELATIONS OF MINOR STRUCTURES TO OVERTHRUSTS

A superb example of the relationship of minor structures, including lineation, to the major structure, has been described from England.[7] In the area described it has been known for some time that thrust plates dip gently northwest. Many have assumed that the relative overthrusting was from the northwest. However, an analysis of the many minor structures show that the relative overthrusting was in a direction N. 20° to 30° W. Only some of the significant data are shown in Fig. 298. Linear features parallel to the movement direction, a, are slickensides, elongated lava pillows, and elongated amygdules (Fig. 298B). Linear features parallel to b are the axes of drag folds (Fig. 298A), tension cracks (Fig. 298B),

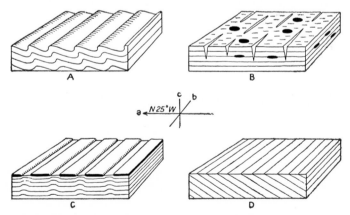

Fig. 298. Relation of minor structures to overthrusting in Tintagel area, North Cornwall, England. A. Drag folds. B. Slickensides shown by short lines on top of block; deformed pillows and amygdules shown in solid black, tension cracks shown by open gashes. C. Boudinage. D. Fracture cleavage. (After Gilbert Wilson.)

[7] Wilson, Gilbert, "The Tectonics of the Tintagel Area, North Cornwall," *Quarterly Journal of the Geological Society of London,* Vol. CVI, pp. 393–432, 1951.

boudinage (Fig. 298C), and fracture cleavage (Fig. 298D). The dip of the axial planes of the drag folds and the dip of the fracture cleavage show that the relative overthrusting was toward the northwest.[8]

[8] For other examples of the relation of minor structures, including lineation, to major structure, see:

Brace, William F., "The Geology of the Rutland Area, Vermont," *Vermont Geological Survey, Bulletin No. 6*, 120 pages, 1953.

Osberg, Philip H., "The Green Mountain Anticlinorium in the Vicinity of Rochester and East Middlebury, Vermont," *Vermont Geological Survey, Bulletin No. 5*, 127 pages, 1952.

CHAPTER 22

Structural Petrology

INTRODUCTION

Petrofabric analysis is not only the study of the spatial relations of the units that comprise a rock, but is also concerned with the movements that produced those arrangements. Petrofabric analysis may be used to investigate rock deformation, as well as the genesis of sedimentary and igneous rocks. *Petrotectonics*, or *structural petrology*, is that phase of the subject that deals with deformed rocks and their tectonic history. A more complete definition and a consideration of the limits of the subject are given below.

The fundamental principles of petrofabric analysis were developed by Bruno Sander[1] and Walter Schmidt.[2] Several excellent treatments are available in English.[3]

Fabric, or *structural fabric*, refers to the arrangements of the units that comprise any kind of external form. These units may be atoms, mineral grains, folds, or, in one sense, still larger units.

If many of the grains in a rock composed of mica, quartz, and feldspar are platy or ellipsoidal in habit and lie parallel to one another, the fabric may be described as *foliated* (p. 336). If many of these platy grains are oval in shape, and if the long axes of the ovals tend to lie parallel to one another, the fabric is *linear* as well as *foliated*. On the other hand,

---

[1] Sander, B., *Einführung in die Gefügekunde der Geologischen Körper*, Pt. 1, 215 pp., 1948; Pt. 2, 409 pp., 1950: Springer-Verlag, Vienna and Innsbruck.

[2] Schmidt, W., *Tektonik und Verformungslehre*. Berlin: Gebrüder Borntraeger, 1932.

[3] Knopf, E. B., and E. Ingerson, "Structural Petrology," *Geological Society of America*, Memoir 6, 1938.

Fairbairn, H. W., *Structural Petrology of Deformed Rocks*, 2d ed. Cambridge: Addison-Wesley Press, 1949.

Turner, F. J., "Mineralogical and Structural Evolution of the Metamorphic Rocks," *Geological Society of America*, *Memoir 30*, 342 pp., 1948; especially pp. 149–282.

Turner, F. J., and J. Verhoogen, *Igneous and Metamorphic Petrology*, New York: McGraw-Hill Book Company, 1951, 602 pp.; especially pp. 503–564.

See also Demay, André, "Microtectonique et Tectonique Profonde," 257 pages, Paris: *Imprimerie Nationale*, 1942.

For review see Knopf, E. B., *American Journal of Science*, Vol. 246, pp. 454–457, 1948.

although many of the grains may be tabular or ellipsoidal, they may lie in a random orientation so that the rock, lacking both foliation and lineation, may be described as *isotropic;* that is, the properties of the rock are equal in all directions.

The type of fabric just described is controlled by the shape of the individual mineral grains. We may also think of the atoms that comprise the individual minerals. Each mineral species is characterized by its own peculiar arrangement of atoms. In each grain of the mineral, this arrangement is repeated regularly in three dimensions, one repetition around each

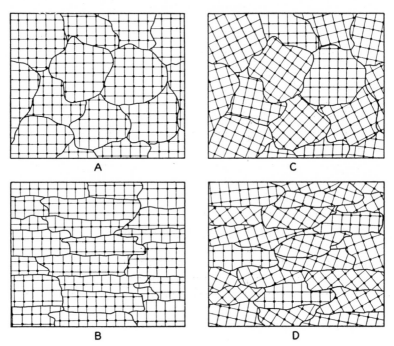

Fig. 299. Diagrammatic two-dimensional representation of preferred orientation. Dots represent centers of atoms. *A.* Space lattice orientation, grains equidimensional. *B.* Space lattice and shape orientation. *C.* No orientation. *D.* Shape orientation, but no space lattice orientation.

point of a theoretical framework or space lattice. In some rocks, the space lattices of all the grains of a single mineral species may have approximately the same orientation. In the diagrams of Fig. 299, which are simple, very diagrammatic, two-dimensional representation of rocks composed of grains of a single mineral species, each dot indicates the center of an atom. In Fig. 299A, the space lattices are parallel. On the other hand, the space lattices may be oriented at random, as represented in Fig. 299C.

In many cases a lattice orientation is associated with a shape orientation (Fig. 299B). But a shape orientation without a space lattice orientation is quite possible. Lenticular grains of quartz may be parallel to one another, but the space lattices may be diversely oriented (Fig. 299D).

Fabric also refers to units of larger size than atoms or minerals. It may, for example, refer to the pebbles in a conglomerate; Figure 291A is a "stretched conglomerate" in which all the long axes lie parallel to one another. Cleavage, joints, lineation, and fold-axes, from this point of view, are all part of the fabric.[4] Going to still higher units, one could even think of folds and thrusts as being part of the fabric of an orogenic belt, and the orogenic belts, in turn, being part of the fabric of the continents.

The relation of cleavage, joints, lineation, folds, and faults to one another has been discussed in previous chapters. Consequently the present chapter will be confined to a discussion of the smaller units comprising rocks, that is, mineral grains and atoms.[5]

If, regardless of whether they are pebbles, minerals, or atoms, the units tend to be oriented in a particular direction, the fabric shows a *preferred orientation*. In Figs. 299A and 299B, the space lattice shows a preferred orientation; in Figs. 299B and 299D, the grains show a preferred orientation according to shape. In contrast to a preferred orientation, we may speak of a *random orientation*.

In many instances, the preferred orientation may be so well marked that there is no doubt of its existence. Obviously, these are all transitions from random orientation to a well-marked preferred orientation. By means of the statistical analysis applied in petrofabric analysis, it is possible to express quantitatively the degree of preferred orientation.

The essence of structural petrology is that the fabric is the result of the conditions existing at the time the rock formed, and particularly that the fabric of deformed rocks has been controlled by penetrative movement, that is, movement that effects every grain and crystal. The fabric of an igneous rock that crystallizes quietly from stationary molten magma will be different from that of an igneous rock that crystallizes from flowing magma. The fabric of a sediment quietly deposited at the bottom of a body of water will be different from that of a rock that has been involved in strong differential tectonics movements. The aim of structural petrology is to determine the nature of the differential movements during the deformation and the number of periods of deformation.

[4] Ingerson, E., "Why Petrofabrics?": *Transactions American Geophysical Union for 1944*, pp. 635–652.

[5] It is the opinion of the author that a broad definition of petrofabrics is unnecessary and undesirable. If, as has been suggested, petrofabrics is detailed structural geology, there is no need for a new term. The author would prefer that petrofabrics refer only to those units that are, at the most, only a few inches long, clearly recognizing that all such studies should be fully integrated with investigations of the larger geological features.

FIELD TECHNIQUE

Inasmuch as one of the aims of structural petrology is to relate the internal structure of the rocks to the larger structural features, a careful field study, conducted by customary field methods, is essential. In particular, such features as foliation, lineation, faults, joints, and all other structural elements in the rock must be measured and recorded on maps.

These field methods are supplemented by structural studies involving the use of the microscope. It is essential, therefore, to collect *oriented specimens* from which thin sections may be cut. An oriented specimen is one the exact arrangement of which in space is known; the fabric of the

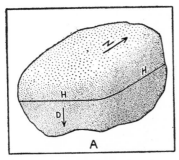 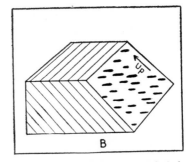

Fig. 300. Methods of labeling specimens in field. *A.* Completely labeled. *B.* Partially labeled; attitude of foliation (parallel lines) and lineation (dark streaks) have been measured in the field.

rock may show either a preferred orientation or a random orientation. The dual use of the word *orient,* in one instance referring to the arrangement of the specimen in space and in the other instance referring to the fabric of the rock, is perhaps somewhat confusing. The specimen may be oriented by reference to the geographic co-ordinates. In Fig. 300A, for example, a horizontal plane (H), north (N), and the down direction (D) are all marked. At any subsequent time it is possible to orient the specimen as it was in its natural relations.

A specimen that possesses foliation and lineation, the attitude of which was recorded in the field, can be properly oriented at any subsequent time, provided that the top or bottom of the specimen is indicated (Fig. 300B).

LABORATORY TECHNIQUE

Thin sections for microscopic study are prepared from the specimens. The sections can be cut in any desired direction, but if only one section is to be prepared, it is usually cut perpendicularly to the schistosity and lineation. It may be necessary to give rather careful instructions to the man making the thin sections.

A conventional set of three mutually perpendicular reference axes are used to describe the fabric of deformed rocks. Those axes are actually defined kinematically, that is, relative to the movements in the rocks (see p. 360). The hand specimens are labeled in the following way (Fig. 301A). The line c is perpendicular to the plane containing the lineation; a is the direction of movement in this plane, whereas b, also lying in this plane, is at right angles to the direction of movement. It is obvious that a subjective element is at once introduced into the labeling of the specimens. A lineation represented by slickensides, for example, is parallel to a; likewise, a mineral streaming (page 359) is also parallel to a. On the

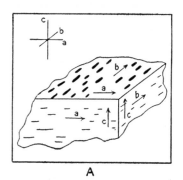
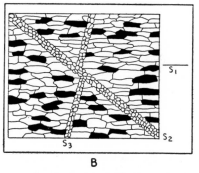

A   B

Fig. 301. Labeling material. *A*. Conventional system of labeling a specimen that has foliation and lineation; c is perpendicular to foliation; a lies in plane of foliation and is parallel to inferred direction of movement; b lies in plane of foliation at right angles to inferred direction of movement. *B*. Thin section showing three *S*-planes. Black = dark mineral; white = light-colored minerals.

other hand, a lineation represented by crinkling, the intersection of bedding and cleavage, or the intersection of two cleavages, is b. Sometimes a final decision can be made only after detailed studies. In some cases, which cannot be discussed here, B and R may be used instead of b. If more than one type of b lineation is present, the more prominent is labeled b, the less prominent b'. If more than one type of a lineation is present, the more prominent is labeled a, the less prominent a'. Similarly, if more than one plane of schistosity is present, the perpendicular to the more prominent one is c, the less prominent one is c'. If the rock is massive, lacking both schistosity and lineation, the thin section may be labeled by geographic directions or by some other system.

For convenience, a plane parallel to the schistosity may be referred to as the ab plane because it contains the a and b axes. The plane perpendicular to the schistosity and to b is the ac plane. The plane perpendicular to the schistosity and parallel to b is the bc plane. Each thin section may be similarly labeled according to the two axes that it contains. Others[6] prefer to designate a thin section by the axis that is perpendicular to it; thus the thin section parallel to the schistosity would be the *c-section* in this terminology.

The thin section is first studied by ordinary microscopic methods, and the minerals are determined. Special attention is given to the orientation and abundance of *S-surfaces*, which may be planes of stratification, schistosity, or shear planes. Figure 301B is an example of a thin section with three *S*-surfaces. The most prominent surface is customarily labeled S_1; the others are designated by Arabic numerals in order of their importance.

A *petrofabric diagram* is then prepared from the thin section. Separate diagrams must be prepared, of course, for each mineral species. Quartz, biotite, muscovite, and calcite are most commonly studied. The diagram may be based on any of the following four properties of the mineral: the space lattice, the cleavage, twin lamellae, or the shape of the mineral. Such diagrams are prepared by means of a *Universal Stage* set on a petrographic microscope. The Universal Stage is so designed that the thin section, by rotation about three mutually perpendicular axes, may be brought into any desired position. The technique is petrographic in character, and its description is beyond the function of this book. Two excellent discussions are available in English.[7] It is possible, however, to understand such diagrams without being familiar with the technique involved in their preparation.

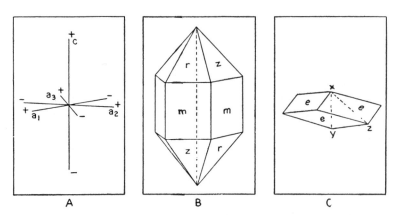

Fig. 302. Hexagonal minerals. *A.* Conventional system of designating axes of hexagonal minerals. *B.* Quartz crystal: $m =$ unit prism; $r =$ positive unit rhombohedron; $z =$ negative unit rhombohedron. Broken line $=$ *c*-crystallographic axis $=$ optic axis. *C.* Calcite crystal: $e =$ negative rhombohedron; $xy =$ *c*-crystallographic axis $=$ optic axis; $xz =$ short diagonal of rhombohedron.

[6] Knopf, E. B., and E. Ingerson, *op. cit.*, p. 218.
[7] Knopf, E. B., and E. Ingerson, *op. cit.*
Fairbairn, H. W., *op. cit.*

The diagrams that consider the space lattice of the minerals are really based on optical properties. The *optic axis* of a hexagonal mineral such as quartz, for example, is parallel to the *c-crystallographic axis*. Figure 302B is a drawing of a perfect quartz crystal, the *c*-crystallographic axis of which is shown by the broken line; this is also the optic axis. Although most quartz grains in rocks are spherical, elliptical, or irregular, each possesses an optic axis. By means of the Universal Stage, the exact orientation of this optic axis relative to the thin section may be determined.

In a thin section, such as that represented by the plane *DEFG* in Fig. 303A, one optic axis of quartz might occupy the position *1*, lying parallel to the plane of the thin section and parallel to *DF*. Another optic axis might be in the position *2*, parallel to the plane of the thin section and parallel to *DE*. A third is in position *3*, lying parallel to the plane of the thin section, but diagonally to the sides. A fourth optic axis, *4*, is perpendicular to the plane of the thin section. A fifth optic axis, *5*, lying in the plane of the thin section, is diagonal to the sides. A sixth optic axis,

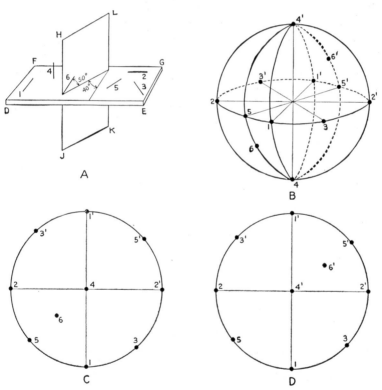

Fig. 303. Meaning of a point diagram. *A*. Thin section is plane *DEFG;* *1, 2, 3, 4, 5,* and *6* represent optic axes of six different quartz crystals. *B*. Spheres showing poles of axes shown in *A*. *C*. Projection on to lower hemisphere. *D*. Projection on to upper hemisphere.

6, is inclined to the plane of the thin section; this is the most general case. This optic axis lies in the vertical plane *HJKL*, which makes an angle of 40 degrees with *DF*; optic axis *6* is inclined 50 degrees to the plane of the thin section.

If each of these grains is imagined to be at the center of a sphere, the optic axis *1* would pierce the sphere at *1* and *1'* (Fig. 303B); optic axis *2* would cut it at *2* and *2'*; *3* at *3* and *3'*; *4* at *4* and *4'*; and *5* at *5* and *5'*. The optic axis *6* would pierce the lower, left-hand, front part of the sphere at *6* and the upper, right-hand, back part of the sphere at *6'*.

Inasmuch as each optic axis pierces the sphere in two places, all the data may be represented on one hemisphere, the upper or lower one. For practical reasons, these data are more satisfactorily plotted on a plane surface that is a projection of the sphere. In Fig. 303C, the data of Figs. 303A and 303B have been plotted on the lower hemisphere. Any optic axis that lies parallel to the plane of the thin section intersects the circumference of the circle at two points, and it can be plotted in either of these two positions; ordinarily only one point is plotted, the choice being arbitrary. Optic axis *2* intersects the circle at *2* and *2'*, and the plot may be made at either of these two points. An optic axis such as *4*, which is perpendicular to the plane of the thin section, lies in the center of the circle. An inclined optic axis, such as *6*, appears between the center and the circumference. The steeper the angle of inclination, the nearer it will be to the center of the circle.

Figure 303D shows the same data plotted on the upper hemisphere. For optic axes parallel or perpendicular to the plane of the thin section, this diagram is identical with Fig. 303C. For inclined optic axes such as *6*, however, the position is diagonally across from that in Fig. 303C. Inasmuch as inclined optic axes are the most common, a plot made on one hemisphere will be a mirror image of that made on the other hemisphere —except, perhaps, for optic axes lying on the circumference of the circle, where an arbitrary choice is permissible. In most petrofabric diagrams the plot has been made on the lower hemisphere.

The exact distance that a point such as *6* appears from the center of the circle depends not only upon its angle of inclination relative to the plane of the thin section, but also upon the type of projection used. In structural petrology, the *Schmidt equal-area net*[8] is used.

When all the optic axes have been plotted, the resulting diagram is known as a *point diagram* (see also p. 112). Figure 304A is an example of a point diagram of the optic axes of quartz plotted on the lower hemisphere.

The optic axis of calcite may be measured and plotted in the same way that the optic axis of quartz is plotted (Fig. 302C).

The biaxial minerals—those with two optic axes—are more difficult to

[8] Knopf, E. B., and E. Ingerson, *op. cit.*, **p. 227.**

study. Biotite, however, is so nearly uniaxial, like quartz and calcite, that point diagrams may be readily prepared. Moreover, the optic axis of biotite is essentially perpendicular to its cleavage, a fact that is a great help in orienting the mineral on the universal stage.

Many petrofabric diagrams show the attitude of the cleavage rather than the orientation of the optic axes. Minerals like biotite and muscovite, which have one good cleavage, are easy to study, but calcite, with three cleavages, is more difficult. The attitude of a line perpendicular to the cleavage is determined and plotted. The point where the perpendicular to a plane intersects the projection sphere is called the *pole* of that plane.

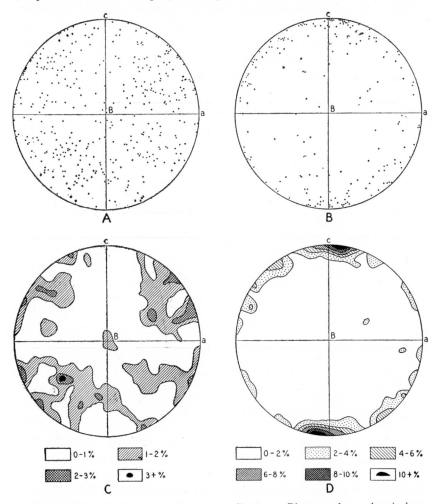

Fig. 304. Point diagrams and contour diagrams. Plots on lower hemisphere. *A.* Point diagram, 400 optic axes of quartz from mica schist, Mt. Clough, New Hampshire. *B.* Point diagram, 200 poles of cleavage of biotite from mica schist, Mt. Clough, New Hampshire. *C.* Contour diagram of *A. D.* Contour diagram of *B.*

The preparation of point diagrams for the poles of cleavage planes is similar to the method used in making point diagrams for the poles of joints, as described on p. 112. Figure 304B is a point diagram of the poles of 200 biotite flakes.

In some diagrams, notably those of calcite, the plot may be based on perpendiculars to twin lamellae (see also p. 378).

The number of grains that must be measured and plotted depends upon the degree of the preferred orientation. In some instances 100 grains are adequate, and usually 200 grains will suffice; if 400 grains reveal no evidence of preferred orientation, it is very probable that none exists.

After the point diagrams have been prepared, they may be converted into *contour diagrams* by the method described on pp. 112–114. Figure 304C shows a contour diagram of the optic axes of quartz; Figure 304D is a contour diagram of the perpendiculars to the cleavage of biotite. Both plots are on the lower hemisphere.

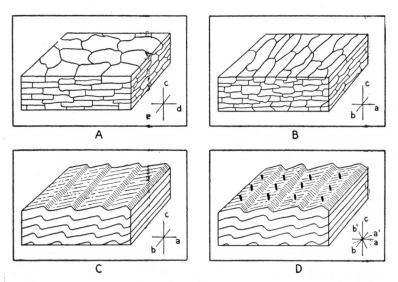

Fig. 305. Symmetry of hand specimens. *A.* Axial symmetry. *B.* Orthorhombic symmetry. *C.* Monoclinic symmetry; wavy lines are schistosity. *D.* Triclinic symmetry; wavy lines are schistosity; black streaks represent an oval mineral lying in the plane of schistosity.

Each high point on a contour diagram is a *maximum*. Actually, there may be several such high points so that several *maxima* may exist.

Most petrofabric diagrams are based on only a small percentage of all the grains of a mineral species in a thin section. A thin section may thus contain several thousand quartz grains, but usually a few hundred are sufficient to indicate whether there is a preferred orientation. Ordinarily, the person preparing the diagram must select the grains at random, and must not make any selection, either conscious or unconscious, of grains of a particular color, size, or shape. A *nonselective diagram* is one prepared by an indiscriminate measurement of grains. A *selective* or *partial diagram* is one prepared by deliberately choosing grains of a certain size, shape, or position within or outside of shear zones. A *collective diagram* is prepared by making a single diagram from several selective diagrams.

Published diagrams should always contain certain fundamental information, preferably on the diagram itself or in the description directly beneath it. The mineral represented by the diagram and the number of grains measured should always be stated. The *a*, *b* and *c* directions and the contour interval should be indicated. A clear statement should be made, either under the figures or at the start of the paper, whether the projection is on the lower or the upper hemisphere. If no statement is made, it may be assumed that the projection is on the lower hemisphere.

SYMMETRY OF FABRIC

The rock fabric may be classified according to its symmetry in somewhat the same way that minerals may be grouped into systems. In fact, the terminology used to describe the symmetry of rocks has been partially borrowed from mineralogy. It was formerly thought that the symmetry of the rock fabric bore a rather simple and direct relation to the movements in the rock during their formation and deformation. It is now realized, however, that the relation is more complicated than that, and broad generalizations are difficult to make. Each case must be considered individually. Moreover, the symmetry shown by the hand specimen may differ from that revealed by the petrofabric diagram prepared from the thin section. A clear distinction must be made, therefore, between the *megascopic fabric symmetry* and *microscopic fabric symmetry*.

The four kinds of fabric symmetry are: (1) spheroidal, or axial; (2) rhombic, or orthorhombic; (3) monoclinic; and (4) triclinic.

Spheroidal symmetry (*axial symmetry*) is the symmetry of a spheroid, either oblate or prolate. There is an axis of symmetry; that is, the fabric is the same in all directions perpendicular to the axis.

A megascopic example is a schist that lacks lineation. The fabric is uniform in all directions within the plane of schistosity. In Fig. 305A the grains appear to be equidimensional in a plane parallel to the schistosity. At right angles to the schistosity, parallel to *c*, the grains are much shorter. Not only is the plane of schistosity a plane of symmetry, but any plane passing through *c* is a plane of symmetry.

Spheroidal symmetry is displayed in a petrofabric diagram by concentration at a point (Fig. 306A). Any diameter of the diagram is a line of symmetry.

Orthorhombic symmetry (rhombic symmetry) is the symmetry of an ellipsoid; the three axes are of unequal length. Figure 305B is a schistose rock with a distinct lineation. If we suppose that each grain is 1 mm. long, 0.5 mm. wide, and 0.1 mm. thick, the rock will have three planes of symmetry, corresponding to the front, side, and top of the block. But the fabric differs parallel to the three principal axes. In the direction *b*, the grains are 1 mm. long; in the direction *a*, they are 0.5 mm. long; and in the direction *c*, they are 0.1 mm. long.

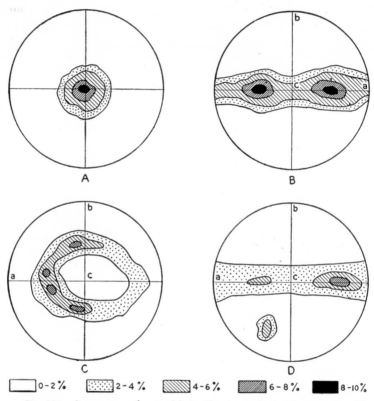

| | 0-2% | | 2-4% | | 4-6% | | 6-8% | | 8-10% |

Fig. 306. Symmetry of petrofabric diagrams. *A.* Axial symmetry. *B.* Orthorhombic symmetry. *C.* Monoclinic symmetry. *D.* Triclinic symmetry.

Figure 306B is a petrofabric diagram showing orthorhombic symmetry. The two principal diameters, *a* and *b*, are lines of symmetry.

Monoclinic symmetry is characterized by a single plane of symmetry which is perpendicular to the lineation. Figure 305C is a metamorphic rock, the schistosity of which has been thrown into tiny asymmetric crinkles. Only the front of the block is a plane of symmetry.

In petrofabric diagrams, monoclinic symmetry is characterized by a single line of symmetry, as in Fig. 306C. This line is usually perpendicular to the *b* fabric axis.

Triclinic symmetry, which has no planes of symmetry, is illustrated by Fig. 305D. The schistosity has been thrown into crinkles trending parallel to the side of the block, but in addition there is a lineation that trends diagonally across the top of the block. Figure 306D is a petrofabric diagram showing triclinic symmetry. There is no line of symmetry in the diagram.

The lines of symmetry in the petrofabric diagrams are not necessarily diameters that pass through the center of the circle. Figure 307A, for example, possesses axial symmetry, whereas the symmetry of Fig. 307B is monoclinic. If the thin section is cut diagonally to the fabric axes

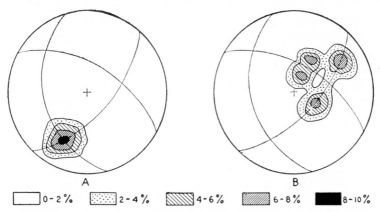

Fig. 307. Eccentric symmetry diagrams. *A.* Axial symmetry. *B.* Monoclinic symmetry.

a, b, and *c,* the whole diagram will be eccentric. Ordinarily, thin sections are cut perpendicularly to one of the megascopic fabric axes because the symmetry is much more readily recognized if the petrofabric diagram is centered.

SYMMETRY OF MOVEMENT

During the formation or deformation of rocks, the individual grains move under the influence of an external force. Detrital sediments settle from stagnant bodies of water under the influence of gravity, or from running water under the combined influence of gravity and the current. In deformed rocks the individual grains move under the influence of tectonic forces. Each type of movement is characterized by a particular symmetry.

Axial symmetry of movement is typified by the settling of sediments from stagnant water. The individual particles move perpendicularly to the surface of the earth under the influence of gravity. Parallel to the surface of the earth, all directions are equal and interchangeable in relation to the movement. The symmetry is that of a spheroid, and it is referable to one axis. The motion involved in the deformation of a sphere into an oblate spheroid under simple compression is also an example of axial symmetry of motion.

Orthorhombic symmetry of movement is exemplified by the motion that occurs when a sphere, subjected to simple compression acting along a vertical line, is constrained on two opposite sides. The sphere would be deformed into an ellipsoid.

Monoclinic symmetry of movement occurs when the cards in a playing pack slide past one another because of shear. Each card moves in the same direction relative to the card directly beneath it. The surfaces along which the movement takes place are *slip planes.*

Triclinic symmetry of movement may be illustrated by a simple example. Water flowing in a stream between two banks, the frictional effect of which is neglected, might represent monoclinic symmetry of movement. Because of friction the bottom layers move more slowly than the upper layers. Any individual particle of water would move directly downstream, but those near the surface move faster. Irregularities and frictional resistance of the banks, however, may cause eddies about vertical axes; these eddies are superimposed on the downstream movement. Such movement is triclinic in character.

On p. 360 it was stated that the three mutually perpendicular reference axes, a, b, and c, are actually based on the movement that causes the fabric. The system advocated by Turner and Verhoogen[9] may be followed. The a axis is the direction of tectonic transport. In monoclinic movement, the ab plane is parallel to the slip planes; a is the direction in which the "cards" are sliding, b lies in the slip plane perpendicular to a, and c is perpendicular to the slip plane. If the movement is orthorhombic, the long axis of the resulting strain ellipsoid is a; b is the intermediate axis, and c is the least axis. If the movement is axial, c is the short axis of the oblate spheroid, but the movement is radially outward perpendicular to c.

CORRELATION OF FABRIC SYMMETRY AND MOVEMENT SYMMETRY

One object of structural petrology is to determine the nature of the movement involved in the formation and deformation of rocks. In many instances, the movement symmetry and fabric symmetry may be directly correlated; that is, an axial fabric symmetry may indicate an axial movement symmetry, and a monoclinic fabric symmetry may indicate a mono-

[9] Turner and Verhoogen, *op. cit.,* p. 532.

clinic movement symmetry. Some simple examples will illustrate this point.

Small mica flakes settling in stagnant water are an example of axial symmetry of movement. These flakes would lie flat on the bottom of the body of water. If a thin section were cut parallel to the bedding, and if a petrofabric diagram were prepared for the normals to the cleavage of the mica, a maximum would appear in the center (Fig. 306A) ; that is, the diagram would show axial symmetry. Thus an axial movement results in an axial fabric.

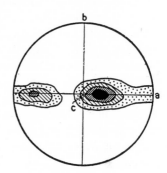

The normals to the cleavage of the mica in the crinkled schist illustrated in Fig. 305C would, in a section cut parallel to the top of the block, give a diagram such as that shown in Fig. 308. This is a monoclinic fabric symmetry, the a-axis being the line of symmetry. In such a crinkled schist each successively higher layer slid to the right relative to the layer directly beneath it. This is a monoclinic symmetry of movement. Thus a monoclinic movement results in a monoclinic fabric.

Fig. 308. Monoclinic symmetry of fabric. Type of diagram expected from poles of mica in a crinkled schist such as that shown in Fig. 305C.

The significance of triclinic symmetry is not clear. It is possible that in some instances triclinic fabric symmetry results from triclinic movement symmetry. In most cases, however, triclinic fabric symmetry is probably the result of two superimposed stages of deformation. Traces of the older deformation were not completely destroyed by the later deformation. Thus in the schist illustrated by Fig. 305D, the diagonal lineation shown by one of the minerals is presumably younger or older than the crinkles. Such an interpretation does not mean that there were two distinct periods of orogeny; the two stages may well have been part of one orogenic period. The deforming forces were acting along somewhat different directions during the two stages.

MECHANICS OF MINERAL ORIENTATION

The reality of the preferred orientation of minerals is a fact that cannot be questioned, but the causes of this orientation are only partially understood. Most students of structural petrology believe that the orientation is a mechanical phenomenon and that recrystallization is not essential to the process of orientation. According to the most widely accepted hypothesis, the deformation is controlled by slip planes in the rock and by glide planes in the minerals.

The rock undergoing deformation is characterized by one or more sets of *slip planes*—that is, surfaces along which differential movements may occur. The slip planes are analogous to the surfaces separating the individual cards in a sliding pack of playing cards. There may be more than one set of slip planes in a rock; the sets may be utilized simultaneously or successively.

As stated on p. 27, some minerals have no glide planes, others have one or more sets; the number depends upon the mineral species. Each grain rotates until a glide plane coincides with or is close to a slip plane; then translation along the glide planes begins (p. 28). In studying the subject of gliding it is essential to consider the glide direction because a mineral cannot glide in any direction in the glide plane. The glide direction must lie essentially parallel to the direction of translation (movement) in the slip plane of the rock. When the glide plane and the glide direction of the mineral are essentially parallel, respectively, to the slip plane and to the direction of movement in the rock, gliding may take place.

Studies in metallurgy suggest that perhaps too much emphasis has been placed on slip planes in structural petrology. Metallurgical investigations indicate that gliding will begin when the grain has rotated to such a position that the shearing stress parallel to the glide direction exceeds a critical value.

The minerals that have been utilized most extensively in structural petrology are quartz, calcite, biotite, and muscovite; dolomite and olivine have been used to a lesser extent, and a few studies have been made on anhydrite and feldspar; occasional studies have been made on other minerals.[10] Knowledge concerning glide planes and glide directions is partly based on experimental data, but much has been inferred from a consideration of fabric diagrams.

Many thin sections of calcite show that a single grain is composed of alternating sheets or layers with different optical behavior. When the nicols of the microscope are crossed, one set may be dark when the other set is light. These are twin lamellae, commonly parallel to the rhombohedron e $(01\bar{1}2)$ (see Fig. 302C). Many petrofabric diagrams of calcite represent the attitude of the perpendiculars to these twin lamellae. Experimental data show that calcite glides on the rhombohedron e $(01\bar{1}2)$; the short diagonal (xz of Fig. 302C) of the rhombohedron is parallel to the translation direction a of the rock. Moreover, the acute angle between this short diagonal and the c-crystallographic axis (yxz of Fig. 302C) generally opens in the a direction. Recent work[11] confirms the importance

---

[10] Fairbairn, H. W., *op. cit.*, pp. 8–38.
[11] Griggs, D., *et al.*, "Deformation of Yule Marble: Part IV—Effects at 150° C.," *Bulletin Geological Society America*, Vol. 62, pp. 1385–1406, 1951.

of twin and translation gliding on e (01$\bar{1}$2). However, Turner[12] cautions: ". . . some other type of intracrystalline movement, leaving no visible trace of its activity, has played a part in deformation."

Quartz, although it is one of the most common minerals in metamorphic rocks and one of those most extensively used in structural petrology, is least understood. It has been suggested by some that quartz possesses several glide planes, but none of these has been revealed by experiments. The various theories that have been proposed to explain the orientation of quartz may be found elsewhere.[13]

TECTONITES

A *tectonite* is a deformed rock, the fabric of which is due to the systematic movement of the individual units under a common external force. A *non-tectonite* is a rock that results from the accumulation of many separate components, each of which moved into place independently of its neighbors; all undeformed sedimentary and igneous rocks belong in this category.

The two principal kinds of tectonites are S-tectonites and B-tectonites. In an S-tectonite, the prominent structure is an S-plane, such as a plane of schistosity, a slip plane, or a bedding plane. The petrofabric diagram of an S-tectonite is generally characterized by one or two, occasionally more, clearly-separated maxima (Fig. 306A).

In a B-tectonite a lineation is prominent, and in some instances S-planes may be absent. The petrofabric diagram of a B-tectonite is usually characterized by a girdle, a more or less complete belt in which the points are concentrated; there may be one or more maxima within this girdle (Fig. 306B).

The girdle characteristic of B-tectonites may develop in one of several ways. (1) Several slip planes intersecting in b might be utilized for gliding. For example, if different calcite grains were to glide parallel to the short diagonal of the negative rhombohedron (xz of Fig. 302C) simultaneously along several such slip planes, the c-crystallographic axis (xy of Fig. 302C) would lie in a girdle about b. (2) If a single slip plane rotating about b were utilized for this same type of gliding, the c-crystallographic axis would lie in a girdle about b. (3) Individual grains might rotate until the plane containing the c-crystallographic axis (xy)

[12] Turner, F. J., and C. S. Chi'h, "Deformation of Yule Marble: Part III—Observed Fabric Changes Due to Deformation at 10,000 Atmospheres Confining Pressure, Room Temperature, Dry," *Bulletin Geological Society of America*, Vol. 62, pp. 887–906, 1951.

[13] Turner, F. J., "Mineralogical and Structural Evolution of the Metamorphic Rocks," *Geological Society of America, Memoir 30*, 342 pp., 1948; especially pp. 255–266.

Fairbairn, H. W., *op. cit.*, especially pp. 8–22.

and the short diagonal of the negative rhombohedron (xz) is more or less parallel to the ac plane of the fabric (Fig. 301B). The grain would then tend to stay in this position and deform by gliding.

ROTATED MINERALS

Rotated minerals such as garnet, albite, and staurolite not only give striking evidence of significant differential movement in rocks, but also permit a rough quantitative estimate of the amount of the movements.[14] Figure 309 illustrates some of the various structural relations of garnet to schistosity that may be observed in thin sections of rocks from metamorphic areas. Figure 309A represents a garnet crystal that is euhedral —that is, has a well-developed crystal habit—because it grew quietly in

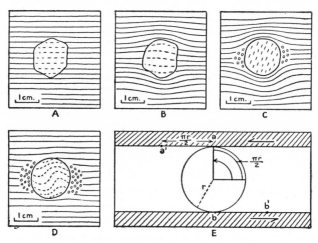

Fig. 309. Rotation of garnets. *A.* Garnet that grew by replacement, no rotation. *B.* Garnet that grew partially by replacement, partially by pushing aside the adjacent schist. *C.* Garnet that rotated after it grew. *D.* Garnet that rotated as it grew. *E.* Calculation of differential movement (see text).

the schist by replacement. Many of the atoms in the garnet entered from the adjacent schist while other atoms diffused out into the adjacent schist. The schistosity is undistorted. Figure 309B is a garnet that formed in a similar manner but as it grew it deformed the schistosity. But Fig. 309C shows another relationship that may be observed in some garnets. Small streaks in the garnet lie at a high angle to the schistosity. Similar impurities in the adjacent parts of the schist are parallel to the schistos-

---

[14] Fairbairn, H. W., *Structural Petrology of Deformed Rocks*. Cambridge: Addison Wesley Press, Inc., 344 pages, 1949; especially pp. 52–57, 158–160.

ity. These relations indicate that the garnet was rotated after it formed. This rotation is presumably the result of differential movements parallel to the schistosity as in the analogy of a sliding pack of cards. Still another relationship is shown in Fig. 309D. This shows that the garnet rotated as it grew. The interior of the garnet had rotated 90 degrees by the time crystallization ceased, but shells progressively further from the center rotated less and less because they are younger.

At least one qualifying remark is necessary. In Figs. 309C and 309D it is apparent that the axis of rotation is perpendicular to the page of the paper. Moreover, it is clear that in a thin section cut parallel to this axis, the streaks of impurities would appear to be parallel to the schistosity. In fact, the relations in such a thin section would be like those in Figs. 309A and B. Therefore, in order to reach the conclusion made in the first paragraph concerning Figs. 309A and B, it is necessary to have two thin sections more or less at right angles to one another.

The axis of rotation of the garnets is b. The direction in the plane of schistosity at right angles to b is a. The perpendicular to the schistosity is c.

To determine the amount of differential movement let us consider a case such as that shown in Fig. 309C, but in which the streaks of impurities lie at a 90 degree angle to the schistosity. Furthermore, let us assume that the rotation of the garnets may be compared to the rolling of a sphere between two boards shearing over one another (Fig. 309E). If r is the radius of the garnet, the outer edge of the garnet has rotated a distance $\pi r/2$ (one-quarter of the circumference). A point on the upper board that was originally at a has moved to a', and a point on the lower board originally at b has moved to b'. The inferred movement of the upper board relative to the lower board is consequently πr. That is, in a layer with the thickness $2r$, the differential movement is πr if the garnets have rotated 90 degrees. If t is the thickness of the bed, then the differential movement is $\pi t/2$. If all the garnets in beds 1,000 feet thick show such rotation, it follows that the top of the beds has sheared 1,570 feet relative to the bottom of the beds. Fairbairn[15] states that the differential movement may often be three times the thickness and in one extreme case was as high as 5.6 times the thickness. Although the analogy to a sphere being rolled between two boards is undoubtedly too idealized, such calculations give clear evidence of the intense differential movements that have taken place.

The schistosity associated with such rotated minerals is obviously not a simple flow cleavage. It could be (1) bedding cleavage, (2) initially a flow cleavage that was later utilized for differential movements, or (3) a slip cleavage that has been transformed into a schistosity (page 341).

[15] Fairbairn, H. W., *op. cit.*, p. 159.

FIELD APPLICATIONS

Space does not permit a discussion of some of the recent field studies that have applied structural petrology, but a few examples, mostly from accessible American journals, may be listed.[16] Applications to the movement of ice are found in several papers.[17]

[16] Balk, Robert, "Fabric of Quartzites Near Thrust Faults," *Journal of Geology*, Vol. 60, pp. 415–435, 1952.

Chi'h, C. S., "Structural Petrology of the Wissahickon Schist Near Philadelphia," *Bulletin Geological Society of America*, Vol. 61, pp. 923–956, 1950.

Cloos, E., "Tectonic Transport and Fabric in a Maryland Granite," *Comptes Rendus, Societé Géologique de Finlande*, Vol. XX, pp. 1–13, 1947.

Cloos, E., and A. Hietanen, "Geology of the 'Martic Overthrust' and the Glenarm Series in Pennsylvania and Maryland," *Geological Society of America, Special Paper 35*, 1941.

Fellows, R. E., "Recrystallization and Flowage in Appalachian Quartzite," *Bulletin Geological Society of America*, Vol. 54, pp. 1399–1432, 1943.

Riley, N. A., "Structural Petrology of the Baraboo Quartzite," *Journal of Geology*, Vol. 55, pp. 453–475, 1947.

[17] Bader. H., "Introduction to Ice Petrofabrics," *Journal of Geology*, Vol. 59, pp. 519–536, 1951.

Rigsby, G. P., "Crystal Fabric Studies on Emmons Glacier, Mount Rainier, Washington," *Journal of Geology*, Vol. 59, pp. 590–598, 1951.

CHAPTER 23

Geophysical Methods in Structural Geology

INTRODUCTION

For many years structural geologists relied exclusively upon data obtained by direct observation. Most of the information came from natural exposures, although some facts were revealed by artificial openings such as mines, tunnels, railroad cuts, and highway cuts. Data obtained from drill holes may also be considered in this category because the cores or cuttings are studied megascopically and microscopically in much the same manner as are surface outcrops. In the last few decades, however, geophysical methods have been greatly amplified, chiefly under the impetus of the petroleum and mining industries. By these methods, much information about the invisible rocks beneath the surface has been obtained. In 1951, $325,000,000 was invested by the petroleum industry alone in geophysical exploration throughout the world.[1]

By the use of geophysical methods it is possible to determine many of the physical properties of the subsurface rocks. These data, if properly interpreted shed much light on the lithology of the rocks, and, if sufficient data are available, on the shape of rock bodies.

Geophysical data are used most successfully when combined with geological information. The geophysical methods and geological methods are so specialized that one individual cannot hope to be fully trained in both fields. Nevertheless, the geologist should be well-versed in the principles of geophysical exploration, and, conversely, the geophysicist should be cognizant of geological principles. Many problems will demand the co-operation of men trained in both fields.[2]

It is beyond the scope of this book to discuss the techniques involved in geophysical studies, and only a rather general discussion of the subject can be presented. For a complete treatment, the student is referred

[1] Hammer, S., "Geophysical Exploration Comes of Age," *Bulletin American Association of Petroleum Geologists,* Vol. 36, pp. 1318–1322, 1952.
[2] Towles, H. C., Jr., "A Study in Integration of Geology and Geophysics," *Geophysics,* Vol. XVII, pp. 876–899, 1952.

to textbooks in geophysical prospecting.[3] But the geologist should be thoroughly familiar not only with the methods that can be used, but also with the extent of their usefulness and their limitations. The broad physical principles underlying the various methods are discussed briefly here, and some examples of geophysical studies of structural problems are presented.

The precision of the information given by geophysical investigations depends upon several factors such as the method employed, the time spent on the problem, the skill and knowledge of the investigator, and the nature of the problem. Although one geophysical method may be most suited for a particular problem, in another case some other method may be more useful.

In many instances, the geophysical methods merely indicate the presence of a rock body that differs in composition from its surroundings; that is, the results are qualitative. In other cases, the numerical data may suggest, with varying degrees of precision, the lithology and areal extent of this body. By some of the methods, the subsurface structure of sedimentary rocks and the shape of rock bodies may be determined with considerable accuracy.

In some instances geophysical methods are used to extend information obtained from a study of surface outcrops. Suppose, for example, that two areas of good exposures are separated by several miles of alluvium. Contacts between formations may be traced beneath the alluvium by some geophysical method; thus the structural relations between the isolated areas may be determined. In other cases, where the exposures are good, it may be desirable to determine the depth to which some of the structural units extend. Some of the geophysical methods may be very useful in achieving this purpose.

In many cases the geophysical methods are employed in areas where surface exposures are rare or absent. In countries that have not been adequately studied geologically, the interpretation of the data may be difficult. In geological provinces that are reasonably well known, however, the correct solution might be readily obtained. If, for example, in the Gulf Coast of the United States a circular area a mile or so in

[3] Heiland, C. A., *Geophysical Exploration.* New York: Prentice-Hall, Inc., 1013 pp., 1940.

Jakosky, J. J., *Exploration Geophysics,* 2d ed. Los Angeles: Times-Mirror Press, 1195 pp., 1950.

Nettleton, L. L., *Geophysical Prospecting for Oil,* New York: McGraw-Hill Book Company, Inc., 1940.

Dobrin, M. B., *Introduction to Geophysical Prospecting.* New York: McGraw-Hill Book Company, Inc., 435 pp., 1952.

Nettleton, L. L., editor, *Geophysical Case Histories,* Vol. I, Tulsa: Society of Exploration Geophysicists, 671 pp., 1949.

Nettleton, L. L., editor, *Early Geophysical Papers of the Society of Exploration Geophysicists* Tulsa: Society of Exploration Geophysicists, 844 pp., 1947.

diameter is occupied by a rock that transmits elastic waves with much greater speed than do its surroundings, a salt dome is probably present. In the Lake Superior region, strong positive magnetic anomalies suggest a deposit of iron ore.

GEOPHYSICAL METHODS

The principal geophysical methods that will be discussed may be classified into four groups: gravitational, magnetic, seismic, and electrical. The first two methods involve the measurement of forces that are inherent in the earth, in contrast to the seismic method in which the forces are artificially introduced by the investigator. Most of the electrical methods also involve the introduction of energy by man, but in some instances natural electrical currents are measured. The investigator cannot control those forces that are naturally present in the earth, and, consequently, the vertical extent of the structural features involved cannot be determined very readily. Whenever the forces are artificially introduced, however, the depth of penetration can be controlled by the investigator; the vertical dimension of the structure can therefore be determined more satisfactorily.

Several other geophysical methods will not be described. Among these are electrical logging, radioactivity logging, and continuous seismic velocity logging.[4] These are chiefly stratigraphic tools, but, of course, a correct understanding of the stratigraphy is essential for a correct structural interpretation. But a brief discussion of airborne radioactivity surveying is included.

GRAVITATIONAL METHODS

Principles

Gravitation is the force by which, due to mass, all bodies attract each other. This force is directly proportional to the product of the masses of the two bodies concerned and is inversely proportional to the square of the distance separating them. This principle may be expressed as

$$F \propto \frac{m_1 m_2}{r^2} \tag{1}$$

Here F is the force, m_1 and m_2 are the masses of the two bodies, and r is the distance between them. In the form of an equation,

$$F = \frac{k \cdot m_1 \cdot m_2}{r^2} \tag{2}$$

[4] Lahee, F. H., *Field Geology*, 5th ed. New York: McGraw-Hill Book Company, 883 pp., 1952.

In this equation m_1 and m_2 are measured in grams, r is in centimeters, and F is in dynes. A *dyne* is the force necessary to give a mass of one gram an acceleration of one centimeter per second per second. If two masses, each weighing a gram, are one centimeter apart, equation (2) becomes $F = k$. That is k, known as the *gravitational constant*, is the force of attraction of two equal masses of one gram each at a distance of one centimeter; $k = 6.673 \times 10^{-8}$ C.G.S. units. This is about 1/15,000,-000,000 part of gravity.

Gravity is the force by which the earth attracts bodies toward it. If a stationary body suspended in air a short distance above sea level is released, it will move toward the earth with a constantly increasing speed; that is, it accelerates. The acceleration is independent of the mass of the released body. It is thus more satisfactory to express the force of gravity in terms of the acceleration it causes. A *gal* is an acceleration of one centimeter per second per second; a *milligal* is one thousandth of a gal. At sea level the acceleration of gravity is approximately **980** gals (approximately **32** feet per second per second).

Because the earth is a rotating oblate spheroid, flattened at the poles, the normal acceleration of gravity differs with latitude; at the equator it is **978.049** gals, at the poles it is **983.221** gals. The general equation is

$$g = 978.049(1 + 0.0052884 \sin^2 \phi - 0.0000059 \sin^2 2\phi) \qquad (3)$$

In this equation g is the normal gravity at sea level, and ϕ is the latitude.

Equation (3) is based on data for the whole earth. In an ideal, homogeneous earth, the value of gravity could be calculated if the latitude were known. Actually, however, gravity usually differs from the theoretical value. This is due in part to the fact that the earth is heterogeneous; even at the surface, the rocks are by no means uniform. If an unusually heavy rock is near the surface, gravity will exceed the theoretical value; if an unusually light rock is near the surface, gravity will be less than the theoretical value.

Some of the gravitational methods, such as those utilizing pendulums and gravimeters, measure the value of gravity directly. Other methods, such as those using torsion balances, measure the rate of change of gravity and the deviation of equipotential surfaces from a spherical shape.

Methods

Pendulum method. By swinging a simple pendulum, we may determine the value of gravity according to the equation

$$g = 4\pi^2 n^2 L \qquad (4)$$

In this equation g is the value of gravity, L is the length of the pendulum, and n is the number of vibrations the pendulum makes in unit time; in the C.G.S. system L is measured in centimeters and n in seconds; g is in gals.

This method has been used for many years by the U. S. Coast and Geodetic Survey and similar organizations to obtain precise values of gravity. A single observation, however, consumes considerable time—several hours—and for this reason the method is not practical for ordinary field mapping.

Gravimeter method. Gravimeters were introduced about 1935. Their great advantage is that the force of gravity can be measured directly within a few minutes. Moreover, within recent years very light gravimeters, weighing as little as five pounds, have been built. Thus areas not accessible to autos and wagons can be investigated. The mechanical gravimeters use the elastic force of springs and the torsion of wires; the deformation is magnified by optical, mechanical, or electrical means to give an accuracy of 1 in 10,000,000. For more complete descriptions the reader is referred to Jakosky.[5]

For work on the continental shelf special apparatus has been designed. The *diving bell,* weighing about two tons, is large enough for a conventional gravimeter and an observer.[6] The maximum depth of operation is 70 feet; moreover, there are several other disadvantages.[7] The *underwater gravimeter*[8] weighs only 300 pounds and can be used to depths of several hundred feet.

Corrections applied in pendulum and gravimeter methods. In order to compare gravity measurements at adjacent stations, it is necessary to make a number of corrections. After the value of gravity is determined by the instruments, the following corrections are made: (1) free air correction; (2) Bouguer reduction; (3) terrain (topographic) correction; (4) isostatic correction.

Free air correction. Most stations are above sea level, and the force of gravity becomes progressively less as the altitude becomes greater. For example, if gravity at some station at sea level were 980.000 gals, gravity measured from a captive balloon 300 meters above the station would be only 979.907 gals. For all stations above sea level, therefore, a correction must be added proportional to the altitude. The correction is +30.86 milligals per hundred meters, or +9.406 milligals per hundred feet.

Bouguer reduction. The rock between the station and sea level increases the value of gravity; the amount is proportional to: (1) the altitude of the station and (2) the density of the rocks between the station and sea level. For example, if the gravity station is at an altitude of 300 meters on a flat tableland underlain by granite, the rock between the station and sea level exerts a gravitational attraction of 33 milligals. This

[5] Jakosky, J. J., *op. cit.,* pp. 369–389.

[6] Frowe, E. W., "A Diving Bell for Underwater Gravimeter Operations," *Geophysics,* Vol. XII, pp. 1–12, 1947.

[7] Jakosky, *op. cit.,* p. 388.

[8] Pepper, T. B., "The Gulf Underwater Gravimeter," *Geophysics,* Vol. VII, pp. 34–44, 1942.

correction, therefore, must be subtracted when one calculates the value of gravity at sea level.

Thus, whereas the free air correction is positive, the Bouguer correction is negative; but the free air correction is the greater—approximately three times as large as the Bouguer correction. Moreover, it is obvious that the free air and Bouguer corrections can be combined into one correction according to the equation

$$g_0'' = g + H(0.0003086 - 0.0000421\delta)\,\text{gals} \tag{5}$$

in this equation g_0'' = gravity at sea level with free air and Bouguer corrections; g = measured value of gravity; H = altitude in meters; δ = density of rocks between station and sea level.

Topographic (terrain) correction. Hills that rise above the instrument, or depressions that descend below it, exert an influence on the measured value of gravity. If good contour maps are not available, it may be necessary for the field party to obtain sufficient data for calculating the topographic data. This is particularly true if considerable relief exists near the station.

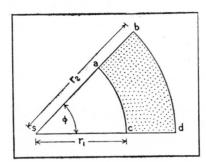

Fig. 310. Calculation of terrain correction in gravity measurements. See text. (After C. A. Heiland.)

One procedure is to divide the country into compartments by radii extending out from the station and by circles concentric about it, as illustrated in Fig. 310, where S is the station. The gravitational effect of each compartment, such as *abcd*, is

$$\Delta g = k \cdot \delta \cdot \phi(r_1 + \sqrt{r_2^2 + h^2} - \sqrt{r_1^2 + h^2} - r_2) \tag{6}$$

In this equation Δg is the gravitational effect of compartment in gals; k = gravitational constant (see p. 386); δ = density of rocks; ϕ = angle between radii; r_1 = radius in centimeters of inner circle bounding compartment; r_2 = radius in centimeters of outer circle bounding compartment; and h = average elevation in centimeters of the compartment above or below the instrument.

Charts and tables for making these corrections are available.[9]

Regardless of whether the average altitude of the compartment is greater or less than that of the instrument, the observed gravity is too low. In other words, the correction Δg should be added to the observed gravity.

[9] Hammer, S., "Terrain Corrections for Gravimeter Stations," *Geophysics*, Vol. 4, pp. 184–194, 1939.

Isostatic correction. A correction for isostatic compensation is unnecessary in the study of local structure. On the other hand, such corrections are of great importance in geodetic work and structure of continental proportions.[10]

Calculation of gravity anomaly. The theoretical or normal value of gravity for a station is calculated by equation (3). The corrected value of gravity is obtained from the observed value by making the free air, Bouguer, and terrain corrections. The difference between the corrected value and the normal value is the *gravity anomaly.* That is,

$$\Delta g_0'' = g_0 - g_0'' \qquad (7)$$

where $\Delta g_0''$ = gravity anomaly, g_0'' = normal gravity, and g_0 = observed gravity, with free air, Bouguer, and terrain corrections. The gravity anomaly is usually expressed in milligals. The gravity anomalies calculated by geodesists include an isostatic correction.

The gravity anomalies for each station are plotted on a map, and then isogams are drawn. *Isogams* are lines of equal gravity anomaly, and they are drawn in the same way as contour lines, interpolating wherever necessary. Figure 311A is an isogam map of the Wellington field in Colorado;[11] the isogam interval is 0.2 milligals.

In some areas, the effects of the local structure may be concealed by a strong regional change in the gravity anomalies, and some method of adjustment must be used. In Fig. 311A, the value of gravity increases toward the south at the rate of 2.2 milligals per mile; the average east-west change is zero. Figure 311B is the adjusted map after the regional effect has been eliminated. Figure 311C is the structure contour map of the region; it is referred to on p. 393.

Torsion balance method. For approximately 20 years, before gravimeters were developed, torsion balances were used for gravitational studies. These instruments do not measure the value of gravity, but give the gradient of gravity and the curvature of equipotential surfaces. Although they are no longer used, an understanding of the fundamental principles involved is necessary in order to read the earlier literature intelligently.

One of the values measured by the torsion balance is the *horizontal gradient* of gravity, also referred to simply as *gradient.* The unit of measurement is the *Eötvös* or *Eötvös unit,* which is 1×10^{-9} dyne per horizontal centimeter.

[10] Daly, R. A., *Strength and Structure of the Earth,* pp. 120–128, New York: Prentice-Hall, Inc., 1940.

Heiskanen, W., "On the Isostatic Structure of the Earth's Crust," *Annales Academiae Scientiarum Fennicae, Ser. A III. Geologica-Geographica,* Vol. 22, 60 pages, 1950. (Helsinki, Finland.)

[11] Wilson, J. H., "Gravity Meter Survey of the Wellington Field, Larimer County, Colorado," *Geophysics,* Vol. 6, pp. 264–269, 1941.

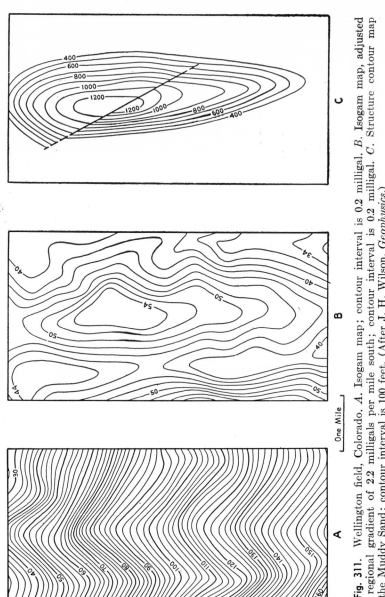

Fig. 311. Wellington field, Colorado. *A.* Isogam map; contour interval is 0.2 milligal. *B.* Isogam map, adjusted for regional gradient of 2.2 milligals per mile south; contour interval is 0.2 milligal. *C.* Structure contour map on the Muddy Sand; contour interval is 100 feet. (After J. H. Wilson, *Geophysics.*)

After the field measurements have been made, corrections similar to those described for the pendulum and gravimeter methods must be made; these are the free air, Bouguer, terrain, and latitude corrections.

The gradient can be shown on maps or on profiles. On maps the gradient is indicated by an arrow pointing in the direction of increasing gravity; the length of the arrow is proportional to the magnitude of the gradient. The tail of the arrow is placed on the map at the point at which the observation is made.

Figure 312 is a gradient map of the Fannett salt dome in Jefferson County, Texas.[12] The arrows point toward the center of the map, indi-

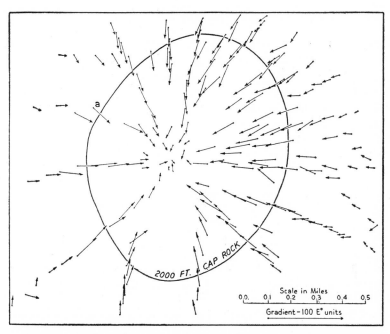

Fig. 312. Horizontal gradient of gravity, Fannett salt dome, Jefferson County, Texas. (After J. B. Eby and R. P. Clark, *American Association Petroleum Geologists.*)

cating that at this point the value of gravity is at a maximum. The highest gradient is near the circular line marked "2,000 ft. cap rock." At a point, such as *a*, the arrow shows that gravity is increasing toward the southeast at a rate of about 33 Eötvös units (see scale in lower right-hand corner of the map).

If the observations are confined to a single line on the map, the gradient may be plotted on a graph in which the horizontal distance is given

[12] Eby, J. B., and R. P. Clark, "Relation of Geophysics to Salt Dome Structures." *Bulletin American Association Petroleum Geologists,* Vol. 19, pp. 356–377, 1935.

on the abscissa and in which the gradient in Eötvös units is given on the ordinate (Fig. 313).

A second value measured by the torsion balance is the *differential curvature*, also known as the *Eötvös curvature value, horizontal directing force*, or *R value*. For the significance of these terms, the reader is referred to textbooks on geophysics.

The torsion balance measures only the gradient of the gravity. But if the absolute value of gravity at one station is known from the pendulum method, the gradient map may be converted into an isogam map. Even if the absolute value of gravity is not known, an isogam map can be prepared on an assumed base.

Relation Between Gravity and Structure

Systematic local differences in gravity are directly related to differences in the density of the underlying rock. In some instances these may have no structural significance; for example, a local lava flow or basic sill in flat-lying sediments would cause differences in gravity. In many instances, however, the indicated lithologic changes are related to the geological structure. Anticlines, buried ridges, salt domes, faults, and igneous intrusions are commonly indicated by changes in gravity.

Many anticlines are expressed by an increase in gravity. This is be-

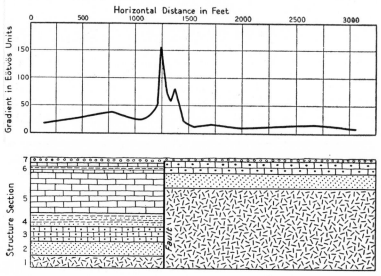

Fig. 313. Hull-Gloucester fault at Leitrim, Ontario. Lower diagram is structure section: *1* = pre-Cambrian, sp. gr. 2.8; *2* = Potsdam sandstone, sp. gr. 2.5; *3* = dolomite, sp. gr. 2.8; *4* = Chazy, shale and sandstone, sp. gr. 2.5; *5* = limestone, sp. gr. 2.7; *6* = shale and limestone, sp. gr. 2.6; *7* = glacial drift, sp. gr. 1.8. Upper diagram is a graph showing horizontal gradient of gravity. (After A. H. Miller, C. A. French, and M. E. Wilson.)

cause the older stratigraphic units tend to be heavier than younger formations. This is notably true where a crystalline basement is overlain by sedimentary rocks. An example of a map showing a correlation between the gravity anomalies and the structure is given in Fig. 311. Figure 311B is the adjusted isogam map of the Wellington field of Colorado. Figure 311C, which covers exactly the same area as does Fig. 311B, is a structure contour map on the Muddy Sand. It shows a doubly plunging anticline with a closure of at least 800 feet. The correlation between the anticline and the adjusted isogam map is apparent.

Salt domes are commonly well-displayed by gravity data. Figure 312 shows the horizontal gradient of gravity for the Fannett salt dome in Texas. The outline of the cap rock at a depth of 2,000 feet below sea level is shown. Gravity increases radially inward toward the center of the dome. Figure 314 is a map of a district in Russia showing the gravity gradient and the isogam map.[13] In this case gravity increases radially outward from the salt domes. Whether a salt dome is a gravity minimum or maximum depends upon the nature of the surrounding sediments, as well as upon the nature and size of the cap rock on the dome.

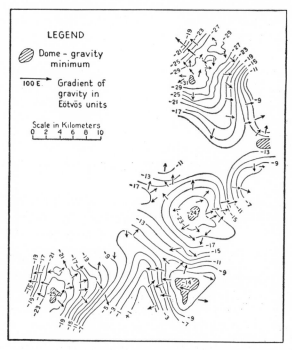

Fig. 314. Horizontal gradient of gravity and isogam map of Emba region, near Dossor, Russia. (After Numerov.)

[13] Numerov, B., "Results of the General Gravity Survey in the Emba District," *Zeitschrift für Geophysik*, Vol. 5, pp. 268–270, 1929.

Faults, if they bring rocks of different density into juxtaposition, will be indicated by gravity data. Figure 313 shows the geological structure section, as well as the gravity gradient, of the Hull-Gloucester fault at Leitrim, Ontario.[14] As would be expected, the gradient reaches a maximum directly over the fault. The maximum is not directly over the outcrop of dipping faults, but its exact position depends upon numerous variables.

In central New England it has been shown recently that many of the gravity anomalies are structurally controlled.[15] Moreover, it is possible to get some idea of the shape of the masses causing the anomaly.[16] It is necessary to know the "density contrast," that is, the difference in density between the rocks causing the anomaly and the surrounding rocks. Different shapes are assumed for the mass causing the anomaly; for each shape the theoretical anomaly curve is computed. The shape that gives a curve most like the observed curve is assumed to be correct. It was possible to reach many interesting conclusions concerning the shape of granite bodies. Other good examples showing the relation of gravity anomalies to plutons have been described from Texas[17] and New York.[18]

In many areas there are large gravity anomalies unrelated to the surface geology.[19] They are generally explained in one of several ways. (1) A sialic (granitic) "root"—that is, a place where the granitic crust is much thicker than normal—would cause negative anomalies (Fig. 194). (2) An upwarp of the heavier sima (basalt) that lies beneath the sialic crust would cause positive anomalies. (3) Inhomogeneities at depth in the crust could cause either negative or positive anomalies, depending upon whether the mass causing the anomaly was lighter or heavier than the "normal" crust.

[14] Miller, A. H., C. A. French, and M. E. Wilson, "Geophysical Survey of the Hull-Gloucester and Hazeldean Faults," *Geological Survey of Canada*, Memoir 165, pp. 190–200, 1931.

[15] Bean, R. J., "Relation of Gravity Anomalies to the Geology of Central Vermont and New Hampshire," *Bulletin Geological Society of America*, Vol. 64, pp. 509–538, 1953.

[16] See also Hubbert, M. K.," A Line Integral Method of Computing the Gravimetric Effects of Two-dimensional Masses," *Geophysics*, Vol. XIII, pp. 215–225, 1948.

[17] Romberg, F., and V. E. Barnes, "Correlation of Gravity Observations with the Geology of the Smoothingiron Granite Mass, Llano County, Texas," *Geophysics*, Vol. IX, pp. 79–91, 1944.

[18] Steenland, N. C., and G. P. Woollard, "Gravity and Magnetic Investigation of the Structure of the Cortlandt Complex, New York," *Bulletin Geological Society of America*, Vol. 63, pp. 1075–1093, 1952.

[19] Bean, R. J., *op. cit.*

Nettleton, L. L., "Relation of Gravity to Structure in the Northern Appalachian Area," *Geophysics*, Vol. 6, pp. 270–286, 1941.

MAGNETIC METHODS

Principles

Magnets are characterized by two *poles*, one of which is known as the *north-seeking* or *north pole*, the other as the *south-seeking* or *south pole*. Like poles repel each other, unlike poles attract. The force between two magnetic poles is proportional to the strength of each pole and inversely proportional to the square of the distance between the poles. That is,

$$F = \frac{SS'}{d^2} K \tag{8}$$

In this equation F is the force; S and S' are the strengths of the two poles; d is the distance between the two poles; and K is a constant of proportionality that depends upon the units chosen. A magnetic pole placed in a field that has a strength of one *gauss* is acted upon by a force of one dyne. In magnetic studies related to geological problems, it is more convenient to use the *gamma*, which is 1/100,000 part of a gauss. That is,

$$1 \text{ gamma} = 1 \text{ gauss} \times 10^{-5}$$

The *magnetic field* of a magnet is that region in space into which the influence of the magnet extends. The *lines of force* of a magnetic field are

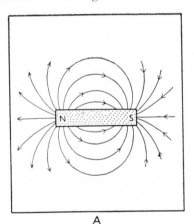

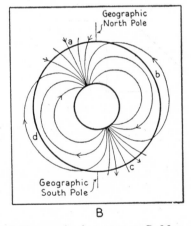

A   B

Fig. 315.   Magnetic fields. *A*. Magnetic field around a bar magnet. *B*. Magnetic field of the earth.

the imaginary lines drawn through the field in such a way that they extend in the direction in which small magnetic poles would tend to move. Figure 315A illustrates the field surrounding a bar magnet. The orientation of lines of force about a magnet is shown very clearly by scattering iron filings in the field because the filings align themselves parallel to the lines of force.

The earth is a gigantic magnet; in a cross section through the earth, the magnetic lines of force are distributed as shown in Fig. 315B. The magnetic poles, far below the surface of the earth, are displaced relative to the geographical poles. Point *a* is on the west side of Hudson Bay at about 70° N. latitude.

A magnetic needle suspended in such a way that it is free to turn in all directions tends to align itself parallel to the lines of force. At points *b* and *d* of Fig. 315B, the needle would be horizontal; at points *a* and *c*, it would be perpendicular to the surface of the earth. At any intermediate point it would be inclined, and the *magnetic dip* is the angle between the lines of force and the horizontal. The *magnetic declination* at a point is the angular difference between geographic north and the vertical plane that contains the inclined needle.

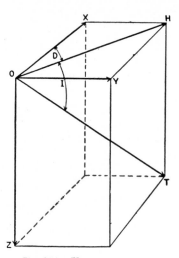

In Fig. 316, which applies to the northern hemisphere, *X* points north and *Y* points east. If *T* is the total intensity of the magnetic force, *H* is the horizontal component, *Z* is the vertical component, *X* is the north horizontal component, and *Y* is the east horizontal component. The magnetic dip *I* is measured in the plane containing *H* and *T*; the magnetic declination *D* is measured in the horizontal plane that contains *H*, *X*, and *Y*.

In the United States, the magnetic dip ranges from 57 to 80 degrees, and the horizontal intensity ranges from 0.15 to 0.26 gauss.

Fig. 316. Vector diagram of the Earth's magnetic field in the Northern Hemisphere. (After C. A. Heiland.)

The lithosphere lacks homogeneity in its magnetic properties. Some rocks are relatively magnetic, others are weakly magnetic. Consequently, the intensity of the magnetism and the attitude of the lines of force differ from place to place.

Technique

Magnetic prospecting methods date back to 1640, and since that time various types of instruments have been devised. The Schmidt vertical intensity magnetometer, the Schmidt horizontal magnetometer, and the Hotchkiss superdip are all of modern design. Simpler instruments are the Swedish mining compass and the dip-needle. In the Schmidt vertical intensity magnetometer, the magnetic system is suspended on a knife edge that is oriented at right angles to the magnetic meridian (magnetic north). It measures the relative value of the vertical component of magnetic intensity. The Schmidt horizontal magnetometer, in which the magnetic system is oriented parallel to the magnetic meridian, measures the value of the horizontal component of the magnetic intensity.

If the Schmidt vertical magnetometer is used, several readings are made with the magnetic system oriented at right angles to the magnetic north. After the system has been turned 180 degrees, several additional readings are made. All the readings, which give the vertical intensity in gammas, are averaged in order to determine the reading for the station. The number of stations occupied depends on the detail with which the work is being done.

Several corrections have to be applied before a map is prepared. A correction for *diurnal variation* is necessitated by more or less systematic daily variations in the magnetic intensity. Another correction must be made because of *magnetic storms*. Both these corrections are made together in one of two ways. A permanent instrument is left at a base station, and observations are made throughout the day on the value of the vertical intensity. Variations from the assumed or true value of the intensity at this station are plotted for the day, a curve is prepared, and the corrections are applied to the field stations. This method necessitates, of course, two instruments and an additional observer. If only one instrument is available, the party must return several times a day to the base station in order to determine the correction. In some instruments, a correction must also be made for variations in temperature, measured by means of a thermometer inside the instrument. If the survey extends over many months, or if surveys made in different years are to be tied together, a correction must be made for long-period changes in the magnetic field of the earth. Charts published by the U. S. Coast and Geodetic Survey give the essential information. In order to show local structure adequately, a correction must be made for the terrestrial variations in the vertical magnetic intensity that is shown in Fig. 315B. This correction is obtained from the most recent "Equal Magnetic Vertical Intensity Chart" published by the U. S. Coast and Geodetic Survey. But on many maps an arbitrary base is chosen, just as in topographic work an arbitrary altitude may be assigned to one point on the map.

For each station, the *magnetic anomaly* is determined algebraically by subtracting the theoretical values of the intensity from the observed value as corrected. The anomalies are then plotted on a map, and lines of equal anomaly are drawn. These lines, called *isonomalies* or *isanomalies*, show magnetic highs and lows. Near the center of the map, illustrated by Fig. 317, there are two magnetic lows.[20] Profiles at right angles to the strike of the geologic structure may also be used, as in Fig. 318.[21]

[20] Eby, J. B., and R. P. Clark, *op. cit.*

[21] Haalck, H., "Zur Frage der Erklärung der Kursker Magnetischen und Gravimetrischen Anomalie, Pt. 2," *Gerlands Beiträge zur Geophysik*, Band 22, pp. 385–399, 1929.

The abscissa represents the distance, and the ordinate represents the magnetic intensity, in this instance given in gauss. Curve Z refers to the vertical intensity, whereas curve X refers to the horizontal intensity.

One of the most recent geophysical tools is the *airborne magnetometer*, which was not fully utilized as a field instrument in the United States until 1944. This type of magnetometer can be carried by helicopter[22] or by plane.[23] The great advantage of this method is that large

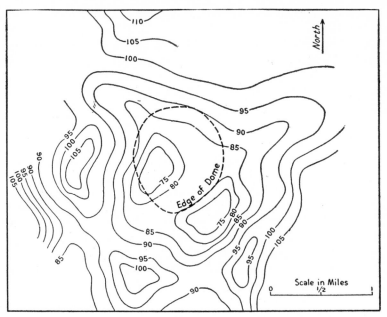

Fig. 317. Isonomoly map of magnetic vertical intensity of the Fannett salt dome, Jefferson County, Texas. Contour interval 5 gamma. (After J. B. Eby and R. P. Clark, *Bulletin of the American Association of Petroleum Geologists.*)

areas can be surveyed very rapidly. The basic instrument is a self-orienting detector element (the "bird"), which hangs down below the plane. The instrument measures in gammas the total magnetic intensity of the earth's field at the point of reading. Surveys are generally flown at altitudes of a few hundred to a thousand feet above the terrain. To prepare a map it is necessary to know the exact course and altitude of the plane, as well as the ground speed of the plane, because the data are recorded

[22] Lundberg, H., "Magnetic Surveys with Helicopters," *Bulletin 488, Institute of Mining and Metallurgy*, pp. 21–27, 1947.
[23] Vacquier, V., *et al.*, "Interpretation of Aeromagnetic Maps," *Geological Society of America, Memoir 47*, 151 pp., 1951.
Balsley, J. R., "Aeromagnetic Surveying," pp. 314–349, in Landsberg, H. E., Editor, *Advances in Geophysics*, Vol. I, 362 pp., New York: Academic Press, Inc., 1952.

at a constant rate. The published maps show the total magnetic intensity (see below).

Relation of Magnetic Intensity to Geological Structure

Normally a magnetic ore body will be indicated by an increase in the vertical magnetic intensity. An anticline or buried ridge may bring a relatively magnetic formation near the surface; this is especially true if crystalline basement rocks are overlain by weakly magnetic sediments. A fault may bring together rocks of differing magnetic properties. Igneous intrusions and salt domes may also be shown by an isonomaly map.

A magnetite ore body at Kiruna, Sweden, profoundly affects the vertical and horizontal intensity of gravity, as shown by Fig. 318. Rather weak magnetic lows are associated with the Fannett salt dome (Fig. 317). In the Witwatersrand district of South Africa, the gold-bearing conglomerates are overlain by shales, some beds of which are highly magnetic. Toward the southwest, all these formations are overlain unconformably by younger formations, usually dolomite, which in places are as much as 3,000 feet thick. By magnetic methods, it proved possible to trace the magnetic shales, then to predict the subsurface location of the gold-bearing conglomerates. On the other hand, a magnetic map of the Cortlandt pluton, New York, shows no clear anomaly associated with the complex as a whole.[24]

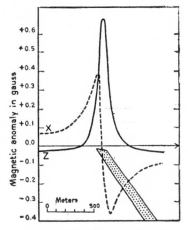

Fig. 318. Profile showing magnetic anomaly associated with magnetite body at Kiruna, Sweden. Z = curve for vertical intensity, X = curve for horizontal intensity. (After Haalck.)

Figure 319 shows by contour lines the total magnetic intensity in gammas, based on an airborne magnetometer survey, of an area in Maine.[25] Actually the total intensity is several tens of thousands of gammas, and, in order to reduce the number of figures, the contours are referred to an arbitrary base of 2,000 gammas. It is apparent that magnetic highs are associated with the serpentine bodies. On the other hand, a broad but equally intense high in the northwest part of the map is unrelated to any visible serpentine.

The interpretation of magnetic maps is sometimes complicated by

[24] Steenland, N. C., and G. P. Woollard, *loc. cit.*

[25] Hurley, P. M., and J. B. Thompson, "Airborne Magnetometer and Geological Reconnaissance Survey in Northwestern Maine," *Bulletin Geological Society of America*, Vol. 61, pp. 835–842, 1950.

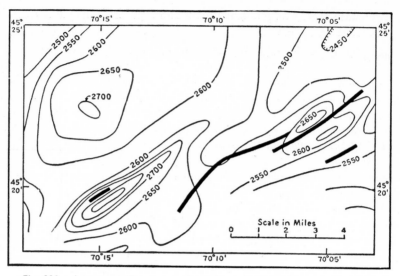

Fig. 319. Aeromagnetic survey. Area in central Maine. Total magnetic intensity given in gammas, but referred to an arbitrary base of 2,000 gammas. Contour interval 50 gammas. Heavy black lines are bodies of serpentine. (After P. M. Hurley and J. B. Thompson.)

remanent magnetism. The interpretation of these maps would be comparatively simple if a magnetic body merely intensified the polarization induced by the earth's field. Some bodies, however, possess a remanent magnetism, the origin of which is not yet clearly understood; in any case, it tends to modify the effects of the magnetic field of the earth. "Whether an ore body may be found by magnetic methods under a given thickness of cover, or at a given height above the terrain if air surveying is used, may depend upon the effectiveness of the combination of remanent and induced polarization." [26]

SEISMIC METHODS

Principles

The essence of the seismic method is the accurate observation of artificially generated elastic waves that are transmitted through the rocks. These waves are generally induced by explosions. The speed of transmission varies with the rock, and, in general, it is a function of the degree of consolidation. Heiland [27] says that in alluvium and glacial drift, the velocities range from 1,900 to 6,400 feet per second; in shales and sand-

---

[26] Hawes, Julian, "A Magnetic Study of the Spavinaw Granite Area, Oklahoma," *Geophysics*, Vol. XVII, pp. 27–55, 1952.
[27] Heiland, C. A., *op. cit.*, pp. 468–472.

stones the velocities are from 3,000 feet to 14,000 feet per second; in granite and gneiss the velocities are from 13,000 feet to 25,000 feet per second; and in salt the velocity is 15,000 to 25,000 feet per second.

All seismic methods are similar in that there is a *shot point* and one or more *receiving points* (Fig. 320). At the shot point, a hole is drilled a few feet to 100 feet deep, occasionally more, depending upon the type of prospecting and upon local conditions. After the charge, which varies from a fraction of a pound to several pounds of dynamite, has been placed, the hole is tamped with water or dirt. The instant of the explosion

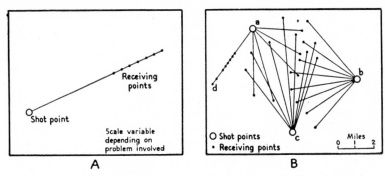

Fig. 320. Seismic surveying. *A.* Profile shooting. *B.* Fan shooting.

may be transmitted to the recording apparatus in various ways. Where the distance between the shot point and the recording apparatus is not great, the instant of shot is transmitted by wire. A contact in an electrical circuit is broken or made at the instant of explosion. If the distance is large, the instant of shot is transmitted by radio.

At each receiving point is a *detector*, known also as a *geophone, phone,* or *pickup*. In some kinds of work, as many as 36 detectors, set up along a profile line a few hundred feet long, record the energy sent out by one explosion. The detectors are connected by wire to amplifiers and a recording camera, often placed in a specially designed truck. The vibrations received by the detectors are recorded on rapidly-moving photographic

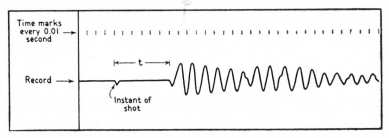

Fig. 321. Seismogram to show interval of time between instant of shot and arrival of first waves at receiving instruments.

paper; a timing device, usually a tuning fork, marks every hundredth of a second. The instant of explosion is also recorded on this same paper. Figure 321 is an example of such a record, which shows that the first impulse arrived 0.06 second after the instant of shot. Knowing the distance, it is possible to calculate the velocity of the elastic waves through the rocks.

$$v = \frac{x}{t} \tag{9}$$

Here v = velocity, x = distance, and t = time.

The data are plotted on a travel-time curve, an example of which is shown in the upper part of Fig. 322. The horizontal scale is the distance from the shot point to the detector; the vertical scale is the time that elapses between the instant of shot and the arrival of the first elastic wave. The less the slope of the curve, the higher the velocity. The velocity can be determined directly from the curve by the equation

$$v = \frac{x_2 - x_1}{t_2 - t_1} \tag{10}$$

In this equation v = velocity, x_2 and x_1 are distances represented by two points on the curve, and t_2 and t_1 are the times represented by the same two points.

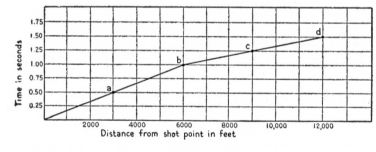

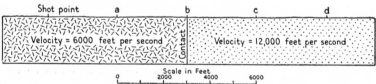

Fig. 322. Travel-time curve (upper diagram) obtained if relations are those shown in cross-section below. (In part after C. A. Heiland.)

In the upper part of Fig. 322, it is apparent that the part of the curve to the left of b indicates a velocity of 6,000 feet per second, whereas the part of the curve to the right of b represents a velocity of 12,000 feet per second.

Refraction Methods

In *fan shooting*, which has been particulary successful in locating salt domes, the receiving points are placed at similar distances near the circumference of a circle, at the center of which the shot point is located (Fig. 320B). For each shot point there are ordinarily 5 to 20 receiving points, which are 4 to 8 miles from the shot point. Several overlapping fans are usually employed.

In a region that has not been previously studied, the normal travel-time curve is determined by "shooting a profile"; that is, the travel-time from a single shot point to 5 or 10 receiving points on the same straight line is determined. In Fig. 320B, the line *ad* is such a profile. If the intervening rocks are relatively homogeneous, the curve should be a straight line.

If a body of unusual composition is present in the area, the travel-times for some of the receiving points on the fan will lie off the normal curve. If a salt dome is present, the travel-times are less, and the points lie below the normal curve—this is because the waves travel faster in salt than in the surrounding sediments. By noting on the map which receiving points are characterized by a lowered travel-time, it is possible to locate the salt dome approximately. Other methods are usually utilized to outline the dome more accurately.

In *refraction profile shooting,* the shot point and the detectors are placed on a straight line. The same shot point may be used for successive locations of the detectors.

By way of introduction, the case of a vertical geological boundary may be considered, although the principles of refraction are not involved. This contact may be a fault, a sedimentary contact, or an intrusive contact. If the velocity of the seismic waves on opposite sides of the contact are different, a distinct break in the travel-time curve will be observed. In the lower diagram of Fig. 322, for example, the velocity in the formation on the left side of the vertical contact is 6,000 feet per second, whereas on the right side the velocity is 12,000 feet per second. The shot point is near the left side of the diagram; at the end of half a second, the seismic waves will have reached *a*. At the end of one second, they will have reached *b*. But after crossing the vertical contact, they will travel at the rate of 12,000 feet per second. One and one-quarter seconds after the instant of shot, the waves will be at *c*, and at the end of 1.5 seconds, they will be at *d*. The travel-time curve is given in the graph above the structure section. No matter where the shot point or the receiving points, the break in the travel-time curve will always be at locality *b*.

Refracted seismic rays obey the same general laws as do refracted light waves. In Fig. 323, the velocity in layer *A* is 10,000 feet per second; in layer *B* the velocity is 20,000 feet per second. If an explosion occurs at

S, the energy moves outward in all directions. Some of it, which follows the path SR (Fig. 323A), is, upon meeting layer B, refracted to follow RT; as in light

$$q = \frac{\sin i}{\sin r} = \frac{v_1}{v_2} \tag{11}$$

In this equation q = index of refraction; i = angle of incidence; r = angle of refraction; v_1 = velocity in upper layer; v_2 = velocity of lower layer.

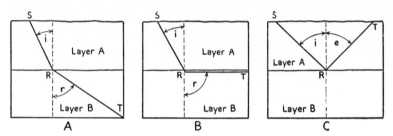

Fig. 323.   Principles of refraction. (See text.)

The greater the angle of incidence, the greater the angle of refraction. There is a critical angle of incidence for which r is 90 degrees; that is, RT is parallel to the contact; in the case illustrated (Fig. 323B), the critical angle is 30 degrees. In the general case

$$\sin c = \frac{v_1}{v_2} = q \tag{12}$$

Here c = critical angle, and the other letters have the same meaning as in equation (11). If the angle of incidence exceeds the critical value, as in Fig. 323C, the energy is reflected; the angle of reflection e equals the angle of incidence i.

The wave that follows the path RT (Fig. 324) travels with the velocity of the lower layer, but it sends energy into the overlying layer. This energy is transmitted upward with the velocity of the upper layer. The angle of emergence is the same as is the angle of incidence. There are an infinite number of such rays; in Fig. 324, rays aa', bb', cc', dd', and ee' are

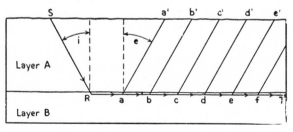

Fig. 324.   Paths followed by refracted ray. (See text.)

only examples. Of the total energy expended at S only a small percentage behaves in this way.

The lower part of Fig. 325 [28] illustrates the character of the wave fronts where the upper layer, 3,000 feet thick, has a velocity of 10,000 feet per second; in the lower layer the velocity is 20,000 feet per second. The shot point is S; the position of the wave front at every tenth of a

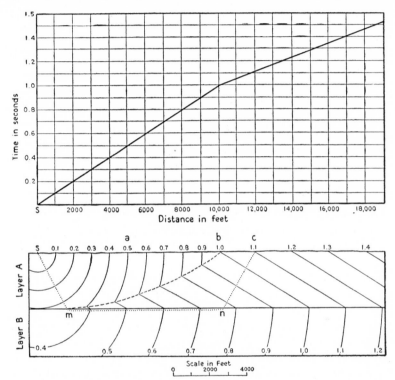

Fig. 325. Travel-time curve for horizontal layers. Lower diagram shows wave front each tenth of a second if S is shot point, if velocity in layer A is 10,000 feet per second, and if velocity in layer B is 20,000 feet per second. Upper diagram is travel-time curve for this case. (After H. R. Thornburgh, *Bulletin American Association Petroleum Geologists.*)

second is shown in Arabic numerals. At the end of 0.5 second, the waves have reached locality a; the energy has traveled directly along the surface of the earth at the rate of 10,000 feet per second. At the end of 1.0 second the energy has reached locality b, also having traveled along the surface of the earth at a speed of 10,000 feet per second. At the end of 1.1 seconds, energy that has followed the more circuitous route $Smnc$ reaches c before energy that has traveled directly from S to c. At all

[28] Modified from Thornburgh, H. R., "Wave-Front Diagrams in Seismic Interpretation," *Bulletin American Association Petroleum Geologists*, Vol. 14, pp. 185–200, 1930.

points to the right of b, the energy that travels in the lower layer arrives first. The travel-time curve for this case is given in the upper part of Fig. 325. The break in this curve occurs directly above b.

A *reversed profile* should be shot in order to ascertain that the contact between the two layers is horizontal; that is, the shot point should be at the right end of the section (Fig. 325), and the receiving points should be at the left end of the section. If the contact is horizontal, the travel-time curve will be identical with that obtained previously.

In actual field practice the travel-time curve is used for determining the velocities in the different layers. The slope of the curve is inversely proportional to the velocity (see p. 402). In Fig. 325, it is apparent from the left end of the travel-time curve that in one second the energy has traveled 10,000 feet; this is the velocity in the upper layer. The right-hand part of the curve, between 1.0 and 1.45 seconds, indicates a velocity of 20,000 feet per second. This is the velocity in the lower layer.

One would suppose that the travel-time curve for the uppermost layer would always intersect the abscissa and ordinate at zero, as in Fig. 325. Often, however, the curve strikes the time scale above zero. This is due to a "weathered zone" in which the rocks, because of fracturing and weathering, are characterized by abnormally low velocities.

The thickness of the upper layer may be calculated in various ways. One equation is

$$d = \frac{x}{2\sqrt{\dfrac{1+q}{1-q}}} \tag{13}$$

In this equation d = depth of the contact; x = "critical" distance on travel-time curve—that is, the distance from the origin to the break in the curve; and q is the index of refraction (see equation 12).

Travel-time curves may be used to obtain velocities and depths of more than two layers.

The problem is more complicated if the contact between two layers is inclined. The reversed profile does not give the same travel-time curve as does the first profile. Depths and angles of dip may be calculated, but space does not permit consideration of the methods employed in such cases.

Reflection Methods

The reflection method can detect reflecting horizons at depths of 300 to 30,000 feet, although it is commonly used for depths of 2,000 to 10,000 feet. If two layers of different velocities are in contact, some of the energy released by the explosion is reflected back toward the surface of the earth. In Fig. 326, S is the shot point, R is a receiving point. Of all the possible rays radiating from S, one is SE; the energy following this path is reflected at E and follows the path ER. The angle of reflection e equals the angle of incidence i.

If the beds are essentially horizontal, *correlation shooting* is employed. The shot point and the receiving points are on the same straight line (Fig. 320A). Six or more geophones operate simultaneously at receiving points that are 20 to 100 feet apart. The distance from the shot point to the middle geophone is 100 to 2,000 feet.

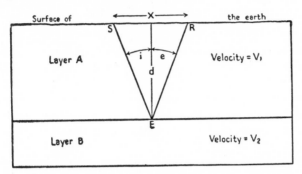

Fig. 326.   Path followed by a reflected wave. (After C. A. Heiland.)

The waves from a reflecting horizon produce in the seismogram a striking change in amplitude, which is followed by one to four oscillations. Figure 329 shows the seismograms for six geophones that are placed 100, 200, 300, 400, 500, and 600 feet from the shot point. Such a record could be obtained from one shot, with the six geophones recording simultaneously. The time is given at the bottom of the figure, each mark representing 1/100 of a second. The instant of shot is marked zero. The greater the distance between the shot point and the receiver, the greater is the time interval between the instant of shot and the arrival of the direct waves. The record of the direct waves is often blurred or lost because of the magnification by the instrument. In the uppermost record, in which the shot point and geophone are 100 feet apart, the reflected waves begin to arrive at 0.2 second. In all the seismograms the reflected waves arrive at approximately the same time, although, as is to be expected, they are a little later where the distance between the shot point and geophone is large.

The depth of a horizontal reflecting horizon is readily calculated:

$$d = \tfrac{1}{2}\sqrt{v_1^2 t^2 - x^2} \tag{14}$$

In this equation d = depth; v_1 = velocity in upper layer; t = time interval between instant of shot and arrival of reflected wave; and x is the distance between shot point and receiving point. The value of v_1 is determined for the surface waves by dividing the distance x by the time interval t.

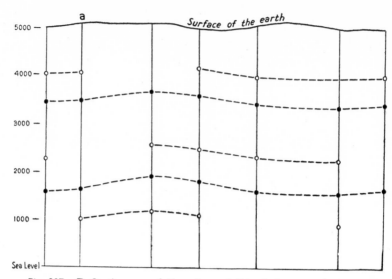

Fig. 327. Reflection correlation logs. Solid circles = good reflection; open circles = fair reflections. Scale in feet along left margin. (Modified after C. A. Heiland.)

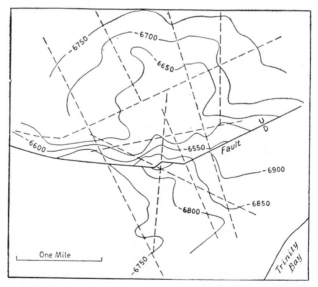

Fig. 328. Structure contour map of the South Cotton Lake area, Chambers County, Texas. Made by reflection method, contoured on a phantom horizon near the top of the Frio sand. Contour interval 50 feet. Broken lines show location of the seismic profiles. Petroleum is trapped in the anticline north of the fault. (After J. M. Wilson, *Bulletin American Association Petroleum Geologists.*)

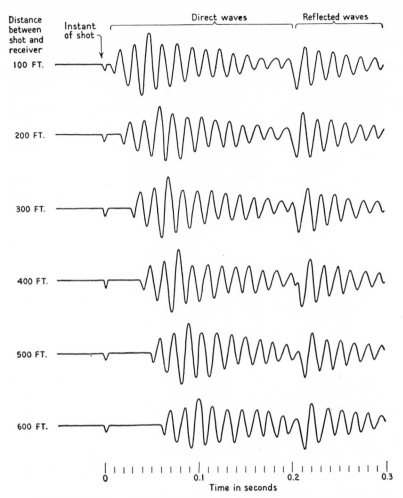

Fig. 329. Direct and reflected waves obtained when the distance between the shot point and the receiving point ranges from 100 to 600 feet. Velocity in layer above reflecting horizon is 10,000 feet per second.

Applying these equations to Fig. 329, it is first necessary to calculate the velocity in the surface layer. The lowest seismogram shows that the waves travel 600 feet in 0.06 seconds, indicating a velocity of 10,000 feet per second. This same seismogram shows that the reflected waves begin to arrive at approximately 0.21 second. Calculating the depth by equation (14), we get a depth of 1,006 feet. Using equation (15), we get a depth of 1,050 feet.

If x is small compared to d, as is the case in *vertical shooting*,

$$d = \tfrac{1}{2}v_1 t \tag{15}$$

These equations assume that the average velocity in the upper layer is the same as the velocity at the very surface of the earth. If a well penetrates one or more layers, it is possible to get the velocity by detonating dynamite at an appropriate depth in the well. It is possible, however, to calculate the *effective average velocity* by the equation

$$V_a = \sqrt{\frac{x_2{}^2 - x_1{}^2}{t_2{}^2 - t_1{}^2}} \tag{16}$$

Here V_a is the average effective velocity, x_2 and x_1 are the distances from the shot point to two separate receiving stations, and t_2 and t_1 are the travel-times for the same receiving stations. More commonly, the squares of the distances are plotted against the squares of the travel-times; the cotangent of the angle that the average curve makes with the abscissa is the square of the average velocity.

Figure 327 illustrates how data obtained from a series of localities may be correlated. All the localities are on the same straight line on the map. Each vertical line gives the data for one locality. Good reflections are shown by solid circles, fair reflections by open circles. At locality *a*, for example, strong reflections were obtained at 3,500 feet and 1,650 feet, fair reflections at 4,100 feet and 1,000 feet. The broken lines show how the reflections may be correlated and the structure deduced.

For inclined strata, *dip shooting* must be employed by reversing the profile. It is possible to calculate both the depth of the reflecting horizon and its dip. After the dip for every reflection is plotted on a structure section, an imaginary, or *phantom horizon,* is sketched on the section to show the structure.

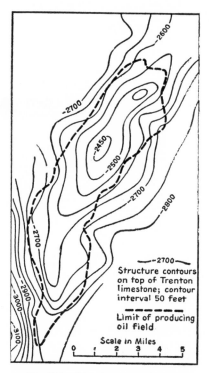

Fig. 330. Structure contour map made by seismic reflection method. Loudon oil field, Illinois. (After P. L. Lyons; permission of Society of Exploration Geophysicists.

Geological Applications of Seismic Methods

Seismic methods are not only useful in recognizing the presence of rock bodies of unusual composition, such as salt domes, but they may also provide some data concerning the characteristics of these rocks.

Moreover, the depth and dip of beds and contacts may be determined. At the present time, the reflection method is the best of all the geophysical methods for obtaining a precise structural picture. Folds, faults, salt domes, and igneous bodies may be delineated.

Figure 328 is a structure contour map of the South Cotton Lake area in Texas based upon a reflection seismograph survey.[29] The broken lines show the location of the profiles. The major features of this map, prepared in 1936, were subsequently verified by drilling. Figure 330 is a structure contour map of the Loudon oil field, Illinois, based on a seismic reflection survey.[30]

ELECTRICAL METHODS

Principles

The electrical methods for deducing geological structure are many and varied, both in technique and in the properties measured. Some methods utilize natural electrical currents that flow through the lithosphere. Other methods use artificial currents that are introduced into the rocks by direct contact or by induction. Only some of the more common methods can be considered.

The flow of electricity may be compared to the movement of water in a pipe. The rate of flow of electricity is measured in amperes. Although the *ampere* might be defined in terms of the magnetic effect of the current, in practice it is defined in terms of its chemical effect. If two silver plates are placed in a jar of silver nitrate solution, and if the positive terminal of a battery is connected to one plate and the negative terminal is connected to the other plate, silver is dissolved from one plate and added to the other. The quantity of electricity that deposits 0.001118 gram of silver is one *coulomb*, and the current that deposits silver at a rate of 0.001118 gram per second is one *ampere*. In geophysical work, measurements are often made in *milliamperes*—that is, in thousandths of an ampere.

All substances offer resistance to the passage of electrical current, just as the friction in a pipe impedes the flow of water. An *ohm* is the resistance offered by a column of mercury 106.3 centimeters long, weighing 14.4521 grams, at 0° centigrade.

The *electromotive force* causes electricity to flow or tend to flow, and it may be compared to the hydrostatic head causing water to flow. The unit of measurement is the *volt*, which is the electromotive force needed to drive a current of one ampere through a resistance of one ohm. In geo-

[29] Wilson, J. M., "South Cotton Lake Field, Chambers County, Texas," *Bulletin American Association Petroleum Geologists*, Vol. 25, pp. 1898–1920, 1941.

[30] Lyons, P. L., "Geophysical Case History of the Loudon Field, Illinois," pp. 461–470, in Nettleton, L. L., editor, *Geophysical Case Histories*, Vol. I, 671 pp., 1948.

physical work, the *millivolt,* one thousandth of a volt, is the unit normally used. *Difference of potential* is the difference in electric pressure between two points in an electric circuit, and it is measured in volts.

The fundamental relationship between current, electromotive force, and resistance is expressed by Ohm's law,

$$R = \frac{E}{I} \tag{17}$$

where R is the resistance in ohms, E is electromotive force in volts, and I is current in amperes.

Resistivity (ρ) or *specific resistance* of a substance is the resistance between opposite ends of a centimeter cube. Resistivity is expressed in ohm-centimeters. *Conductivity* (γ) is the reciprocal of resistivity.

$$\rho = \frac{1}{\gamma} \tag{18}$$

Resistivity is a very important tool in geophysical work because, whereas it is very high for rocks, it is very low for metals. The resistivities of a few common rocks and minerals are given in Table 2.[31] The resistivity of a rock under natural conditions, however, is not controlled so much by the mineralogy as by the composition of the water in the pore spaces.

Table 2
Resistivity of Some Rocks and Minerals

Rock	Resistivity
Basalt and trap	10,000 to 10,000,000
Granite	30,000 to 1,000,000,000
Shale	10,000 to 10,000,000
Sandstone	30,000 to 100,000
Limestone	3,000 to 400,000
Chalcopyrite	0.1 to 10
Pyrite	0.002 to 1.5
Cuprite	0.1
Magnetite	0.008 to 0.5

A rock in which the pore spaces are filled with salt water will have a resistivity only 1/100 to 1/1000 that of the same rock in which the pores are filled with fresh water.

If electricity flows from one end of a thin homogeneous rectangular plate to the other, as from A to B in Fig. 331, we may think of the electricity as moving along an infinite number of current flow lines, some of which are illustrated by broken lines. Along each of these lines there is a drop in potential. If the difference in potential between A and a, A and b, A and c, A and d, A and e, and A and f is the same, it follows that there is no difference in potential along the line $abcdef$, which is therefore an *equipotential line.* There are an infinite number of such equipotential

    [31] From Birch, F., *et al.*, "Handbook of Physical Constants," pp. 304–316, *Geological Society of America, Special Paper No. 36,* 1942.

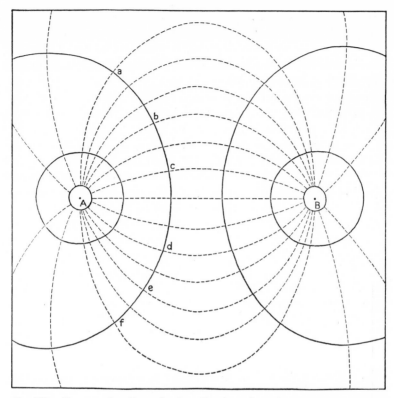

Fig. 331. Current flow-lines (broken lines) and equipotential lines (solid lines) about two electrodes *A* and *B*.

lines, at right angles to the current flow lines, and in Fig. 331 some of them are shown in solid lines. Within the lithosphere, which is three-dimensional, we must think of equipotential surfaces. All points on an equipotential surface are at the same potential. Usually it is feasible to map only the equipotential lines, and not the equipotential surfaces.

Natural Electrical Currents

Spontaneous electric currents. Methods which use natural electrical currents are usually called self-potential methods. Sulphide ore bodies set up spontaneous electric currents.

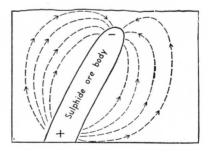

Fig. 332. Spontaneous electric current about a sulphide ore body. (After S. F. Kelly.)

At the surface of the earth the current flows toward the body (Fig. 332), and, consequently, there is a drop in potential as the ore is approached. In order to produce measurable currents, the top of the ore body should be within 300 feet of the surface. The drop in potential along the surface of the earth as one approaches this *negative potential center* over the ore body may be as great as 700 millivolts. The intensity and shape of this field may be determined by preparing potential profiles, or by surveying equipotential lines.

A *potential profile* follows a straight line perpendicular to the strike of the geological structure if its strike is known. Wooden pegs are laid out on the line of the profile every 20 to 100 feet. The measuring instruments consist of two "porous pot" electrodes connected by wires to a potentiometer reading to 1 millivolt. One electrode is placed at peg *A*, the other at peg *B*. The difference in potential is read on the potentiometer. The first electrode is then moved to peg *B*, the other to peg *C*, and a new reading is made. The process is repeated for all the pegs on the line. The readings are commonly plotted as curves. The horizontal scale is the distance along the profile, the vertical scale is the difference in potential,

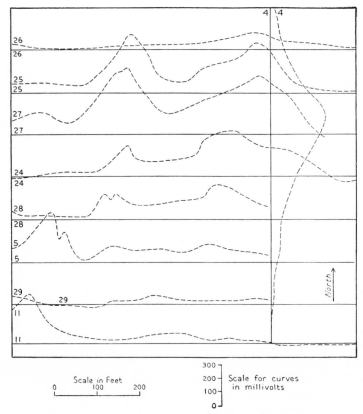

Fig. 333. Combined map and potential profiles of spontaneously generated electric currents at Noranda Mines, Ltd., Quebec. (After S. F. Kelly.)

calculated by algebraic addition. Thus if the drop in potential from A to B is 10 millivolts, and the drop from B to C is 7 millivolts, the total drop from A to C is 17 millivolts. If there is a drop from A to B of 10 millivolts, but an increase of 7 millivolts from B to C, the total drop from A to C is only 3 millivolts. Peg A is arbitrarily assigned a value of zero on the vertical scale.

Ordinarily, a series of such profiles are run parallel to one another, the number depending upon the character of the investigation. Moreover, at least one profile at right angles to the others, and crossing them all, is essential in order that all the profiles may be tied to the arbitrarily chosen starting point. An example of such a series of profiles is given in Fig. 333.[32] This figure is essentially a map with profiles superimposed on it. Each solid east-west line is a line along which a potential profile was run; the solid north-south line serves a similar function. The potential profile is shown by a broken line. Each profile is numbered in order that it may be correlated with the correct line on the map; each line serves as the base of a graph. The millivolt scale for the profiles is given below the map. The point on the map represented by the intersection of lines *11* and *4* was arbitrarily assigned a value of zero. A maximum of 470 millivolts is found on profile *27*.

From such profiles, a map of equipotential lines may be deduced, just as a contour map can be constructed from a series of topographic profiles (Fig. 334).

Equipotential lines may be surveyed by the same instruments, although a milliammeter may be used instead of a potentiometer. One of the "porous pot" electrodes is placed in the ground, and the other is placed in successive trial locations, until no current flows through the measuring instrument; that is, until either an ammeter or potentiometer would read zero. This means that two electrodes are on an equipotential line. One electrode is then moved to the location of the second electrode, and the second is moved on to find a new location on the equipotential line. If possible, the equipotential line should be followed back to the starting point. Several such equipotential lines may be surveyed, although one line will ordinarily indicate rather clearly the center of the electrical disturbance. No numerical values can be assigned to these equipotential lines unless they are tied together by a potential profile.

In these methods, some corrections have to be applied for polarization of the electrodes and for topography.

Although spontaneous electric currents are used most extensively in the search for ore bodies, they may be employed in other ways. A notable example is the Luushia anticline of Katanga; beds rich in graphite are brought nearer the surface by the anticline. The spontaneous currents

---

[32] Kelly, S. F., "Geophysical Delineation of Structure in Mining Operations." *Transactions American Geophysical Union*, Pt. 3, pp. 245–269, 1939.

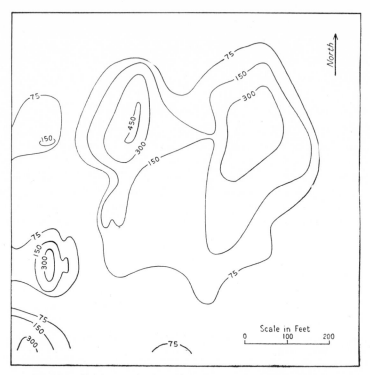

Fig. 334. Equipotential lines for same area shown in Fig. 333.

generated by the graphite cause a negative potential over the anticline; a negative potential thus indicates the presence of an anticline. Anthracite coal causes strong spontaneous currents, but a positive potential center occurs above anthracite beds. Some faults are characterized by spontaneous currents, apparently due to differences in the conductivity of solutions in the fractures along the fault.

Telluric currents. Telluric currents are natural currents of electricity flowing through the lithosphere, and are of solar origin.[33] Most electrical methods are not useful for depths greater than 6,000 feet, but the telluric currents give information for greater depths.

Even at a single locality, the character of the telluric currents is constantly changing because of diurnal variations and magnetic storms. It is necessary, therefore, to occupy a base station with which measurements made at a mobile station may be compared. The "preferential direction" of the currents is determined, as is the ratio of the intensity at the mobile station to the intensity at the base station. The telluric currents are influenced by inhomogeneities in the lithosphere; they avoid rocks of high resistivity and tend to flow around them. If a circular, highly resistant

[33] Schlumberger, M., "The Application of Telluric Currents to Surface Prospecting," *Transactions American Geophysical Union*, Pt. 3, pp. 271–280, 1939.

mass is at the surface of the earth, the telluric currents flow around it. If a lump of resistant material is at depth, the currents not only go around it, but also rise over it.

This method has been used in a study of Alsatian salt domes, which affect both the trend and the intensity of the telluric currents.[34] In southern Sumatra, the depth of the crystalline basement rocks is excellently portrayed by this method. A study of salt domes in Texas has given promising results.[35]

Artificial Currents

Principles. In most electrical methods, the ground is artificially energized, either by direct introduction of currents or by induction. The power may be provided from available power lines or by mobile generators.

Surface potential methods. In the *point electrode method* direct current is introduced by two electrodes known as the *power pegs* or *current electrodes,* which may be iron pegs or coils of copper wire. These two electrodes should be on a line parallel to the strike of the strata, if such information is available, and should be a mile or more apart. If the field were homogeneous, the current flow lines and the equipotential lines would be symmetrically distributed about the two electrodes, as in Fig. 331. If, however, bodies of unusually low or unusually high resistivity are present, the flow lines and equipotential lines are distorted. The *potential profile* or *equipotential lines* may be surveyed in the same way as is outlined for spontaneous currents; two electrodes, known as reading pegs, are used in the same way that they are used for spontaneous currents.

In the *line electrode method* various alternate arrangements may be employed. Either d.c. or a.c. current may be used. Two uninsulated copper wires, 2,000 to 2,500 feet long, are placed parallel to one another about 2,000 to 2,500 feet apart. The area is then surveyed to locate equipotential lines as in other methods. Any inhomogeneity in the rocks will be shown by distortion of the equipotential lines.

Resistivity methods. These methods are particularly suitable for horizontal or gently dipping beds. The resistivity, defined on p. 412, can be calculated if the current and potential are known. Two current electrodes introduce the energy to the ground, but the number and arrangement of the reading electrodes vary with different methods. In the Wenner-Gish-Rooney method, two additional electrodes are placed in line with the current electrodes, and all four electrodes are the same distance apart (Fig. 335A).

$$\rho = 2\pi a \frac{V}{I} \tag{19}$$

[34] Schlumberger, M., *op. cit.*

[35] Boissonnas, E., and E. G. Leonardon, "Geophysical Exploration by Telluric Currents, with Special Reference to a Survey of the Haynesville Salt Dome, Wood County, Texas," *Geophysics,* Vol. XIII, pp. 387–403, 1948.

In this equation $\rho =$ resistivity in ohms per unit distance; $a =$ distance between electrodes; $V =$ difference in potential between two inner electrodes; and I is the current.

In the Lee partitioning method, a fifth electrode is placed halfway between the middle electrodes (Fig. 335B).

$$\rho = 4\pi a \frac{Vc}{I} \tag{20}$$

Here $Vc =$ difference in potential between the central electrode and either adjacent electrode; other terms are as in equation (19).

There are several other methods for measuring resistivity.

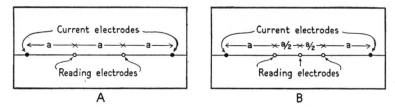

Fig. 335. Arrangement of current electrodes and reading electrodes in two different resistivity methods. *A.* Wenner-Gish-Rooney method. *B.* Lee partitioning method.

The greater the interval between the power electrodes, the greater is the depth of penetration, which is essentially equal to the distance a (Fig. 335). As a is increased, a layer of contrasting resistivity may be penetrated. In such cases, the *apparent resistivity* is measured at the surface. By calculations and graphs, it is possible to determine the depth to the lower layer and to determine the true resistivities of the upper and lower layers. The problem can also be solved for three horizontal layers. It is thus possible to make structure contours on subsurface horizons. If one or more drill holes are available, such a map can be related directly to the stratigraphy of the region.

Resistivity methods may be used either qualitatively or quantitatively in determining the geological structure. If the separation of the power electrodes is a constant value, variations in the resistivity indicate different kinds of rock at the same depth beneath the surface. Figure 336 shows the influence of an anticline on the resistivity curve.[36] The resistivity of the Devonian limestone is much higher than that of the Mississippian and Pennsylvanian shale. If, however, an anticline brings up a formation of low resistivity, the curve would be the reverse of that in Fig. 336. Salt has a high resistivity, and salt domes usually appear as resistivity highs; in

[36] Hubbert, M. K., "Results of Earth Resistivity Survey on Various Geologic Structures in Illinois," *American Institute Mining Metallurgical Engineers, Transactions,* Vol. 110, *Geophysical Prospecting,* pp. 9–39, 1934.

some instances, however, the reverse is true because strata of low resistivity lie directly above the dome. Many faults are zones of low resistivity because of electrolytes in the solutions along the fault.[37] Formations of contrasting resistivity may be brought into contact along the fault, and this affects the resistivity curves.

Electrical methods are especially valuable in prospecting for ore bodies with high conductivity. They are useful in the search for water supplies and placer deposits because the sands and gravels in the stream

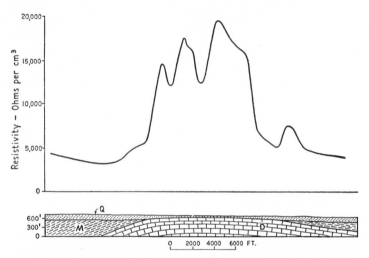

Fig. 336. Resistivity profile across an anticline. $D =$ Devonian limestone; $M =$ Mississippian-Pennsylvanian shale and sandstone; $Q =$ glacial till. (After M. K. Hubbert, *American Institute of Mining Metallurgical Engineers*.)

channels have different electrical properties from the bedrock. The same is true in the study of the foundations for dams and other engineering projects.[38]

RADIOACTIVITY

In recent years methods have been devised to map geological contacts on the basis of the varying content of radioactive elements in different rocks. Radioactive disintegration involves emission of α, β, and γ rays. The α-rays are essentially positively charged helium atoms that lack two electrons. The β-rays are electrons (negatively charged). The γ-rays are electromagnetic radiations.

[37] See also Hawley, P. F., "Fault Location by Electrical Prospecting—an Example," *Geophysics*, Vol. VIII, pp. 391–403, 1943.

[38] See also Jakosky, *op. cit.*, pp. 554–579.

The chief sources of such radiation from rocks are uranium, thorium, and potassium. Inasmuch as the amounts of these elements are unlike in different rocks, a means of mapping formations is suggested. Geiger counters and scintillometers are instruments that measure mostly γ-radiation. For airborne surveys a scintillometer is mounted in a plane that is flown a few hundred feet above the ground.

Such airborne surveys "show that radiation intensity is related to the areal distribution of various rock types; thus such surveys provide a reconnaissance technique for delineating major geologic features with rapidity and at low cost. In geologic reconnaissance, rock types can be distinguished both where rock outcrops occur and where residual soils blanket the bedrock." [39]

[39] Stead, F. W., R. M. Moxham, and F. J. Davis, "Progress in Airborne Radioactivity Surveying," *Bulletin Geological Society of America*, Vol. 64, 1953.

Laboratory Exercises

EXERCISE 1

Outcrop Pattern of Horizontal and Vertical Strata

PATTERNS

If strata are horizontal, each stratigraphic horizon,[1] such as the top or bottom of a bed, is everywhere at the same altitude. Horizontal beds are shown in Fig. 54A. The outcrop of the top or bottom of a horizontal bed thus follows topographic contours. The width of outcrop of a horizontal bed depends upon the thickness of the bed and upon the topography. The width of outcrop of a bed of uniform thickness is greatest where the slopes are gentle—that is, where the contours are far apart.

The relation between the attitude of a bed, the outcrop pattern displayed by the bed, and the topography may be remembered by the "rule of V's." This rule states in part that the outcrop of a horizontal bed forms a V as it crosses a valley and that the apex of the V points upstream (formation shown by circles in Fig. 54A). The top and bottom contacts of the bed are parallel to topographic contours.

If an horizon is exposed at one place in a region of horizontal beds, it is obviously possible to predict the location of the horizon everywhere else on the map. If the exposure of the horizon coincides with a contour, the location and the pattern of the horizon will be identical with that of the contour. If the altitude of the exposure of the horizon falls between two contours, interpolation is necessary in order to locate the position of the horizon on the map. In regions of low relief the error of the predicted location may be considerable.

The top and bottom of a vertical bed will appear on the map as straight lines parallel to the strike of the bed. Topography has no control on the outcrop pattern of vertical beds. The outcrop pattern of a vertical bed is shown in Fig. 54B.

STRUCTURE SECTIONS

Structure sections show the geological structure as it would appear on the sides of an imaginary vertical trench cut into the earth. Sometimes they portray the structure as observed on vertical cliffs, in highway cuts, or in mine openings. More commonly they are predictions based on exposures at the surface of the earth. Consequently they are only an approximation to the truth, their precision depending upon the simplicity of the structure, the number of exposures, and the skill of the geologist.

In regions of low relief the surface of the earth may be represented by a straight line, but ordinarily the top of the structure section shows

---

[1] *Horizon* is used in this book to refer to a surface having no thickness.

the topography. The first step, therefore, in preparing a structure section is to make a topographic profile. Such a profile is prepared from the topographic map in the following way. In Fig. 337A the structure section is to be made along the line *AB*. A strip of blank paper is laid across the topographic map, the top of the strip coinciding with the line of the section. A mark is made on this strip of paper at each place that a contour crosses the line of the section. The altitude represented by each of these marks may be written on the strip.

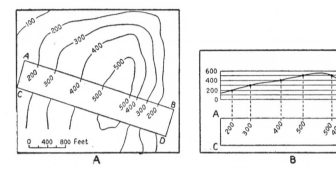

Fig. 337.   Preparation of topographic profile. *A. AB* is line along which profile is to be made. *ABCD* is strip of blank paper laid over topographic map. *B*. Plotting profile; scale along left side of profile is same as horizontal scale of the map.

A base on which to plot the profile is then prepared, as shown in the upper part of Fig. 337B. The horizontal scale is the same as that of the map. The altitude above sea level of each horizontal line is written on this diagram; each line thus corresponds to a contour. Generally the vertical scale should be the same as the horizontal scale; otherwise the geological structure becomes distorted. If the strata are horizontal, however, it is sometimes necessary to exaggerate the vertical scale.

The strip of paper prepared from the topographic map is then placed under the diagram (Fig. 337B). Each pencil mark on the strip is then projected upward to the appropriate altitude line and a dot is made. These dots are then connected by a smooth line to make the topographic profile.

To add the geology to the profile, place a new strip of paper along the line of the section on the map and make a pencil mark wherever a geologic contact crosses the line of section. This strip is then placed beneath the topographic profile, and the contacts are projected vertically upward to the profile. If the beds are horizontal, horizontal lines drawn through these points are the geological contacts in the profile.

PROBLEMS

1. In Fig 338, in the envelope, assume that the base of a horizontal bed of sandstone 150 feet thick is exposed on the east side of Bear Moun-

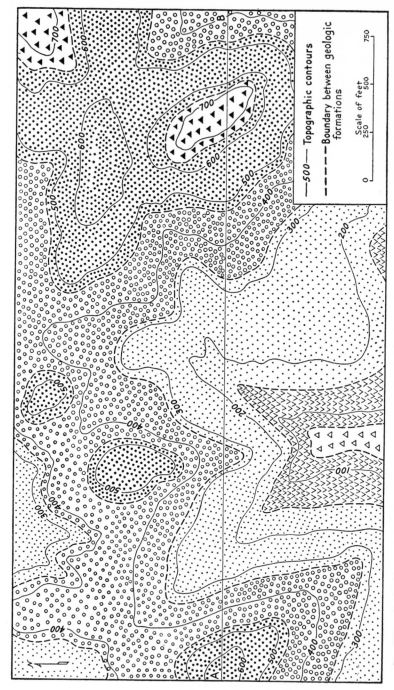

Fig. 339. Geologic map for Problem 3, Exercise 1. Scale, 1 inch = 500 feet. Open triangles = rhyolite; checks = basalt; small dots = sandstone; open circles = conglomerate with quartzite pebbles; heavy dots = volcanic tuff; and solid triangles = volcanic conglomerate.

tain at an altitude of 1,500 feet. Color in blue (inking the contacts) those parts of the area in which the sandstone constitutes the surface formation.[2]

2. In Fig. 338 assume that the base of a series of vertical limestone beds 1,056 feet thick is exposed at bench mark 1,342 near the southern edge of the map. The beds strike N. 30° E. and are younger toward the northwest. Color in red (inking the contacts) that part of the area in which the limestone outcrops.[2]

3. In Fig. 339 different patterns are used to show various geological formations. (a) What is the attitude of the strata? (b) Describe briefly the relationship of the outcrop pattern to the topography. (c) Draw a topographic profile and geologic section along the line *AB*.

If the instructor desires, he may use one or more of the following folios of the *Geological Atlas of the United States,* published by the U. S. Geological Survey: 200, Galena-Elizabeth, Illinois-Iowa; 109, Cottonwood Falls, Kansas; 208, Colchester-Macomb, Illinois; 206, Leavenworth-Smithville, Missouri-Kansas; 87, Camp Clarke, Nebraska; 202, Eureka Springs-Harrison, Arkansas-Missouri; 176, Sewickley, Pennsylvania; 178, Foxburg-Clarion, Pennsylvania.

[2] This can be done directly on the map or on a piece of tracing paper placed over the map.

EXERCISE 2

Patterns of Dipping Strata; Three-point Problems

RULE OF V'S

It has been shown in Exercise 1 that the contacts of horizontal beds follow topographic contour lines, and that wherever such strata cross a valley their outcrop pattern forms a V that points upstream. It was also shown that topography has no influence on the pattern of vertical beds, the outcrop pattern of which forms straight lines parallel to the strike of the beds.

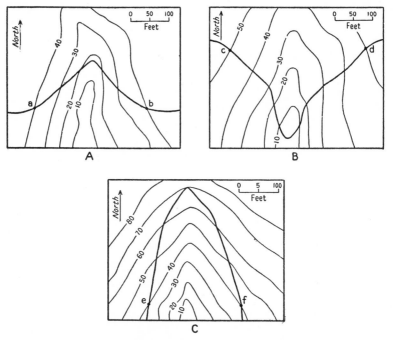

Fig. 340. Rule of V's (see text).

The outcrop pattern of beds that dip upstream forms a V that points upstream, as shown in Fig. 55. The contacts of the bed are not parallel to topographic contours. Figure 340A shows the same thing. The horizon, known to outcrop at a and b, strikes N. 90° E. and dips 11.3° N.; that is, it drops 20 feet vertically every 100 feet horizontally. The heavy line shows the expected outcrop pattern.

The outcrop pattern of beds that dip downstream at an angle greater than the stream gradient forms a V, the apex of which points downstream. In Fig. 340B let us assume that an horizon strikes N. 90° E. and dips downstream at an angle of 11.3 degrees; that is, it drops 10 feet vertically every 50 feet horizontally. Moreover, the stream gradient is 10 feet vertically every 100 feet horizontally. If the horizon is known to outcrop at c and d, the heavy line shows the expected outcrop pattern.

The outcrop pattern of beds that dip downstream at an angle less than the gradient of the stream forms a V that points upstream. The contacts of the beds are not parallel to topographic contours. In Fig. 340C let us assume that the horizon strikes N. 90° E. and dips south (downstream) at an angle of 5.7 degrees; that is, it drops 10 feet vertically every 100 feet horizontally. Moreover, the stream gradient is 10 feet vertically every 50 feet horizontally. If the horizon outcrops at e and f, the heavy line shows the predicted outcrop pattern.

Application of the rule of V's to geological maps enables one to determine the approximate dip of beds from the outcrop patterns. By use of the three-point method, which will be described later, it is possible to determine the value of the dip with considerable precision.

OUTCROP PATTERN OF DIPPING BED

The outcrop pattern of an horizon can be predicted if a contour map showing the topography is available, if the dip and strike of the horizon are known, and if the location of one exposure of the horizon is given. This is possible, however, only if the horizon is truly a plane surface— that is, if its dip and strike are constant.

Figure 341 illustrates the procedure that may be followed. The horizon outcrops at X. The ground surface is represented by 100-foot contours. Inasmuch as the horizon is known to strike N. 90° E. and to dip

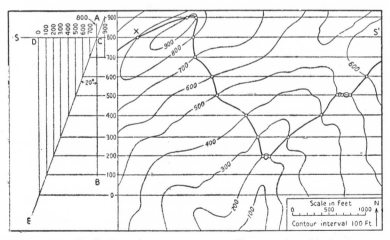

Fig. 341. Prediction of outcrop pattern. If a stratigraphic horizon at X strikes N. 90° E. and dips 20° S., the expected outcrop pattern is shown by the heavy line passing through the open circles.

20° S., it is possible to predict its position at any place in the area. The position of the horizon may be represented by structure contours, which are more fully described in Exercise 6.

Draw the line *SS'* through the outcrop *X* parallel to the strike of the horizon (N. 90° E.). Inasmuch as the outcrop is at an altitude of 800 feet, at every place on this line the horizon has an altitude of 800 feet. Now make a vertical section at right angles to the strike by drawing *AB* perpendicular to the strike of the bed at any convenient distance from the map. The intersection of *AB* and *SS'* may be designated by *C*. At *C* lay off the angle *BCE* equal to the dip of the horizon, in this instance 20 degrees. *CE* is the trace of the horizon on the vertical section. Along *SS'* from point *C* lay off 100-foot units (equal to the topographic contour interval), using the same scale as that of the map.

Through each 100-foot point above or below *C* draw a line parallel to *AB* to an intersection with line *CE*. The intersections are points on the bedding plane; they are 100 feet apart vertically. From each of these intersections draw lines parallel to *SS'*. These lines are 100-foot structure contours on the horizon. At each point where a structure contour intersects a topographic contour of the same altitude, the horizon will outcrop. The locations of these intersections have been marked by small circles. Connecting these circles, as shown in Fig. 341, shows the predicted outcrop pattern.

THREE-POINT PROBLEMS

The method of working a three-point problem is the opposite of constructing an outcrop pattern. It is possible to calculate the dip and strike of an horizon if the location and altitude of three points on that horizon are known and if the horizon is truly a plane and not a warped surface.

A simple illustration of a three-point problem will be given first. Figure 342A is a map giving the location and altitude of three points on an horizon; these points are *A*, *B*, and *C*. Inasmuch as the strike of any plane is a line connecting points of equal altitude on that plane, line *AB*

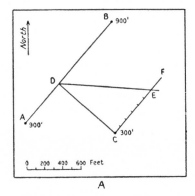
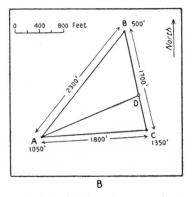

    A   B

Fig. 342. Three-point method. Location and altitude of a plane are given at *A*, *B*, and *C*. Dip and strike of the plane can be determined.

is the strike of the horizon under consideration because A and B are at the same altitude. The dip is measured at right angles to the strike, and in this case it is toward the southeast. A perpendicular is dropped from C to AB, the intersection being labeled D. To find the value of the dip a vertical triangle is rotated to the surface around DC as an axis. CF is erected perpendicular to DC. The difference in altitude between points C and D, 600 feet, is set off, on the same scale as the map, along the line CF. The angle CDE is the dip of the horizon.

A more general problem is illustrated by Fig. 342B. The location and altitude of three points on the horizon are shown. Some point, to be determined, between points B and C, will have the same altitude as A (1,050 feet); a line connecting that point with A will be the strike of the horizon. The unknown point can be located by proportion:

$$\frac{\text{Altitude of } A \text{ minus altitude of } B}{\text{Altitude of } C \text{ minus altitude of } B} = \frac{\text{Distance } BD}{\text{Distance } BC}$$

where D is the point we wish to find. Solving the equation, we obtain BD = 1,100 feet. This distance is set off from point B using the same scale as the map. AD is the strike of the horizon. The dip may be found in the same way as in Fig. 342A.

PROBLEMS

1. Figure 343 is a topographic map on which two geologic horizons are shown, one by a broken line and the other by a dotted line. In the vicinity of point a what is the attitude of the horizon shown by the broken line?

2. In Fig. 343 what is the attitude of this same horizon in the vicinity of b?

3. In Fig. 343 what is the attitude of the horizon shown by the dotted line in the vicinity of c?

4. In Fig. 343 what is the attitude of this same bed in the vicinity of d?

5. In Fig. 344, in the envelope, assume that at 3,000 feet at the north end of the summit of Bald Mountain the base of a bed of limestone which strikes N. 90° E. and dips 15° N. is exposed. Draw on the map the outcrop pattern of the base of the limestone.[1]

6. In Fig. 344 assume that the base of a bed of sandstone is exposed on top of Scragg Hill at an elevation of 1,780, at the X on Gale River marked 1,160, and at the X on Gale River marked 1,040. Find the dip and strike of this bed by the three-point method, assuming that the bed is a perfect plane.[1]

7. In Fig. 344 assume that a tuff horizon, which strikes due north, is exposed at 2,525 feet on the top of Bickford Mountain and at B. M. 990. What is the dip of the tuff horizon? [1]

8. In Fig. 344 assume that a vertical quartz vein striking N. 20° E. is exposed on Meadow Brook at an altitude of 1,400 feet. It is expected that

[1] This work can be done directly on the map or on a piece of tracing paper.

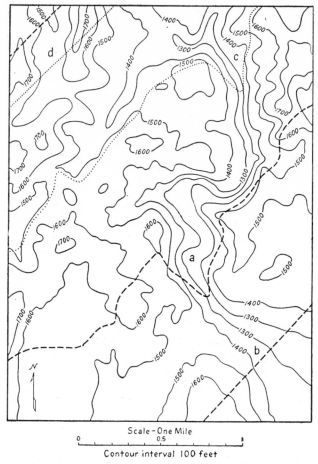

Fig. 343. Map for use in Problems 1, 2, 3, and 4 in Exercise
2. Topographic contour interval is 100 feet.

an ore shoot will be found at the intersection of this vein with the base
of the limestone that outcrops on Bald Mountain. Indicate where on the
map one should look for the outcrop of the ore shoot.[2]

9. In Fig. 344 how deep a vertical shaft, sunk from the top of Bickford Mountain, would be necessary in order to intersect the base of the
limestone? [2]

If the instructor desires, he may use one or more of the following folios
of the *Geological Atlas of the United States,* published by the U. S. Geological Survey: 142, Cloud Peak-Fort McKinney, Wyoming; 56, Little
Belt Mountains, Montana; 174, Johnstown, Pennsylvania; 175, Birmingham, Alabama; 153, Ouray, Colorado; 141, Bald Mountain-Dayton,
Wyoming.

[2] This work can be done directly on the map or on a piece of tracing paper.

EXERCISE 3

Thickness and Depth of Strata

INTRODUCTION

It is essential in structural, stratigraphic, and economic problems to be able to calculate the thickness and depth of strata. A stratum is tabular in shape, like a sheet of paper. Strata may be horizontal, inclined, or vertical. The thickness is measured perpendicular to the plane of the bedding (t of Fig. 345). The depth is the vertical distance meas-

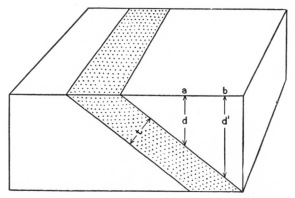

Fig. 345. Thickness and depth. Bed of sandstone shown by dots; shale above and below is left blank. t = thickness of sandstone: d = depth of top of sandstone at point a; d' = depth of top of sandstone at point b.

ured from any defined point on the surface of the earth to the top of the desired stratum. In Fig. 345, d is the depth at a, and d' is the depth at b.

If the whole stratum is favorably exposed in a cliff, the thickness may be measured directly by tape. Ordinarily, however, a direct measurement is impossible, and the thickness must be calculated by means of data obtained from a map, such as the top of the block in Fig. 345.

EQUATIONS

The fundamental equations for calculating the thickness of beds and the depth of beds are given below. The derivation of some of the simpler equations is given. For a more complete discussion the reader is referred to a series of papers by Palmer and Mertie.[1] Other papers dealing with the subject have been written by Miller and Mandelbaum and Sanford.[2]

Case a

Thickness, if the ground surface is horizontal, and if the breadth of outcrop of the bed is measured at right angles to its strike. As shown in

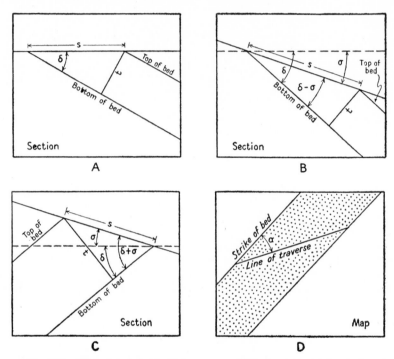

Fig. 346. Measurement of thickness. $t =$ thickness; $\delta =$ angle of dip of bedding; $s =$ slope distance between outcrop of top of bed and outcrop of bottom of bed; $\sigma =$ angle of slope of ground; $a =$ angle between strike of bedding and trend of traverse. *A.* Ground horizontal. *B.* Bedding dips in same direction that ground slopes. *C.* Bedding dips in opposite direction to that in which ground slopes. *D.* Map for case in which traverse is not at right angles to strike of bedding.

[1] Palmer, H. S., "New Graphic Method for Determining the Depth and Thickness of Strata and the Projection of Dip," *U. S. Geological Survey Professional Paper 120*, pp. 122–128, 1918.

Mertie, J. B., Jr., "Graphic and Mechanical Computation of Thickness of Strata and Distance to a Stratum," *U. S. Geological Survey Professional Paper 129*, pp. 39–52, 1922.

Mertie, J. B., Jr., "Stratigraphic Measurements in Parallel Folds," *Bulletin Geological Society of America*, Vol. 51, pp. 1107–1134, 1940.

[2] Miller, F. S., "Graphs for Obtaining True Thickness of a Vein or Bed," *American Institute of Mining and Metallurgical Engineers, Contribution No. 136*, 6 pp., 1944.

Mandelbaum, H., and J. T. Sanford, "Table for Computing Thickness of Strata Measured in a Traverse or Encountered in a Bore Hole," *Bulletin Geological Society of America*, Vol. 63, pp. 765–776, 1952.

cross section in Fig. 346A,

$$\sin \delta = \frac{t}{s}$$

or
$$t = s \sin \delta \tag{1}$$

where t = thickness of the bed, δ = angle of dip of the bed, and s = breadth of the outcrop at right angles to the strike, measured along a horizontal surface.

Case b

Thickness, if the ground surface slopes in the same direction that the bed dips, and if the breadth of outcrop is measured at right angles to the strike of the bed. As shown in cross section in Fig. 346B,

$$\sin (\delta - \sigma) = \frac{t}{s}$$

or
$$t = s \sin (\delta - \sigma) \tag{2}$$

where t = thickness of bed, δ = angle of dip of the bed, σ = angle of slope of the surface of the ground, and s = breadth of outcrop measured at right angles to the strike and along the surface of the ground, *not* the map distance.

Case c

Thickness, if the ground surface slopes in the opposite direction to that in which the bed dips, and if the breadth of outcrop is measured at right angles to the strike of the bed. As shown in a cross section in Fig. 346C,

$$\sin (\delta + \sigma) = \frac{t}{s}$$

or
$$t = s \sin (\delta + \sigma) \tag{3}$$

where symbols are the same as for equation (2).

Case d

Thickness, if the ground surface is sloping, and if the breadth of outcrop is not measured at right angles to the strike of the bed. A plan is shown in Fig. 346D.

$$t = s (\sin \delta \cos \sigma \sin \alpha + \sin \sigma \cos \delta) \tag{4}$$
and
$$t = s (\sin \delta \cos \sigma \sin \alpha - \sin \sigma \cos \delta) \tag{5}$$

where t = thickness, s = slope distance (*not* map distance), α = azimuth of traverse—that is, the horizontal angle between the strike of the stratum and the direction in which the slope distance is measured, δ = dip of the bed, and σ = angle of slope of the surface of the ground in the direction of the traverse.

Equation (4) is used if the dip of the bed and the slope of the ground are in opposite directions. Equation (5) is used if the dip of the bed and the slope of the ground are in the same direction.

Case e

Depth, if the ground surface is horizontal, and if the distance is measured at right angles to the strike of the bed. As shown in a cross section in Fig. 347A, in which p is the point at which the depth is to be determined,

$$\tan \delta = \frac{d}{s}$$

or
$$d = s \tan \delta \tag{6}$$

where d = depth to the bed, δ = angle of dip of the bed, and s = distance along surface of ground between the outcrop of the bed and the point at which the depth of the bed is to be calculated.

Case f

Depth, if the ground surface slopes in the same direction that the bed dips, and if the distance is measured at right angles to the strike of the bed. As shown by a cross section in Fig. 347B, in which p is the point at

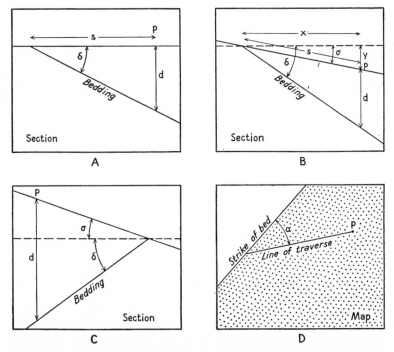

Fig. 347. Measurement of depth to a stratigraphic horizon. d = depth at point p; δ = angle of dip of bedding; σ = angle of slope of ground; s = slope distance between outcrop of bed and point p; α = angle between strike of bedding and trend of traverse. *A.* Ground horizontal. *B.* Bedding dips in same direction that ground slopes. *C.* Bedding dips in opposite direction to that in which ground slopes. *D.* Map for case in which traverse is not at right angles to strike of bedding.

which the depth is to be determined

$$\cos \sigma = \frac{x}{s} \quad \text{and} \quad x = s \cos \sigma$$

$$\sin \sigma = \frac{y}{s} \quad \text{and} \quad y = s \sin \sigma$$

$$\tan \delta = \frac{d + y}{x} = \frac{d + y}{s \cos \sigma}$$

$$d + y = s \cos \sigma \tan \delta$$

or $\qquad\qquad d + s \sin \sigma = s \cos \sigma \tan \delta$

or $\qquad\qquad\qquad d = s \cos \sigma \tan \delta - s \sin \sigma$

or $\qquad\qquad\qquad d = s \left(\cos \sigma \tan \delta - \sin \sigma \right) \qquad\qquad (7)$

where $d =$ depth, $s =$ slope distance, $\sigma =$ angle of slope, and $\delta =$ angle of dip of bed.

Case g

Depth, if the ground surface slopes in the opposite direction from that in which the bed dips, and if the distance is measured at right angles to the strike of the bed. From Fig. 347C, in which p is the point at which the depth is to be determined, the following equation may be derived:

$$d = s \left(\cos \sigma \tan \delta + \sin \sigma \right) \qquad\qquad (8)$$

where the symbols have the same meaning as in equation (7).

Case h

Depth, if the ground surface is sloping and the distance is not measured at right angles to the strike of the bed. A plan is shown in Fig. 347D, p is the point at which the depth is to be determined.

$$d = s \left(\tan \delta \cos \sigma \sin \alpha + \sin \sigma \right) \qquad\qquad (9)$$

and $\qquad d = s \left(\tan \delta \cos \sigma \sin \alpha - \sin \sigma \right) \qquad\qquad (10)$

where $d =$ depth, $s =$ slope distance, $\alpha =$ azimuth of traverse (that is, the horizontal angle between the strike of the bed and the direction of the traverse), $\delta =$ dip of the bed, and $\sigma =$ slope of the surface of the ground in the direction of the traverse.

Equation (9) is used if the dip of the beds and the slope of the ground are in opposite directions. Equation (10) is used if the dip of the bed and the slope of the ground are in the same direction.

DIAGRAMS TO SCALE

Solutions of the problems by the construction of diagrams to scale may be modeled after the diagrams in Figs. 346 and 347. A scale of 1 inch equals 200 feet should give sufficient accuracy for the problems at the end of this exercise.

ALIGNMENT DIAGRAMS

Figures 348, 349, 350, and 351 are alignment diagrams. Figures 348 and 349 may be used if the breadth of outcrop or distance perpendicular to the strike of the bed is known and if the ground is horizontal; Figure 348 is for thickness, and Fig. 349 is for depth. In Fig. 348 a line drawn from the "width of outcrop" on the left-hand scale to the "dip" on the right-hand scale gives the thickness on the central scale. Figure 349 is used in the same way to determine depth. These two diagrams may be

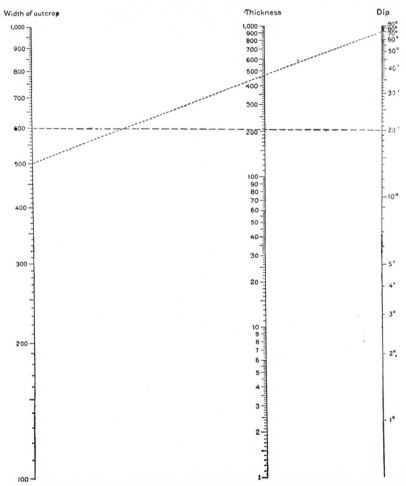

Fig. 348. Alignment diagram for computing thickness. This form is to be used only where breadth (width) of outcrop is measured at right angles to strike of bed. If ground surface is horizontal, if width of outcrop is 500 feet, and if dip is 70 degrees, the thickness is 470 feet. If the ground surface is horizontal, if width of outcrop is 600 feet, and if dip is 20 degrees, the thickness is 205 feet. (After H. S. Palmer.)

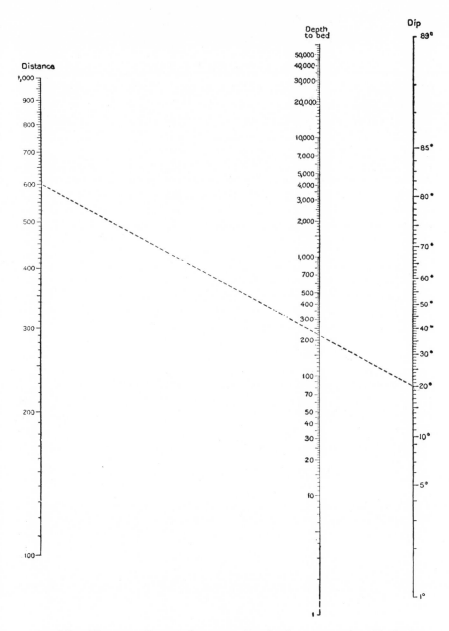

Fig. 349. Alignment diagram for computing depth to a stratigraphic horizon. This diagram is to be used only where distance to the outcrop of the horizon is measured at right angles to the strike of the horizon. If the ground surface is horizontal, if the distance to the outcrop is 600 feet, and if dip of bed is 20 degrees, the depth is 220 feet. (After H. S. Palmer.)

used also where the ground is sloping if the breadth of outcrop perpendicular to the strike of the bedding is known. But "width of outcrop" on the diagram is the slope distance, and "dip" is the dip plus (or minus) the slope angle. If the bedding dips in the opposite direction to that in which the ground slopes, the slope angle is added to the dip; if the bedding dips in the same direction as that in which the ground slopes, the slope angle is subtracted from the dip.

Figures 350 and 351, which are in the envelope, are more complicated diagrams and may be used for sloping ground where the breadth of outcrop is not measured perpendicular to the strike.

Using Fig. 350, the thickness diagram, we first locate a point which we may call a on the left-hand scale, on which "azimuth of traverse" means the angle between the strike of the beds and the line along which the breadth of outcrop is measured. Thus if the breadth of outcrop is measured perpendicular to the strike of the beds, the "azimuth of traverse" is 90 degrees. If the strike of the beds is north, whereas the breadth of outcrop is measured in a northeasterly direction, the "azimuth of traverse" is 45 degrees. The upper half of the scale is used if the bed and the ground slope in opposite directions; the lower half of the scale is used if the bed and the ground slope in the same direction.

A second point, which for convenience we may call b, is located on the triangle near the center of the diagram. The intersection of the angle of dip, given on the horizontal scale, and the angle of slope, given on the vertical scale, is located; this is point b.

A line drawn from a to b is extended to its intersection with the scale labeled t'. The point of intersection may be called c.

A new point, which we may call d, is located on the slope-distance scale; this point is the breadth of outcrop of the bed measured along the sloping surface of the ground. It is *not* the map distance, unless the surface of the ground is horizontal. If c is on the upper half of the diagram, d is likewise located on the upper half. If c is on the lower half, so is d.

A line connecting c and d is extended to intersect the right-hand vertical scale (t scale); this intersection is point e, which is the thickness of the bed. If points c and d are on the upper half of the diagram, read the t scale as though it were numbered from 0 at the top to 2,000 at the bottom. If points c and d are on the lower half of the diagram, read the t scale as though it were numbered from 0 at the bottom to 2,000 at the top.

The alignment chart for depth, Fig. 351, is used in a similar way.

PROBLEMS

The student must submit for each problem a neat diagram showing the relations.

1. Determine the thickness of a shale that strikes N. 90° E. and dips 34° S.; the breadth of outcrop, measured in a due north direction, is 375 feet The region is one of no relief. Solve this problem in the following

order: (a) by construction of a diagram to scale; (b) by the alignment diagram in Fig. 348; (c) by the alignment diagram in Fig. 350; and (d) by the equation.

2. Determine the thickness of a sandstone that is exposed on the east side of a mountain; the sandstone strikes N. and dips 26° W. The top of the sandstone is exposed at an altitude of 2,000 feet, and the bottom is exposed at an altitude of 1,625 feet. The distance between the top and bottom of the sandstone, measured along the slope and perpendicular to the strike is 2,450 feet. Solve in the following order: (a) by the alignment diagram in Fig. 348; (b) by the alignment diagram in Fig. 350; and (c) by the equation.

3. A stream flows in a southerly direction across a limestone that strikes N. 45° W. and dips 40° SW. Determine the thickness of the limestone if the base of the limestone is exposed at an altitude of 2,700 feet, and the top is exposed at an altitude of 2,100 feet. The breadth of the limestone along the stream, as shown on a map, is 2,000 feet. Solve in the following order: (a) by the alignment diagram in Fig. 348; (b) by the alignment diagram in Fig. 350; and (c) by the equation.

4. In a region of no relief a conglomerate strikes N. 30° E. and dips 45° SE. The top and bottom of the conglomerate are 4,300 feet apart as measured along an east-west line on the surface. Calculate the thickness of the conglomerate in the following order: (a) by the alignment diagram in Fig. 348; (b) by the alignment diagram in Fig. 350; and (c) by the equation.

5. A sandstone is exposed on the west slope of a mountain range. The sandstone strikes north and dips 34° E. The top of the bed is exposed at an altitude of 1,610 feet, the bottom at an altitude of 1,255 feet. The *map distance* between the top and bottom of the bed, measured in a direction N. 70° W., is 1,000 feet. Calculate the thickness of the sandstone: (a) by the alignment diagram in Fig. 350; (b) by the equation.

6. A gold-bearing conglomerate strikes due N. and dips 17° W. The surface of the ground is flat. At a distance of 925 feet west of the exposure, how deep a vertical shaft must be sunk to reach the conglomerate? Solve (a) by the alignment diagram in Fig. 349; (b) by the alignment diagram in Fig. 351; and (c) by the equation.

7. A bed of coal that strikes N. 45° E. and dips 36° NW. outcrops on the northwest side of a mountain at an altitude of 1,000 feet. At an altitude of 700 feet down the slope to the northwest a distance of 800 feet, measured perpendicular to the strike of the coal bed and along the slope, a vertical shaft is sunk to the coal bed. How deep must the shaft be? Solve (a) by the alignment diagram in Fig. 351; and (b) by the equation.

EXERCISE 4

Structure Sections of Folded Strata and Apparent Dips

METHOD

In the preparation of structure sections the topographic profile is prepared as indicated in Exercise 1. The contacts between geologic formations are also transferred in the manner indicated.

If the structure section that is to be constructed is approximately at right angles to the general trend of the structure, dips can be used as they appear on the map without any correction. The strike-dip symbols on the map are seldom located right on the line of the structure section. How close a symbol must be in order to be used depends upon the complexity of the geology. In regions in which the structure is simple, symbols a mile or so away may be used. The student should use a protractor in laying off the dips on the structure section.

The depth of the section depends on many variables. In this exercise it is suggested that they go to about half a mile below sea level. The beds should be connected above the ground surface by broken lines in order to emphasize the structure. Care must be taken to connect the horizons properly. The thickness of a formation should be approximately constant throughout the section.

A title, a legend, the scale, and the orientation should appear on the structure sections.

If the strike of a bed is not at right angles to the strike of the structure section, the apparent dip in the structure section is not the same as the true dip. The difference between true dip and apparent dip is illustrated by Fig. 352. If a bed strikes N. and dips 45° E., the apparent dip on a vertical east-west face is the same as the true dip. But on a

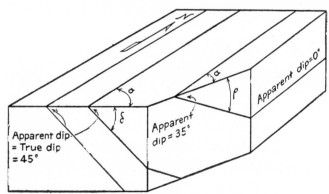

Fig. 352. Apparent dip and true dip. (See text.)

vertical face striking northeast the apparent dip is 35°. On a vertical north-south face the apparent dip is zero. If the strike of the bed is within 10 or 20 degrees of perpendicular to the strike of the structure section, the discrepancy ordinarily may be neglected.

The apparent dip of a bed in any desired direction may be calculated from the true dip by the equation

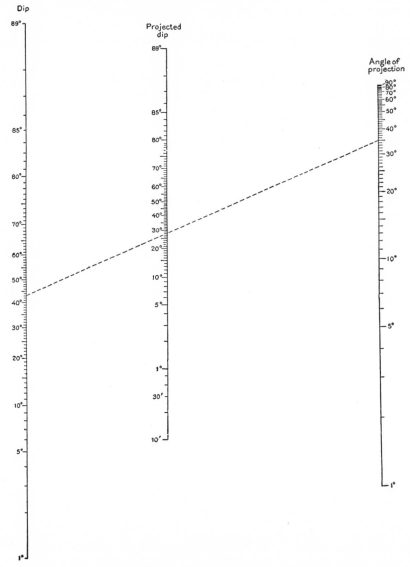

Fig. 353. Alignment diagram for computing apparent dip (projected dip). If true dip is 43 degrees, the apparent dip on a vertical section making a 35 degree angle with the strike of the bedding would be 28 degrees. (After H. S. Palmer.)

$$\tan \rho = \tan \delta \sin \alpha$$

where ρ is the apparent dip on a vertical plane, δ is the true dip, and α is the angle between the strike of the bed and the direction of the apparent dip.

Ordinarily the apparent dip can be determined with sufficient precision by using the alignment diagram of Fig. 353. The true dip is given on the left-hand scale; the angle between the strike of the bed and the strike of the vertical section upon which the apparent dip is plotted is given in the right-hand scale. A line connecting the points on these two scales gives the apparent dip on the central scale.

Examples of the use of the alignment diagram may be cited. If the strike of an horizon is N. 45° E. and the dip is 30° NW., what is the apparent dip on a vertical section that trends N. 5° W.? The point on the left-hand scale is 30 degrees. The point on the right-hand scale is 50 degrees. A line connecting these two points crosses the central scale at 24 degrees. Therefore 24 degrees is the apparent dip in a N. 5° W. direction.

Tables and charts for apparent dip are given in Lahee.[1]

The reverse problem is to calculate the true strike and dip if two apparent dips are known. The apparent dips must be measured on vertical faces. Moreover, the two vertical faces cannot have the same strike. The general principles are illustrated in Fig. 354A. Suppose that the apparent dip is known on two vertical faces, one striking in the direction OB and the other in the direction OA. Draw two rays from a central point O.

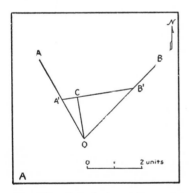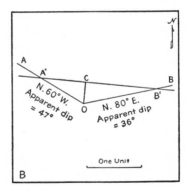

Fig. 354. Calculating strike and true dip from two apparent dips. (See text.)

These two rays, OA and OB, are parallel to the vertical faces on which the apparent dips are measured. Moreover, they extend from O in the direction of the apparent dip. Lay off along each ray, using any convenient scale, the value of the *cotangent of the apparent dip*, OA' on OA, and OB' on OB. Connect A' and B'; the direction of this line is the direction of strike of the bed. Drop a perpendicular, OC, from $A'B'$ to O. The magnitude of this line CO equals the cotangent of the true dip.

[1] Lahee, F. H., *Field Geology*, 5th ed., Appendices XIII and XIV. New York: McGraw-Hill Book Company, 1951.

Figure 354B is a specific example. On a vertical face trending N. 80° E. the apparent dip is 36° in the direction N. 80° E. On a vertical face trending N. 60° W. the apparent dip is 47° in a direction N. 60° W. On *OB* plot *OB′*, which is 1.38 units long (the cotangent of 36°). On *OA* plot *OA′*, which is 0.93 unit long (the cotangent of 47°). The strike (the trend of *A′B′*) is N. 85° W. The true dip is the angle whose cotangent is the length of *CO*, which is 0.40 unit; that is, the true dip is 68°.

PROBLEMS

1. Make a topographic profile and geologic structure section along the indicated line on the map given you by your instructor. One of the following folios of the *Geologic Atlas of the United States,* issued by the U. S. Geological Survey, may be used: **221,** Bessemer-Vandiver, Alabama; **175,** Birmingham, Alabama; **227,** Hollidaysburg-Huntingdon, Pennsylvania.

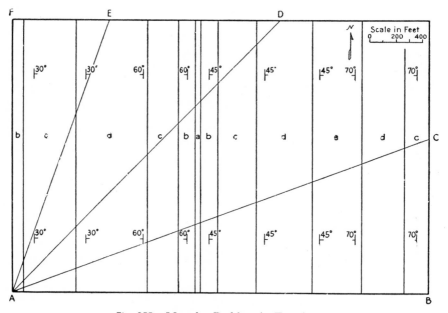

Fig. 355. Map for Problem in Exercise 4.

2. From Fig. 355 draw a series of structure sections along the lines *AB, AC, AD, AE,* and *AF.* Connect the beds above the ground surface by broken lines in order to show the structure more clearly.

3. The apparent dips on different pairs of vertical faces are given below. Determine the strike and dip of the bedding for each of the three cases.

	Value of Apparent Dip	Direction of Apparent Dip
(a)	20°	N. 90° W.
	40°	N.
(b)	60°	N. 60° E.
	70°	S. 45° E.
(c)	5°	N. 70° E.
	30°	N. 30° E.

4. The strike of a bed can be measured on the flat top of an outcrop, but the true dip cannot be measured. The apparent dip may be observed on a vertical face *not* perpendicular to the strike of the bedding. For each of the two cases given below determine the true dip.

	Value of Apparent Dip	Direction of Apparent Dip	Strike of Bed
(a)	45°	N. 60° E.	N. 90° E.
(b)	50°	N. 45° W.	N. 15° W.

5. Work this problem on an 8½ by 11 inch sheet of plain white paper. To insure adequate space use the short dimension of the sheet as the N-S direction and place a road intersection 4 inches in from the east edge of the paper and 3 inches down from the top. Use a scale of 1 inch = 400 feet.

Data. Well No. 1. Located 600 feet south of the road intersection, elevation 435 feet. Depth to fault 2,435 feet. Depth to unconformity 1,935 feet.

Well No. 2. Located 1,000 feet east of the same road intersection, elevation 200 feet. Depth to the fault 2,700 feet. Depth to unconformity 1,700 feet.

Well No. 3. Located 600 feet north of the same road intersection, elevation 100 feet. Depth to the fault 2,100 feet. Depth to the unconformity 1,600 feet.

Well No. 4. Located 1,000 feet west of the same road intersection, elevation 300 feet.

Find the following: (a) strike of the fault; (b) dip of the fault; (c) apparent dip of the fault in a north-south direction; (d) apparent dip of the fault in an east-west direction; (e) depth at which Well No. 4 hits the fault; (f) depth at which Well No. 4 hits the unconformity; (g) draw the line along which the fault plane intersects the unconformity on your scale diagram.

EXERCISE 5

Geometrical Reconstruction of Folds

METHOD

Application

Two principal geometrical relations between successive bedding planes in a fold are possible. The folds may be parallel or similar (see p. 56). This exercise gives a method of reconstructing parallel folds if the location of several exposures is given and if the attitude of the beds in those exposures is known. The method cannot be used for reconstructing similar folds nor is it suitable for reconstructing tight or complicated folds.[1] Moreover, the distance between exposures must be less than the distance between the axes of folds.

Principle

Figure 356 shows the method of reconstructing parallel folds.[2] The attitude of strata at points A, B, C, D, and E is shown. These points are

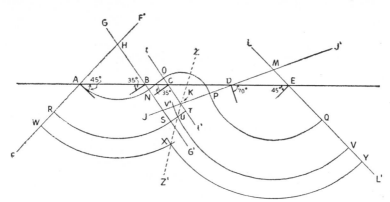

Fig. 356. Geometrical construction of folds. Dip of beds is known at A, B, C, D, and E. (After Busk.)

on a line perpendicular to the trend of the folds. If the strike of the section is not at right angles to the strike of the bedding, the apparent dip in the direction of the section must be calculated for each outcrop. Perpendiculars to the bedding at each outcrop are constructed and extended to intersect the perpendiculars to the bedding of adjacent outcrops. FF',

[1] Gill, W. D., "Construction of Geological Sections of Folds with Steep-Limb Attenuation," *Bulletin American Association Petroleum Geologists*, Vol. 37, pp. 2389–2406, 1953.

[2] Busk, H. G., *Earth Flexures*. Cambridge: Cambridge University Press, 1929.

the perpendicular to A, intersects GG', the perpendicular to B, at H. The dip of the bedding is the same at any point along FF' as it is at A. Similarly, the dip at any point on GG' is the same as that at B. With H as a center, and HA as the radius, an arc is swung from A to intersect GG' at N. Inasmuch as the dip at B and C is the same in this problem, the perpendiculars to the bedding at these points will not intersect. The horizon is extended from N, parallel to the dip of the beds, to intersect II' at O. With K, which is the intersection of II' and JJ', as a center, and KO as the radius, an arc is constructed to intersect JJ' at P. With M, which is the intersection of JJ' and LL', as a center, and MP as a radius, an arc is swung from P to intersect LL' at Q. $ANOPQ$ is the position of the horizon outcropping at A.

In reconstructing an horizon at R, we find that the horizon falls at T below the intersection K. In such a case the distance QV is set off on line LL' equal to the distance AR. From V, with M as a center and MV as the radius, an arc is swung to intersect JJ' at V'. The position of the horizon that occurs at R is $RSUV$.

At the depth at which horizon W occurs, the dip at C no longer has any influence. WXY shows the form assumed by the horizon at W.

ZZ' is the trace of the axial plane of the central anticline on the vertical section. ZK bisects angle IKJ'; KZ' passes through points U and X.

Interpolation

The accuracy of the reconstructed fold depends upon the number of dip and strike readings in the section. If outcrops are missing in a critical locality, the reconstruction may not be accurate. A key bed, for example, may be recognizable in several different localities. Its position, as predicted by the method outlined above, may not correspond to its actual position. Dips may then be interpolated to make the fold pattern fit the field facts. The method is outlined below.

In Fig. 357, points A, B, C, and D show the location and attitude of folded beds. When the fold is reconstructed according to the method given above, the horizon at A should reappear at J. The theoretical position of the horizon is $AHIJ$. If field mapping has shown that the horizon at A is the same as that at D, then a dip must be interpolated at some point in the section to erase the apparent discrepancy. A dip should be interpolated for a point between the two outcrops that are farthest apart —that is, between B and C.

With G as a center and GD as a radius, an arc is constructed to intersect EE' at K. For arc HI two arcs that are tangent to each other and tangent to H and K will be substituted. From K, KL is drawn perpendicular to EE'. From H, HM is drawn perpendicular to VV'. These two lines intersect at N. H and K are connected by a straight line, HK. A perpendicular to HK, drawn through point N, is extended to intersect EE' at R and VV' at S. With R as a center and RK as a radius, arc KT is constructed. Arc HT is drawn with S as a center and SH as a radius. $AHTKD$ is the pattern of the fold. A perpendicular to OP at X gives the interpolated dip, which is the angle UXC.

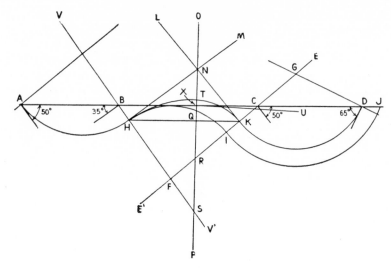

Fig. 357. Geometrical Construction of Folds. Dip of beds is known at *A*, *B*, *C*, and *D*. Same stratigraphic horizon crops out at *A* and *D*. (After Busk.)

PROBLEMS

1. A traverse is made due east across a series of rocks that strike north-south. The following data are obtained on the dip of the beds. The left-hand column gives the distance in feet from the west end of the traverse; the right-hand column gives the dip.

Distance in Feet	*Dip*
0	35° E.
1000	20° W.
2100	35° E.
2400	20° W.
3100	15° E.
4200	40° E.
5000	40° E.
5900	35° W.
7000	25° E.
7500	18° W.

(a) Reconstruct the folds, assuming parallel folding. (b) If a distinctive bed outcrops at the west end of the traverse, at what depth (or height, in which case it would be eroded) would the bed be located at the east end of the section (distance 7,500)?

2. A traverse is made due south across a series of rocks that strike N. 90° E. The following data are obtained on the dip of the beds. The left-hand column gives the distance in feet from the north end of the traverse; the right-hand column gives the dip.

Distance in Feet	Dip
0	45° S.
2300	30° N.
3500	25° S.
5300	40° N.
7000	28° S.

(a) Reconstruct the folds, assuming parallel folding. (b) If a distinctive bed outcrops at the north end of the traverse, at what depth (or height, in which case it would be eroded) would the bed be located at the south end of the section? (c) Actually the distinctive bed outcrops at the south end of the traverse (distance 7,000). Adjust the section to allow for the known position of the distinctive bed. Do this by interpolating a dip between the 5,300-foot and 7,000-foot points. What is the location and value of the interpolated dip?

3. A traverse is made in a due east direction across a series of rocks that strike N. The following data are obtained on the dip of the beds. The left-hand column gives the distance in feet from the west end of the traverse. The right-hand column gives the dip.

Distance in Feet	Dip
0	60° E.
1600	10° W.
2400	10° W.
2700	25° W.
3600	10° E.
4000	35° E.
5700	60° E.
6800	0°

(a) Reconstruct the folds, assuming parallel folding. (b) On the surface of the earth what is the horizontal distance of the crest of the anticline from the west end of the section? (c) At a depth of 1,000 feet what is the horizontal distance of the crest of the anticline from the west end of the section? (d) At a depth of 2,000 feet?

EXERCISE 6

Structure Contours and Isopachs

STRUCTURE CONTOURS

A structure contour is an imaginary line connecting points of equal altitude on a single horizon, usually the top or bottom of a sedimentary bed. A structure contour map thus shows the form of the horizon. Structure contours are analogous to topographic contours, which show the form of the surface of the earth.

The dip of an horizon represented by structure contours can be calculated with great precision. For a given contour interval, the closer the structure contours are to each other on a map, the steeper is the dip, just as the closer topographic contours are to each other, the steeper is the slope. The method of determining the dip quantitatively is discussed on p. 85.

The method of preparing a structure contour map is illustrated by Fig. 358. First of all, some horizon must be chosen to be represented by the structure contours; it may be the top or bottom of a coal bed, the top of an oil-bearing stratum, or the top or bottom of some bed that is readily recognizable. Wherever this horizon is exposed at the surface of the earth, the altitude may be plotted on the map. The data may also come from drill holes or mines. If the thicknesses of the various stratigraphic units have been precisely determined, it is possible to predict at what depth the key horizon occurs, even though it is not exposed or penetrated by drill holes or mines.

The altitudes of numerous points on the top of a bed of limestone are given in Fig. 358. It is decided to use a structure contour interval of 100 feet. In the lower left-hand corner of Fig. 358 the altitude of the top of the limestone at one point is shown to be 800 feet. The 800-foot structure contour will pass through this point. Otherwise it is necessary to interpolate proportionally between each pair of points for which data are given. In the northeast corner of the map, two points on the horizon being contoured have the altitudes of 740 feet and 960 feet, respectively. The 800-foot and 900-foot contours will pass between these two points. The difference in altitude between these two points is 220 feet. The distance of the 800-foot contour from the 740-foot point will be 6/22 of the total distance between the two points. The distance of the 900-foot contour from the 740-foot point will be 16/22 of the total distance between the two points. The location of contours over all the map may be found in the same way. The contours obtained in this way may be modified somewhat in order to smooth out sharp curves.

If the altitudes are given on some bed other than the one being contoured, the thickness of the beds must be taken into consideration. That is, if altitudes are given on a bed 1,000 feet stratigraphically above the horizon being contoured, the structure contour is 1,000 feet below the altitude given on the map. Strictly, we should use the depth factor rather than the thickness (Figs. 346A and 347A). Since, however, the dip is unknown prior to the completion of the structure contour map, it is impossible to make this correction. Moreover, if the dip does not exceed 10 degrees the correction is negligible. The error is usually much less than the probable error in the thicknesses of the formations.

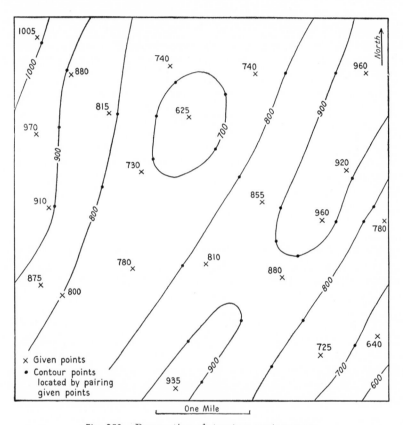

Fig. 358.   Preparation of structure contour map.

If an area is entirely enclosed by one or more contours, it is known as a *closed structure;* this usage is not to be confused with the use of the term *closed fold* (p. 45). The closure of a fold is the vertical distance between the highest and the lowest contours that completely enclose the fold. The precision of the measurement of the closure of a fold, as determined from a structure contour map, depends upon the contour interval. If a fold has a closure less than the contour interval that is used, the closure may not appear on the map. A minus (−) before a contour indicates depth below some level plane, usually sea level.

ISOPACHS

A bed or formation is not constant in thickness. If the thickness is known at many localities, it is possible to draw *isopachs,* which are lines connecting points at which the bed is of equal thickness. Suppose, for example, that a formation is known to be 100 feet thick at three localities that are designated *a, b,* and *c,* but 300 feet thick at three other localities designated *e, f,* and *g.* The 100-foot isopach would pass through *a, b,* and *c,* and the 300-foot isopach would pass through *e, f,* and *g.* The 200-foot isopach would lie between the 100-foot and the 300-foot isopachs; if no other data were available, it would be placed halfway between them. In the preparation of isopach maps from data at numerous localities, inter-polation is performed in the same way as in the preparation of structure contour maps.

PROBLEMS

Figure 359 shows a series of structure contour maps. Assume they are all on the same horizon and that the surface of the earth is a plain 1,500 feet above sea level.

1. In Fig. 359A what is the dip in feet per mile and in degrees between 1 and 2? Between 2 and 3?

2. In Fig. 359B what is the dip in feet per mile and in degrees between 4 and 5?

3. In Fig. 359C what is the depth to the key horizon at point 6?

4. In Fig. 359D what is the depth to the key horizon at point 7?

5. Draw a cross section along the indicated line for each of the six maps. Exaggerate the vertical scale 10 times.

6. Figure 360, in the envelope, is a geological map. Formation *B* is the oldest of the exposed formations, and formation *G* is the youngest. The altitude of many points on the contacts is given. Well records show that the formations have the following thicknesses: *F* is 50 feet; *E* is 160 feet; *D* is 80 feet; *C* is 290 feet; *B* is 200 feet; and *A,* which does not outcrop, varies in thickness. Well records indicate that *A* is 200 feet thick in the northeast corner of the map; seven miles due west of here it is 500 feet thick. In the southeast corner of the map it is 250 feet thick; six miles due west it is 450 feet thick. Other drill records indicate that the variation in thickness is uniform throughout the area.

Prepare a structure contour map on the top of formation *A,* using a contour interval of 100 feet.[1]

7. On a piece of tracing paper prepare an isopach map for formation *A* in Problem 6.

8. On a piece of tracing paper prepare a structure contour map on the base of formation *A* in Problem 6.

If the instructor desires, he may use one or more of the following folios of the *Geological Atlas of the United States,* published by the U. S. Geo-

---

[1] This may be done directly on the map or on a piece of tracing paper placed over the map.

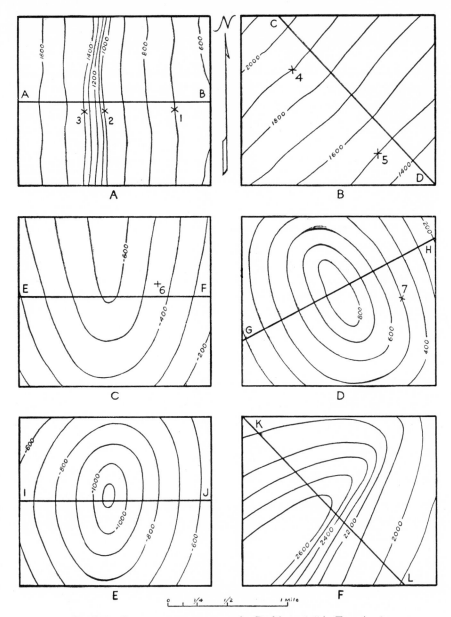

Fig. 359. Structure contour maps for Problems 1–5 in Exercise 6.

logical Survey: 185, Murphysboro-Herrin, Illinois; 189, Barnesboro-Patton, Pennsylvania; 174, Johnstown, Pennsylvania; 175, Birmingham, Alabama; 133, Ebensburg, Pennsylvania; 125, Rural Valley, Pennsylvania.

The instructor may want to use some of the excellent structure contour maps in the series entitled "Oil and Gas Investigations" issued by the U. S. Geological Survey.

EXERCISE 7

Trigonometric Solution of Fault Problems

METHOD

The types of faults and the definition of terms relating to the movement along faults are given on pp. 124–146.

The solution of the problems should be accompanied by a plan, as well as by one or more structure sections that show the fault and the disrupted beds.

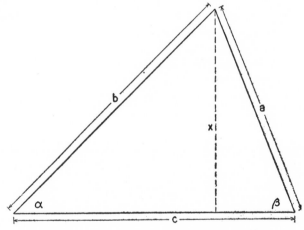

Fig. 361. Triangle to illustrate the *Law of Sines*.

The law of sines, which can be used to solve any triangle, is useful in this exercise. This law states that the sines of angles are proportional to the sides opposite the respective angles. As shown in Fig. 361, if abc is the triangle, and x is a perpendicular to c,

$$\sin \alpha = \frac{x}{b}$$

$$\sin \beta = \frac{x}{a}$$

$$\frac{\sin \alpha}{\sin \beta} = \frac{\frac{x}{b}}{\frac{x}{a}}$$

$$\frac{\sin \alpha}{\sin \beta} = \frac{xa}{xb}$$

455

and
$$\frac{\sin \alpha}{\sin \beta} = \frac{a}{b}$$

The following problem, illustrated by a structure section given in Fig. 362A, will be solved to illustrate the method used.

A horizontal tunnel extends east-west and intersects a fault that strikes north and dips 40 degrees to the west. At a distance of 500 feet east of this intersection the tunnel cuts a bed of sandstone that strikes north and dips 30 degrees east. At a distance of 700 feet west of the fault

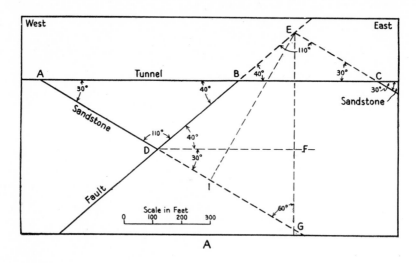

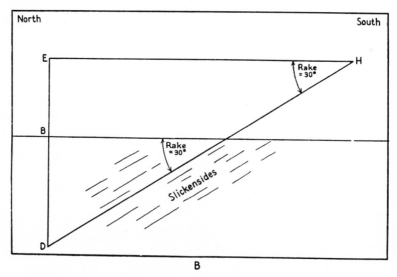

Fig. 362. Trigonometric solution of fault problems. *A*. Vertical cross section of a thin bed of sandstone that is displaced along a fault. *B*. Slickensides on fault rake 30° N.

the tunnel cuts the same sandstone, also striking north and dipping 30 degrees east. The slickensides on the footwall rise from north to south (Fig. 362B) and make an angle of 30 degrees with a horizontal line in the fault plane; that is, the rake of the slickensides is 30 degrees north.

Calculate the net slip, dip slip, strike slip, heave, throw, stratigraphic separation, vertical separation in a plane perpendicular to the fault, and horizontal separation in the same plane.

From Fig. 362A, which is a vertical section at right angles to the strike of the fault, we obtain

$$Dip\ slip = DB + BE$$

In triangle ABD

$$\frac{\sin 110°}{\sin 30°} = \frac{AB}{DB}$$

and

$$BD = \frac{AB \sin 30°}{\sin 110°}$$

In triangle EBC

$$\frac{\sin 110°}{\sin 30°} = \frac{BC}{BE}$$

and

$$BE = \frac{BC \sin 30°}{\sin 110°}$$

$$Dip\ slip = DB + BE = \frac{700 \sin 30°}{\sin 110°} + \frac{500 \sin 30°}{\sin 110°}$$

$$Dip\ slip = 638\ feet$$

From Fig. 362B

$$Strike\ slip = EH$$

$$\tan 30° = \frac{DB + BE}{EH} = \frac{638}{EH}$$

$$EH = 1105\ feet$$

$$Net\ slip = DH$$

$$\sin 30° = \frac{DB + BE}{DH} = \frac{638}{DH}$$

$$DH = 1276\ feet$$

From Fig. 362A, triangle DEF

$$Throw = EF$$

$$\sin 40° = \frac{EF}{DB + BE}$$

$$EF = (DB + BE) \sin 40°$$

$$EF = 638 \sin 40° = 410\ feet$$

$$Heave = DF$$

$$\cos 40° = \frac{DF}{DB + BE}$$

$$DF = (DB + BE) \cos 40°$$

$$DF = 638 \cos 40° = 488\ feet$$

From Fig. 362A, triangle DEI

$$Stratigraphic\ separation\ =\ EI$$

$$\sin{(30° + 40°)} = \frac{EI}{DB + BE}$$

$$EI = 638 \sin 70° = 599\ \text{feet}$$

From Fig. 362A, triangle DEG

$$Vertical\ separation\ =\ EF + FG$$

$$\frac{\sin{(30° + 40°)}}{\sin 60°} = \frac{EF + FG}{DB + BE}$$

$$\frac{\sin 70°}{\sin 60°} = \frac{EF + FG}{638}$$

$$EF + FG = 692\ \text{feet}$$

From Fig. 362A

$$Horizontal\ separation\ =\ AB + BC$$
$$AB + BC = 1200\ \text{feet}$$

PROBLEMS

These problems are to be solved by trigonometry.

1. A bed that strikes N. 45° W. and dips 45° SW. is broken by a strike fault that dips 45° NE. The hanging wall has moved 1,600 feet directly down the dip of the fault plane. Calculate (a) net slip, (b) strike slip, (c) dip slip, (d) throw, (e) heave, (f) horizontal separation in a vertical plane perpendicular to the strike of the fault, (g) vertical separation in the same plane, and (h) stratigraphic throw.

2. A sandstone that strikes N. 45° W. and dips 60° SW. is broken by a strike fault that dips 35° SW. The sandstone outcrops 250 feet northeast of the fault and 150 feet southwest of the fault. Assuming the movement to have been directly down the dip of the fault plane, calculate the (a) net slip, (b) dip slip, (c) strike slip, (d) throw, (e) heave, (f) horizontal separation in a vertical plane perpendicular to the strike of the fault, (g) vertical separation in the same plane, and (h) stratigraphic throw.

3. A north-south tunnel cuts a fault that strikes N. 90° E. and dips 65° S. The strata also strike N. 90° E., but dip 35° N. The hanging wall has gone down diagonally toward the east; the rake of the net slip is 35 degrees; and the value is 1,500 feet. Calculate the (a) dip slip, (b) strike slip, (c) throw, and (d) heave.

4. A fault plane strikes N. 90° E. and dips 40° N. A coal bed, striking N. 90° E. and dipping 65° S., is exposed 500 feet north of the fault and again 800 feet south of the fault. The rake of the slickensides on the fault is 30 degrees toward the west. Assuming that the slickensides are parallel to the net slip, calculate the (a) net slip, (b) dip slip, (c) strike slip, (d) heave, (e) throw, and (f) stratigraphic throw. (g) Is this a normal or a reversed fault?

EXERCISE 8

Projections

METHOD

An object having three dimensions may be shown on a single plane by means of projection. The projection of a point on a plane is a point. The projection of a line on a plane is generally a line. The plane upon which points or lines are projected is the *plane of projection*. The *direction of projection* is the direction in which a point is projected into the plane of projection. *Normal projection,* in which the direction of projection is perpendicular to the plane of projection, is used in this exercise.

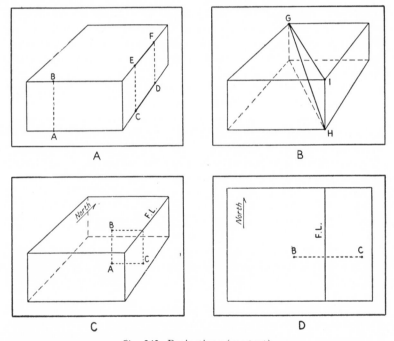

Fig. 363. Projections (see text).

Normal projections are illustrated in Fig. 363. Points and lines have been projected into the horizontal plane represented by the upper surface of the blocks. In Fig. 363A, point B is the projection of point A; line EF is the projection of line CD. In Fig. 363B, line GI is the projection of line GH into this plane.

The line of intersection of two planes is the trace of one plane upon the other. The trace of one plane of projection upon a second plane of projection is called a *folding line*. In normal projection the angle between two planes having a common folding line is always 90 degrees.

In most cases one plane of projection is horizontal, whereas the others are vertical. In geology the horizontal plane is a plan, corresponding more or less precisely with the map. A map portrays the relations on the surface of the earth, regardless of its topographic irregularities. A plan is made on a plane surface. In areas of low relief the geological map may be treated as a plan, and, whenever the term *map* is used in the ensuing descriptions, it is to be considered synonymous with the word *plan*. In geology the other planes of projection are structure sections. However, a plane of projection does not have to be either horizontal or vertical.

To represent a plan (map) and a section on one plane (the plane of the paper), it is necessary to rotate the section into the plane of the map around the folding line as an axis. In the following problems it is best to consider the section as lying below the folding line; the section will then be rotated upward into the horizontal plane. In Fig. 363C, point B is the projection of point A into a horizontal plane; point C is the projection of point A into the vertical plane represented by the side of the block. Figure 363D shows the projection after the vertical plane has been rotated into the plane of the paper about the folding line ($F. L.$) as an axis.

The attitude of a line is defined by the strike of its horizontal projection and by its plunge (see p. 46).

The following problem, similar to those at the end of the exercise, illustrates the procedure to be followed.

Problem: As shown in Fig. 364, a vein that strikes N. 40° E. and dips 40° NW. intersects a vein that strikes N. 30° W. and dips 55° NE. Draw the projections of the intersection of the two veins (a) on a horizontal plane, (b) on a vertical plane striking north-south, and (c) on a vertical plane striking parallel to the direction of plunge of the intersection. (d) Show the trace of the N. 40° E. vein on the N. 30° W. vein. (It will be necessary to rotate the N. 30° W. vein into the horizontal to show the projection.) (e) What is the attitude of the intersection?

Solution: Draw AB and CD parallel to the respective strikes of the veins, as shown in Fig. 364. The veins intersect at point O. Construct a folding line FF' perpendicular to AB; construct a folding line GG' perpendicular to CD. These folding lines may be constructed at any convenient point along AB and CD.

Using these folding lines as the horizontal, now make cross sections. Draw HH' parallel to and at an arbitrary distance h from FF'; construct II' at the same distance from GG'. HH' and II' represent a level which will be called the *lower reference plane;* it is h distance below the level of the plan (map). Throughout any one problem the elevation of the lower reference plane remains constant. F'' is the intersection of FF' with AB; G'' is the intersection of GG' with CD. Draw angles $FF''J$ and $G'G''K$ equal to the respective dips of the two veins. $F''J$ intersects HH' at J'; $G''K$ intersects II' at K'. Draw $J'M$ and $K'L$ parallel to AB and CD, respectively. These two lines represent the horizontal projections of contours on the two veins at h distance below the plan; that is, these two lines are the horizontal projection of the intersection of the two veins with the lower reference plane. Point N is the horizontal projection of the intersection of the two veins on the lower reference plane, and point O is the intersection of the two veins on the plan. Therefore line ON is the horizontal projection of the intersection of the two veins. The strike of the intersection in this case is N. 6° W.

Draw line PP' in a north-south direction through some arbitrary point. This line is the trace of a north-south vertical plane on the plan.

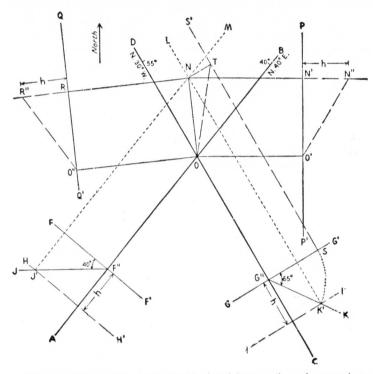

Fig. 364. Projection to find attitude of intersection of two veins: one striking N. 40° E., dipping 40° NW.; the second striking N. 30° W., dipping 55° NE.

The vertical plane must be rotated into the upper reference plane (the plan) around PP' as the axis of rotation to show the projection of the intersection ON on the vertical plane.

Project point O to O' in the north-south plane; similarly project point N to N' in the north-south plane. Draw a line through NN' and extend it to the right of N'. Lay off point N'' at a distance h from point N'. Point N'' is the intersection of the two veins in the lower reference plane projected into a north-south vertical plane; line $O'N''$ is the intersection of the two veins projected into the north-south vertical plane.

Through some arbitrary point construct line QQ' parallel to line ON. Line QQ' is the trace on the plan (map) of a vertical plane that strikes parallel to the direction of the plunge of the intersection of the two veins. This vertical plane must be rotated into the horizontal around the folding line QQ' in order to show the projection of the intersection of the two veins upon it. Project point O into this plane to O''; similarly project point N to R in this same plane and extend line NR to the left of R. From point R, lay off RR'' equal to h. Point R'' is the intersection of the two veins with the lower reference plane projected into a vertical plane that strikes parallel to the intersection of the two veins. Line $O''R''$ is the intersection of the two veins projected to this same plane. Angle $RO''R''$, 31°, is the plunge of the intersection of the two veins.

To draw the trace of the N. 40° E. vein on the N. 30° W. vein, it is necessary to rotate the N. 30° W. vein into the plan (map). CD, the trace of the vein on the plan, is used as the axis of rotation. Using the line $G''K'$ as the radius and the point G'' as the center, draw an arc to intersect GG' at S. Through point S draw a line SS' parallel to the strike of the N. 30° W. vein. This line, SS', is the trace of the N. 30° W. vein on the lower reference plane, now rotated into a horizontal position. From point N, construct NT perpendicular to SS'. N is the horizontal projection of a point on the lower reference plane; this point on the lower reference plane falls at T when it is rotated to the surface. Line OT is the trace of the N. 40° E.

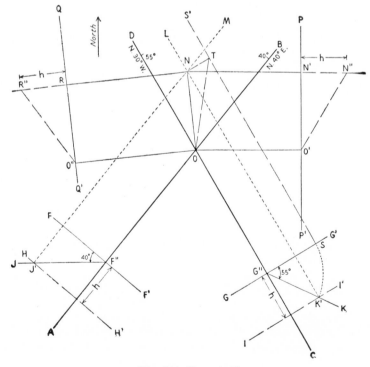

(Fig. 364. Repeated.)

vein on the N. 30° W. vein. Angle *DOT*, 39°, is the rake of the trace of the N. 40° E. vein on the N. 30° W. vein.

PROBLEMS

1. A vertical vein that strikes N. 30° W. intersects a vein that strikes N. 45° E. and dips 60° SE. Determine the direction and amount of plunge of the intersection.

2. The two limbs of a fold strike N. 45° W. and N. 30° E., and dip 35° NE. and 75° W., respectively. What is the direction and amount of plunge of the fold?

3. A vein that strikes N. 50° E. and dips 45° SE. intersects a vein that strikes N. 70° W. and dips 60° SW. Draw the projections of the intersection (a) on a horizontal plane, (b) on a vertical plane striking north-south, (c) on the plane of the N. 50° E. vein, and (d) on a vertical plane striking parallel to the direction of the plunge of the intersection. (e) In which of these projections can the plunge be measured directly? (f) What is the direction and amount of the plunge of the intersection?

4. A vein that strikes N. 50° E. and dips 50° NW. intersects a vein that strikes N. 10° W. and dips 30° E. Perform the same operations and answer the same questions as in Problem 3.

EXERCISE 9

Measuring Lengths, Areas, and Stratigraphic Thicknesses by Descriptive Geometry

LENGTHS OF LINES

To measure the length of a line we project the line onto a vertical plane parallel to its direction of plunge. The method for constructing such a projection was described in Exercise 8. An example is given here in Fig. 365.

A thin, cylindrical body of copper ore crops out at point A at an altitude of 3,050 feet. The same ore-body was located underground in a tunnel at point B, 400 feet south and 200 feet east of its outcrop at point A, and at an altitude of 2,680 feet. To find the length of the ore-body above the tunnel, draw a folding line QQ' parallel to AB, the map projection of the ore-body. From A, draw a line perpendicular to QQ', locating A'. From B, draw a similar line and extend it beyond Q'. Measure the distance $Q'B'$ equal to the difference in altitude, 370 feet, using the same scale as the map. The line $A'B'$ is the length of the ore-body, 580 feet, and the angle $B'A'Q'$, 40 degrees, is its plunge.

AREAS OF PLANES

To measure the area of a plane figure, we must make a projection in the plane in which the figure lies. Such a projection can be made by one of two methods.

2.

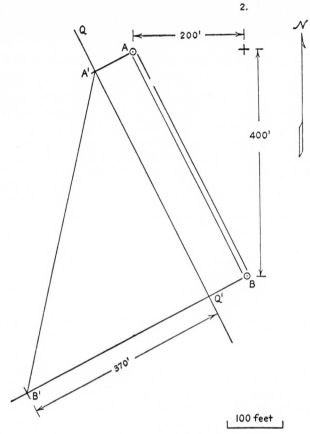

Fig. 365. Length of a line.

The first method was described in Exercise 8 (see Fig. 364, p. 461). An arc is swung from the edge view of the N. 30° W. vein (line $G''K'$) to determine a segment of $G''G'$ equal in length to $G''K'$. This segment is $G''S$. Through S the line SS' is passed parallel to $G''D$. This line is the projection in the plane of the N. 30° W. vein of the line $K'N$; and the line OT is the projection in the plane of the N. 30° W. vein of the line whose projection in the horizontal plane is ON. This method of obtaining projections in sloping planes by drawing arcs is very useful where only a few points have to be projected. However, if a large number of points have to be projected, the finished drawing, which is essentially two different views superimposed on each other, is hard to read.

A method of solving the problem in complicated cases is to make a completely new projection from the edge view of the plane. In Fig. 366, a coal bed striking N. 40° W. and dipping 50° NE. is explored by two horizontal tunnels, lying in the bed, along the lines AB and CD. The tunnel along the line CD is 100 feet lower than the tunnel along the line AB. In the upper tunnel the coal bed is cut off by faults at A and B; in the lower tunnel it is cut off by the same faults at C and D. The intersections of the faults and the coal bed are shown in plan by the dot-dash lines. The coal bed is 5 feet thick. We wish to find the volume of coal in the block between the two tunnels and between the two faults, by drawing a projection of the coal bed in the plane of the bed.

First we draw an edge view of the plane of the coal bed. To do this, draw the folding line PP' through the point N perpendicular to AB extended. Draw NR making an angle of 50 degrees with PP' (the dip of the coal bed). Measure NQ on ABN extended, equal to 100 feet (the difference in altitude of the two beds), and through Q draw a line parallel to PP'. In the vertical plane perpendicular to the coal bed, represented by PP' and NO, this last line we have drawn is 100 feet below PP'. The point O, where this line intersects the line NR, is a point on the bed 100 feet below the tunnel AB. As is to be expected, this point lies on the line CD extended.

Now, to obtain a projection in a plane parallel to the plane of the coal bed, we must project the points A, B, C, and D onto a plane perpendicular to the vertical plane and passing through NO. To do this, draw lines NV and OW perpendicular to NO. At any convenient distance on NV, locate the point B'. Returning to the plan view, erect a line BE perpendicular to AB at B, and intersecting CD at E. Similarly at B' erect a line perpendicular to NV and intersecting OW at E'. Measure $B'A'$ equal to BA; $D'E'$ equal to DE; and $C'D'$ equal to CD. The lines $A'B'$ and $C'D'$ are the projections of the tunnels in the plane of the coal bed, and the lines $A'C'$ and $B'D'$ are the traces of the faults on the coal bed. If the area of $A'B'C'D'$ be now measured, at the scale of the map, and multiplied by the thickness of the coal bed, the volume of coal can be determined.

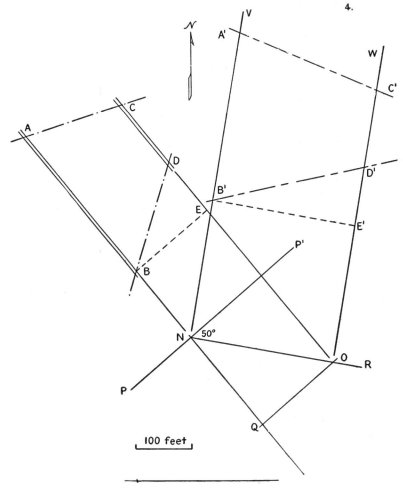

Fig. 366.   Area of a bed.

STRATIGRAPHIC THICKNESSES

To measure stratigraphic thicknesses in regions of bedded rocks by the methods of descriptive geometry, we make a projection of the contacts between different rocks on a vertical plane perpendicular to the strike of the beds. The thickness of a bed is then measured along a line perpendicular to the trace of the bedding in this vertical section. The construction of such vertical projections has already been described in Exercise 2,

p. 427. In Fig. 341, the line AE is the projection of the bed passing through X, striking N. 90° E. and dipping 20° south, on the due north vertical plane SCB. An example of the use of such constructions to obtain stratigraphic thicknesses is illustrated in Fig. 367.

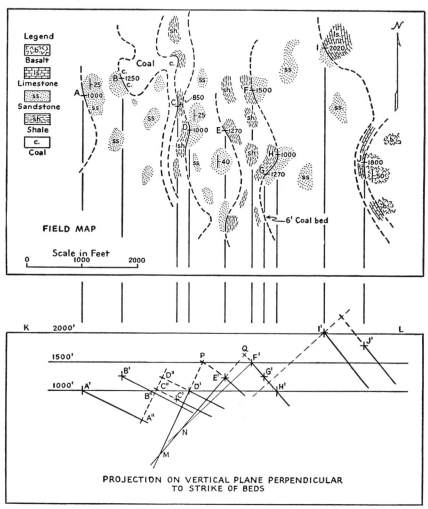

Fig. 367. Stratigraphic thickness.

Figure 367 is a plane-table map of a series of bedded rocks striking due north and dipping east. The points A through J were carefully located by surveying and their altitudes determined as indicated on the map. Dips and strikes on the beds were carefully measured; all the reliable ones are plotted on the map. The points F, G, and H are on the top of the same 6-foot coal bed. The scale of the map is shown graphically.

To measure graphically the thickness of the beds, draw a folding line *KL* perpendicular to the strike of the beds (Fig. 367). Consider this line to have the altitude 2,000 feet. Draw lines parallel to *KL* at altitudes of 1,500 feet and 1,000 feet using the same scale as the map. Through the points *A*, *B*, *C*, etc., draw lines parallel to the strike and extend them to cut line *KL*. On these lines locate the points *A'*, *B'*, *C'*, etc., at their proper altitudes in the vertical projection. Through the points *A'*, *D'*, *E'*, and *J'* draw lines making angles with the line *KL* equal to the dip of the beds at those points. The points *F'*, *G'*, and *H'* fall on the same straight line; the angle between this line and the 1,500 foot line parallel to *KL* is the dip of the coal bed at *F*, *G*, and *H*. Where the dip changes between two adjacent points, reconstruct the bedding by the geometric method described in Exercise 5.

The thicknesses of the various beds are measured along lines perpendicular to the trace of the bedding in the vertical projection plane. Thus the thickness of the lowest sandstone bed is the distance *A"B"*; of the lower coal bed, the distance *B"C"*; and of the lower shale bed *C"D"*. The thickness of the middle sandstone bed is *D'P*, where *P* is the point of intersection of the arc *E'P* (swung about the center *M*) with *D'M* extended. Similarly, the thickness of the upper shale bed is the distance *E'Q*.

When the stratigraphic thicknesses have been measured, a stratigraphic column can then be drawn up, using any convenient scale. It should show lithology by appropriate symbols and thicknesses by figures along the side. Such a column is illustrated in Fig. 368.

PROBLEMS

1. On a featureless plain a vertical north-south dike and an east-west vertical fault intersect. A thin vein striking N. 45° E. and dipping 30° NW. is exposed in the area southeast of the intersection. The vein terminates toward the northeast against the fault at a distance of 212 feet from the intersection of the dike and the fault. The vein also terminates toward the southwest against the dike. (a) Determine the area of the vein beneath the surface of the plain. (b) A shaft connects the vein with the point where the fault and the dike intersect at the surface of the earth. If the shaft is as short as possible, what is its length and where does it intersect the vein?

2. On the 200 foot level of a mine two veins, which may be designated *A* and *B*, are cut off by a vertical fault which strikes N. 30° E. Vein *A* strikes N. 90° E. and dips 30° S; vein *B*, which strikes N. 40° W. and dips 70° SW., intersects vein *A* 200 feet west of the intersection of vein *A* with the fault. (a) Determine the area of both veins below the 200 foot level between their mutual intersection and the fault. (b) Determine the length of the line of intersection of veins *A* and *B* below the 200 foot level.

3. On the 2,000-foot level of a mine, a vein, which strikes N. 90° E. and dips 40° S., terminates against a dike and a fault. The dike strikes

N. 10° W. and dips 40° E.; the fault, which strikes N. 40° E. and dips 60° E., intersects the vein 2,000 feet east of the intersection of the vein with the dike. (a) What is the area of the vein below the 2,000-foot level? (b) If the vein averages 5 feet thick, what is the volume below the 5,000-foot level? (c) If the ore is 12½ cubic feet per ton and runs $10 of gold per ton, what is the total value of the gold?

4. Figure 369 is a plane table map of a badland area in a coal field.

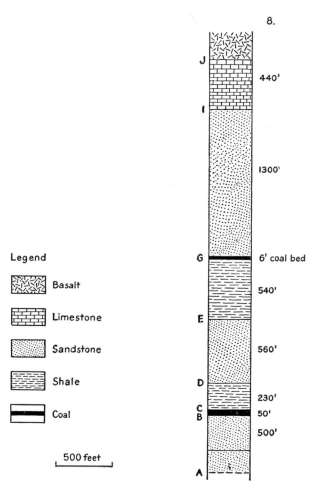

8.

Legend

Basalt

Limestone

Sandstone

Shale

Coal

500 feet

J

I

G   6' coal bed

540'

E

560'

D

C   230'

B   50'

500'

A

440'

1300'

Fig. 368. Stratigraphic column determined from Fig. 367.

Points 1 through 7 were located by triangulation from the two plane table stations on the west side of the creek. Point 1 is at the base of the coal measures, where they rest on granite. Points 2, 3, and 4 are on the base of a coal bed 20 feet thick. The section between the coal bed and the base of the formation consists of sandstone. Point 5 is the top of a coal bed 40 feet thick. The section between the coal bed at 2 and the coal bed at

5 is shale. Point 6 is at the base of a coal bed 10 feet thick. The section between 5 and 6 is sandstone. From 6 to 7 is interbedded sandstone and shale. At point 7 is the base of a very thick conglomerate formation. Assuming the dip of all the beds to be the same, prepare a stratigraphic column of the coal measures, on a scale of 1 inch equals 100 feet, showing lithology by appropriate symbols and thickness by figures at the right of the respective lithologic units.

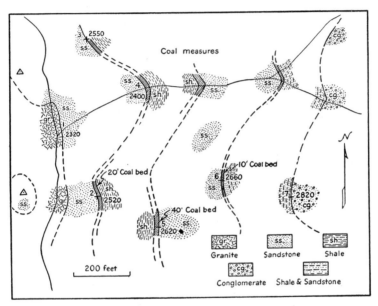

Fig. 369. Map for Problem 4 in Exercise 9.

EXERCISE 10

Solution of Three-point Problems and Vertical Fault Problems by Descriptive Geometry

THREE-POINT PROBLEM

The method used in this exercise for the solution of three-point prob-- lems is based on the graphic solution of similar triangles. The following problem illustrates the procedure to be followed:

Given: Points *A*, *B*, and *C*, all on top of a sandstone bed. Point *B* lies N. 45° W. of *A* at a *map distance* of 300 feet. Point *C* lies N. 60° E. of *A* at a *map distance* of 400 feet. The elevations of points *A*, *B*, and *C* are 950, 1,100, and 1,350 feet, respectively.

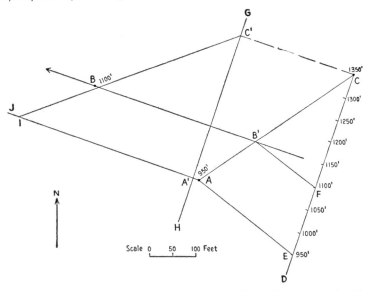

Fig. 370. Graphic solution of three-point problem. Location and alti- tude of *A*, *B*, and *C* are known.

To Find: The strike and dip of the top of the bed of sandstone. In all such cases the top of the bed must be a plane surface.

Construction (Fig. 370): Locate the three points according to the data given, using some convenient scale. Draw line *AC*, connecting the *highest* and the *lowest* of the three points. Some point along this line has the same altitude as the intermediate point *B*.

Along line *CD*, drawn in some convenient direction from point *C*, lay off *CE* equal to the difference in elevation between pcints *A* and *C* using

473

any convenient scale. On the same line, using the same scale, lay off *CF* equal to the difference in elevation between points *B* and *C*.

Connect points *A* and *E* by a line. Through point *F* draw a line parallel to line *AE* to intersect line *AC*. This intersection, point *B'*, is the point having the same altitude as point *B*. The line connecting points *B* and *B'* is the strike of the top of the bed.

At any convenient place draw line *GH* perpendicular to the strike of the bed. Project points *A* and *C* into this line to points *A'* and *C'*. Line *CC'* is the strike line on the top of the bed at an altitude of 1,350 feet, and line *AA'* is the strike line on the top of the bed at an altitude of 950 feet. The dip is therefore from point *C'* toward point *A'*—that is, toward the southwest.

Now make a vertical section along line *GH*. Erect the perpendicular *A'J* to *GH* at point *A'*, and on this line, using the same scale as the horizontal map scale, lay off *A'I* equal to the difference in altitude between points *A* and *C*. Connect points *I* and *C'*. Angle *A'C'I* is equal to the dip of the top of the sandstone.

VERTICAL FAULT

The following example illustrates the graphic method of determining the displacement of a fault if the attitude and location of two displaced horizons on both sides of the fault are known.

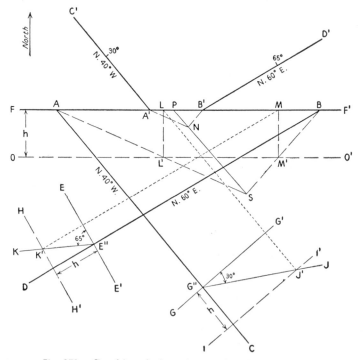

Fig. 371. Graphic solution of a vertical fault problem.

Given (Fig. 371) : On a surface of no relief, fault FF' strikes N. 90° E. and dips vertically; a vein striking N. 40° W. and dipping 30° NE. is exposed at A and A' on the south and north sides of the fault, respectively; another vein, striking N. 60° E. and dipping 65° NW., is exposed at B and B' on the south and north sides of the fault, respectively.

Find: (a) the net slip, (b) the plunge of the net slip, (c) the strike of the horizontal projection of the net slip, and (d) the relative movement along the fault plane.

Construction: Draw AC and $A'C'$ parallel to the strike of the N. 40° W. vein, and draw BD and $B'D'$ parallel to the strike of the N. 60° E. vein (Fig. 371). Draw EE' and GG' perpendicular to the strikes of the veins at convenient places, such as points E'' and G''. Using these lines as the horizontal, we shall now make structure sections.

Draw HH' parallel to and at some arbitrary distance h from EE'; draw II' parallel to and at a distance h from GG'. These lines represent a level which we will call the *lower reference plane*; it is h distance below the surface plan. Draw angles $G'G''J$ and $EE''K$ equal to the respective dips of the N. 40° W. and N. 60° E. veins. Draw $J'L$ and $K'M$ parallel to AC and BD, respectively. These lines represent the horizontal projection of contours on the two veins; at all points on these contours the two veins are exactly distance h below the horizontal surface represented by the plan. Point L is the horizontal projection of the intersection of the fault, the lower reference plane, and the N. 40° W. vein on the south side of the fault. Point M is the horizontal projection of the intersection of the fault, the lower reference plane, and the N. 60° E. vein on the south side of the fault.

We will now make a vertical section along line FF'—that is, in the plane of the fault. Draw OO', h distance away from and parallel to FF'. This construction, in reality, amounts to rotating the vertical fault into the plane of the map (plan). Draw LL' and MM' perpendicular to FF'. Inasmuch as L' and M' are points on the section, h distance below L and M on the surface plan, they represent points on the veins in the cross section.

Draw AL' and BM'; extend them to an intersection at S. AS and BS represent the traces of the two veins on the fault plane (in the cross section), and S represents their intersection on the south wall. Draw $A'N$ and $B'N$ parallel to AS and BS, respectively. $A'N$ and $B'N$ represent the traces of the two veins on the fault plane on the north wall, and N is their intersection.

Draw NS. This line is the total displacement in the fault plane between the two points N and S, which were together before the faulting; NS is therefore the net slip.

Extend NS to intersect FF' at P. The angle SPF' is the rake of the net slip; in a vertical fault the rake and plunge are equal.

The net slip must lie in the fault plane. Inasmuch as the fault plane is vertical and strikes N. 90° E., the strike of the horizontal projection of the net slip is also N. 90° E. Point S is at a lower elevation in the vertical section along the fault than point N and is to the east of a vertical line through point N; therefore the south side of the fault has moved down toward the east relative to the north side of the fault.

PROBLEMS

1. The top of a coal bed crops out at an altitude of 500 feet. A second outcrop of this horizon lies 1,000 feet (map distance) due north at an altitude of 1,300 feet; and a third outcrop lies 600 feet (map distance) due W. from the first outcrop at an altitude of 800 feet. Determine the strike and dip of the coal bed.

2. A vertical fault strikes N. 90° E. across a featureless plain. Two veins, which may be called A and B, are disrupted by the fault. The data are as follows: "Distance" is measured toward the east from the point on the map at which the southern segment of vein A abuts against the fault.

Vein	Strike	Dip	Distance on South Wall	Distance on North Wall
A	N. 10° W.	40° E.	0 feet	150 feet
B	N. 60° E.	50° N.	500 feet	400 feet

Determine (a) the value of the net slip; (b) the plunge of the net slip; (c) the strike of the horizontal projection of the net slip; and (d) the relative movement along the fault (that is, which block has gone up relatively).

3. A large vertical fault strikes N. 90° E. across a gold mining property 500 feet north of the vertical shaft. Two hundred feet below the surface and 500 feet due N. of the shaft, vein A is exposed on the south side of the fault; vein A strikes N. 30° W., dips 45° NE. Two hundred feet below the surface, 500 feet north and 300 feet east of the shaft, vein B is exposed on the north side of the fault; vein B strikes N. 45° E., dips 60° NW. The rake of the net slip along the fault is 60° W., with the net slip 50 feet, north block up relative to the south block.

Three hundred feet below the surface and 600 feet north of the shaft is an east-west tunnel. Where, along this tunnel, should veins A and B be crossed?

EXERCISE 11

Solution of Inclined Fault Problems
by Descriptive Geometry

METHOD

The following example illustrates the graphic method of determining the displacement on a fault that dips at an angle other than 90 degrees, if the attitude and location of each of two displaced horizons are known on both sides of the fault.

The example also shows the method of locating a disrupted horizon on one side of a fault, if the location and attitude of the disrupted horizon on the opposite side of the fault are known; the direction and amount of movement along the fault must also be known.

Given (Fig. 372): On a surface of no relief, fault FF' strikes N. 90° E. and dips 40° S.; a vein striking N. 30° W. and dipping 35° NE. is exposed at A and A' on the south and north sides of the fault, respectively; another vein, striking N. 30° E. and dipping 60° NW., is exposed at B and B' on the south and north sides of the fault, respectively; a third vein, striking N. 40° E. and dipping 70° SE., is exposed at X (Fig. 373) on the south side of the fault.

To Find: (a) the net slip of the fault, (b) the strike of the horizontal projection of the net slip, (c) the plunge of the net slip, (d) the relative movement along the fault—that is, which block moved up—and (e) the location of the third vein on the north side of the fault.

Construction: As shown in Fig. 372, draw AC and $A'C'$ parallel to the strike of the N. 30° W. vein, and draw BD and $B'D'$ parallel to the strike of the N. 30° E. vein. Draw EE', FF', and GG' perpendicular to BD, AC, and FF', respectively, at any convenient points such as E'', F'', and G''. Using these lines as horizontals, we shall now make cross sections.

Draw HH' parallel to and at an arbitrary distance h from EE'; construct II' and JJ' in a similar way. These lines represent a level that we shall call the *lower reference plane;* it is h distance below the surface plan. Lay off angle $GG''K$ equal to the dip of the fault; $G''K$ intersects JJ' at K'. Lay off angle $EE''L$ equal to the dip of the N. 30° E. vein; $E''L$ intersects HH' at L'. Lay off angle $F'F''M$ equal to the dip of the N. 30° W. vein; $F''M$ intersects II' at M'. From K' draw $K'O$ parallel to FF'. From L', draw a line parallel to BD to intersect $K'O$ at P. From M', draw a line parallel to AC to intersect $K'O$ at Q. $K'O$, $L'P$, and $M'Q$ represent contours on the fault and the veins; at all points on these lines the respective fault or vein is exactly h distance below the surface of the plan. The intersections of the two veins with the fault on this lower reference plane are at P and Q.

477

We shall now make a section in the plane of the fault. It is necessary to rotate the fault plane into the plane of the map in order to show this section. Line FF' is used as the axis of rotation. Using $G''K'$ as the radius and G'' as the center, draw an arc to intersect GG' at R. $G''R$ is the true slope distance in the fault plane between the surface plan and the lower reference plane. From R, draw RR' parallel to FF'. $BG''RR'$ is a section in the plane of the fault.

From Q, construct a line perpendicular to $K'O$ to intersect RR' at Q'. From P, construct a line perpendicular to $K'O$ to intersect RR' at P'. Q' and P' represent the intersection of the veins with the lower reference plane, viewed in the fault plane.

Draw AQ' and BP' to an intersection at S'. AS' and BS' represent the trace of the two veins on the south wall of the fault plane; S' represents their intersection on the south wall. Draw $A'N'$ and $B'N'$ parallel to AS' and BS', respectively. N' represents the intersection of the trace of the two veins on the north wall. Draw $N'S'$, which is the net slip.

Draw AQ and BP to an intersection at S. AS is the horizontal projection of the intersection of the N. 30° W. vein and the fault. BS is the horizontal projection of the intersection of the N. 30° E. vein and the fault. S is the horizontal projection of the intersection of the two veins on the south wall of the fault plane. Draw $A'N$ and $B'N$ parallel to AS and BS, respectively. Draw NS, which is the horizontal projection of the net slip.

To determine the plunge of the net slip, it is necessary to find the altitude of the points for which N and S are the horizontal projections. Draw a line from S, parallel to FF', to intersect $G''K$ at T; and draw a line from N, parallel to FF', to intersect $G''K$ at U. Lines perpendicular to FF' are then erected, one from T and the other from U. These perpendiculars intersect FF' at T' and U'. $T'U'$, on the same scale as the map, whatever it may be, is the difference in altitude between the points of which N and S are the horizontal projections.

Lay off NS on a separate part of the paper. Drop a perpendicular from S to S' such that $S'S = T'U'$. Draw NS'. SNS' gives the vertical angle that the net slip makes with its horizontal projection; it is the plunge of the net slip. As a check on your work, NS' in this diagram should equal $N'S'$ in the main construction.

The point of intersection of the two veins on the south side of the fault with the fault plane lies at a lower altitude and to the east of the corresponding intersection on the north side of the fault. The relative movement along the fault is such that the south side has moved down and to the east in relation to the north side. Extend $N'S'$ to intersect FF' at V. Angle $S'VB$ is the rake of the net slip.

Figure 373, which illustrates the method used to locate the N. 40° E. vein on the north side of the fault, shows data concerning the fault identical with that in Fig. 372. FF' is the trace of the fault on the map. $K'O$ is the horizontal projection of the intersection of the fault and the lower reference plane, and RR' is this intersection after it has been rotated into the plane of the map.

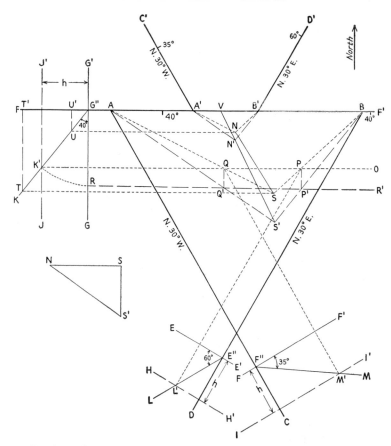

Fig. 372. Graphic solution of an inclined fault problem. Two veins, one striking N. 30° W. and dipping 35° NE., the other striking N. 30° E. and dipping 60° NW., are displaced along the fault *FF'*.

The location of the N. 40° E. vein on the south side of the fault is shown. Draw *XY* parallel to the strike of the vein. At some convenient point along *XY*, such as *A''*, draw *AA'* perpendicular to *XY*. At *h* distance (the same distance as used in Fig. 372) from *AA'*, draw *BB'* perpendicular to *XY*. Lay off angle *A'A''C* equal to 70°, the dip of the N. 40° E. vein. From *C'*, the intersection of *A''C* with *BB'*, draw a line parallel to the strike of the N. 40° E. vein to intersect *K'O* at *D*. *C'D* represents a contour on the vein; at all points on this line the vein is exactly *h* distance below the surface of the plan. The intersection of the vein with the fault on this lower reference plane is at *D*. From *D* draw a line perpendicular to *K'O* to intersect *RR'* at *D'*. *D'* represents the intersection of the vein with the lower reference plane, viewed in the fault plane.

Draw *EE'*, which passes through points *X* and *D'*. *EE'* is the trace of the N. 40° E. vein on the south wall of the fault plane. Figure 372 shows that the north block has moved up and to the west; therefore the trace of the vein on the north wall of the fault plane will be above and to the west of EE'. At any convenient point along EE', as at X, lay off angle $G''XH$ equal to the rake of the net slip, which is the angle $S'VB$ of Fig. 372; and on XH, lay off XH' equal to the net slip, which is $N'S'$ of Fig. 372. Through H', draw II' parallel to EE'. II' is the trace of the vein on the north side of the fault. From X', draw $X'Y'$ parallel to XY. Point X' represents the intersection of the vein with the fault on the north side of the fault, and $X'Y'$ is the trace of the N. 40° E. vein on the plan, north of the fault.

PROBLEMS

1. A vertical fault strikes due E. across a featureless plain. Three veins, which may be called A, B, and C, are disrupted by the fault. The data are as follows: "Distance," is measured from west to east along the fault, the starting point being indicated by 0 distance.

Vein	Strike	Dip	Distance on North Wall	Distance on South Wall
A	N. 10° W.	30° E.	0 feet	100 feet
B	N. 10° W.	45° SW.	350 feet	240 feet
C	N. 40° E.	50° SE.	400 feet	?

(a) Determine the net slip, the rake of the net slip, the strike of the horizontal projection of the net slip, and the relative movement on the fault—that is, which block moved relatively upward. (b) Locate vein C on the south side of the fault.

2. A fault plane exposed on a featureless plain strikes N. 90° E. and dips 60° S. Two veins, which may be called A and B, are disrupted by the fault. The data are as follows:

Vein	Strike	Dip	Distance on North Wall	Distance on South Wall
A	N. 40° E.	30° SE.	100 feet	0 feet
B	N. 20° W.	75° W.	300 feet	250 feet

Determine the net slip, the rake of the net slip, the plunge of the net slip, the strike of the horizontal projection of the net slip, and the relative movement on the fault.

3. A fault plane, exposed on a featureless plain, strikes due E. and dips 60° N. Three veins, which may be called A, B, and C, are disrupted by the fault. The data are as follows:

Vein	Strike	Dip	Distance on North Wall	Distance on South Wall
A	N.	50° E.	0 feet	100 feet
B	N. 40° W.	75° NE.	250 feet	200 feet
C	N. 30° W.	75° SW.	350 feet	?

(a) Determine the net slip, the plunge and rake of the net slip, the strike of the horizontal projection of the net slip, and the relative movement on the fault. (b) Locate vein C on the south side of the fault

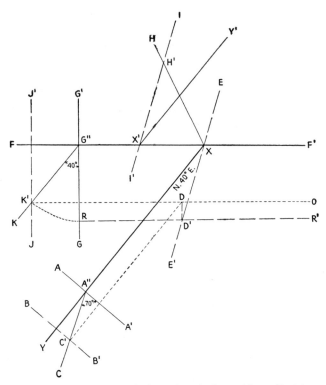

Fig. 373. Graphic solution of a fault problem. Position of N. 40° E. vein is known on south side of fault, *FF'*. Net slip is same as in Fig. 373. Problem is to find position of N. 40° E. vein on north side of fault. N. 40° E. vein dips 70° SE.

EXERCISE 12

Stereographic Projection in Structural Geology

By the use of the stereographic projection some of the simpler problems in structural geology that we have already attacked might have been solved more rapidly. This same projection is used especially in mineralogy, and its use in structural geology has been emphasized by Bucher.[1] Although it is possible to determine directions and angles by this method, it is not possible to get distances.

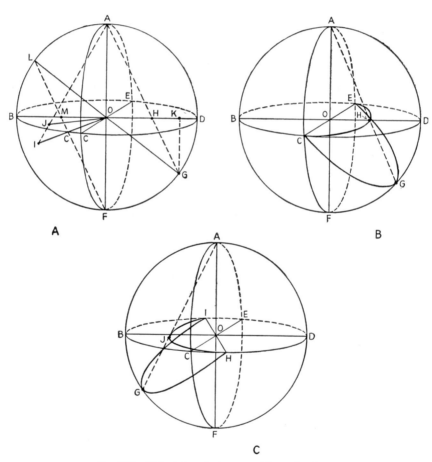

Fig. 374. Principles of stereographic projection.

[1] Bucher, W. H., "The Stereographic Projection, a Handy Tool for the Practical Geologist," *Journal of Geology,* Vol. 52, pp. 191–212, 1944.

The principles of the stereographic projection are illustrated in Fig. 374. Figure 374A shows a sphere; the AF axis is vertical, the BD axis is horizontal east-west, and the CE axis is horizontal north-south. $BCDE$ is a horizontal plane, $ACFE$ is a vertical north-south plane, and $BFDA$ is a vertical east-west plane. Let us consider a line that plunges due east at an angle of 40 degrees. Now assume, as is always done in this projection, that the line passes through O, the center of the sphere. Since the line plunges due east, it must lie in the plane $BFDA$. The pole of this line is G on the lower hemisphere and L on the upper hemisphere. If G were projected vertically upward to the equatorial plane, the point of projection would be K. In the stereographic projection, however, the line of projection is drawn from G to the upper pole of the sphere (A), so that the point of projection is H. That is, on the equatorial plane HO represents GO in space. If a reader were presented with this equatorial projection, the fact that HO strikes east-west would tell him that the bearing (horizontal projection) of GO is east-west. Since H is east of O and the projection is on the lower hemisphere, the line represented by HO must plunge to the east. The distance HO is a function of the angle of plunge. An appropriate scale gives the angle in degrees (see below). An east-west line with zero plunge would be represented by OD (or by OB). A north-south line with zero plunge would be represented by OE (or by OC). A vertical line would be represented by a point at O.

It is apparent that only one hemisphere need be used. If the upper hemisphere were used, the projection would be the mirror image of that on the lower hemisphere. In structural problems it is better to use the lower hemisphere.

Assume that another line plunges 25° SW. The pole on the lower hemisphere is at I, the projection of which on the equatorial plane is J.

The method of representing planes is shown in Figs. 374B and 374C. Assume a plane that strikes north-south and dips 40° E. If such a plane is imagined to pass through the center of the sphere at O (Fig. 374B), its intersection with the lower hemisphere is CGE. The projection of G onto the equatorial plane is H, and the line CGE is represented by CHE. If a reader were presented with this equatorial projection, he could tell that the plane strikes north-south. Because CHE lies east of O, the plane dips east. The distance HD, if one knows the scale (see page 485), gives the dip of the plane. A horizontal plane would be represented by the equatorial plane itself. A vertical north-south plane would be represented by COE; a vertical east west plane by the line BOD.

If a plane strikes northwest and dips 50° SW., its projection on the equatorial plane is HJI (Fig. 374C).

The meridian stereographic net, 10 centimeters in diameter, is shown in Fig. 375, which is in the envelope. This net represents the equatorial plane of a sphere of that diameter. The long arcs, or meridional arcs, are the projection of great circles that lie 2 degrees apart on the lower hemisphere, as they would appear when seen from the upper pole of the sphere. The short arcs, or polar arcs, represent small circles drawn about the poles at 2 degree intervals.

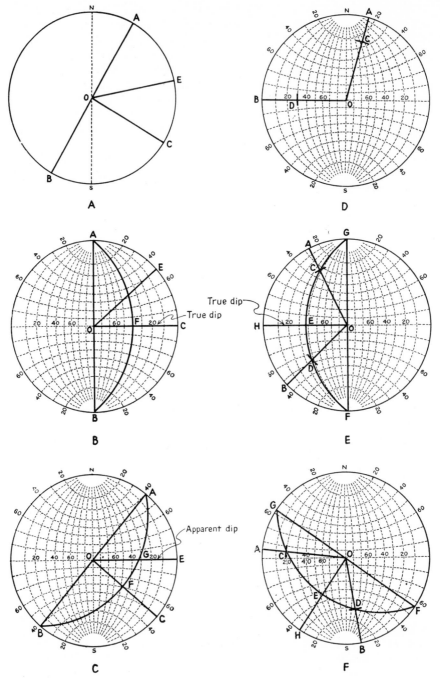

Fig. 376. Use of stereographic projection, Examples 1 and 2, Exercise 12.

The attitude of a line may be determined from the net. The line OC in Fig. 376F may be taken as one example. The bearing (strike of the horizontal projection) may be read from the margin of the net. That is, OC, if projected to the margin at A, indicates that the bearing is N. 85° W. The plunge is measured by AC. ACO is rotated until it lies along the east-west line of the net. Each division on Fig. 376F represents 10 degrees; the angles are measured from the outside of the circle. Hence AC is 18 degrees, which is the plunge of the line represented by OC.

OC in Fig. 376E strikes N. 27° W. If OCA is rotated counterclockwise to coincide with the east-west axis, AC can be measured to be 18 degrees. OC in Fig. 376C indicates a horizontal line striking S. 50° E. (N. 50° W.).

A plane is represented in the stereographic projection by the line of strike, drawn through the center O, and the trace of the great circle in which it cuts the lower hemisphere. Thus in Fig. 376F a plane striking N. 58° W. and dipping 36° SW. is represented by the curve $GCEDF$ and the line of strike is GOF. The dip is determined by rotating GOF clockwise until it coincides with the north-south line. HE could then be measured as 36 degrees.

Example 1. A bed strikes N. 30° E. and dips 40° SE. Find its apparent dip in a section trending N. 80° E.

As in Fig. 376A, draw on a piece of tracing paper, placed over the stereonet, AOB representing the strike of the bed; OC, perpendicular to AOB, representing the direction of dip of the bed; and OE, representing the line of section. Place the tracing paper over the stereonet and rotate it until OC coincides with the east-west direction, as in Fig. 376B. Measure the true dip, CF, along CO and trace the great circle AFB, which represents the trace of the bed on the lower hemisphere. Now rotate the paper until OE coincides with the east-west direction of the stereonet (Fig. 376C). The apparent dip EG may be read as 32 degrees.

Example 2. In a gully the following apparent dips were found on a shale bed: 20° in a direction N. 85° W. and 30° in a direction S. 10° E. Find the strike and dip of the shale.

Plot the directions of the apparent dips, OA and OB, on tracing paper. Then place the paper over the stereonet and plot the amount of the apparent dips, AC and BD, by successively rotating each of these directions to the east-west position (Fig. 376D). Now rotate the tracing paper until points C and D' lie on the same great circle (Fig. 376E). Draw the plane $CEDOFG$ which is the plane of the dipping shale bed. The true dip is 36 degrees, as indicated by HE. The strike may be determined by rotating the tracing paper until the apparent dips have their proper orientation (Fig. 376F). It is N. 58° W.

Example 3. A vein striking N. 20° E. and dipping 30° NW. intersects a bed which strikes N. 45° W. and dips 20° SW. What is the direction and amount of plunge of the line of intersection? What is the rake of the intersection measured in the plane of the vein?

Plot the vein, AOB, and the bed, COD, on tracing paper laid over the stereonet by the methods of the foregoing problem (Fig. 377A). OE is the line of intersection of the bed and the vein with a direction of S. 58° W.

EF is its plunge, which may be measured as 19 degrees by rotating the tracing paper until *OF* coincides with the east-west line of the stereonet. *BE* is the rake of the intersection in the plane of the vein. It may be found by rotating the tracing paper until the strike of the vein, *COD*, coincides with the polar diameter of the stereonet. The rake is 42° S.

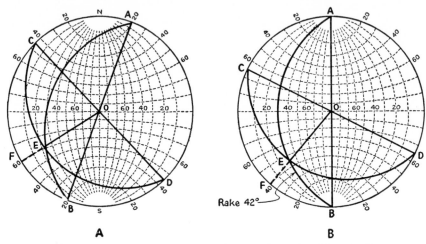

Fig. 377. Use of stereographic projection, Example 3, Exercise 12.

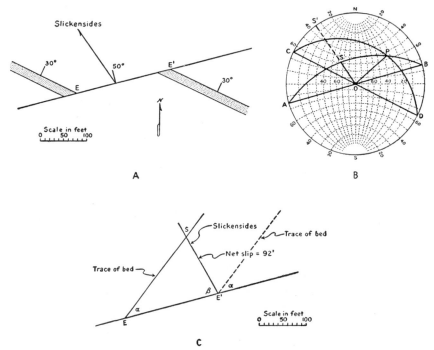

Fig. 378. Use of stereographic projection, Example 4, Exercise 12.

Example 4. The map in Figure 378A shows a bed that has been displaced by a fault. The dip of the fault (50° NW.) and the dip of the bed (30° NE.) are shown on the map and also the bearing of slickensides on the fault; What is the direction and amount of the net slip?

Plot the plane of the fault, *AOB*, the plane of the bed, *COD*, and the direction of the slickensides, *OS'*, on the stereographic projection by the methods discussed above (Fig. 378B). The direction in space of the net slip is given by its trend, *OS* (N. 35° W.), and its plunge, *SS'* 48° NW. These slickensides rake 75° W. (*AS*) in the plane of the fault. *OP* is the intersection of the bed with the fault plane and this intersection rakes *PB* or 38° E. in the plane of the fault.

Figure 378C is an auxiliary construction of the plane of the fault. *EE'* represents the horizontal separation of the beds in the plane of the fault. Plot $\alpha = PB$ = rake of the intersection of the bed in the fault plane. Plot $\beta = AS$ = the rake of the net slip (as shown by slickensides) in the fault plane. Then *E'S* (92 feet) is the length of the net slip.

PROBLEMS

1. Given the following data on a limestone bed:

Value of Apparent Dip	Direction of Apparent Dip
40°	N. 80° W.
50°	N. 20° E.

(a) Find the strike and dip of the bed.

(b) What is the apparent dip in an east-west direction?

2. The two limbs of a fold strike N. 50° W. and N. 30° E., and dip 35° NE. and 50° NW. respectively.

(a) What is the plunge of the fold?

(b) If a fault striking N. 80° W. and dipping 60° S. intersects this fold, what will be the rake of the intersections of these two limbs in the fault plane?

3. A vein striking N. 30° E. and dipping 40° NW. is displaced by a fault that strikes N. 70° E. and dips 60° S. The horizontal separation of the vein measured along the trace of the fault is 200 feet; the part of the vein north of the fault lies west of the part to the south. The bearing of slickensides in the fault plane is N. 45° W. If the relative displacement along the fault is assumed to be parallel to the slickensides, what is the net slip and what is the relative movement of the north side of the fault with respect to the south side?

4. A vein and a distinctive limestone bed intersect a fault which strikes N. 70° W. and dips 70° N. The attitudes of the vein and the bed, and the relative positions of the intersections with the fault plane measured from east to west horizontally along the trace of the fault are as follows:

	Strike	Dip	Intersection with the Fault (in feet)	
			North Wall	South Wall
Vein	N. 20° E.	50° E.	0	600
Bed	N. 30° W.	60° W.	400	200

What is the net slip and the direction and plunge of the net slip?

EXERCISE 13

Chronology in Structural Geology

No additional instructions are necessary for this exercise.

PROBLEMS

1. In Fig. 379, in the envelope, the topographic contours are shown in light lines. The contact between the pre-Cambrian and the Cretaceous formations is shown by heavy lines. (a) Make a structure contour map of the contact between the pre-Cambrian and Cretaceous formations (Be-

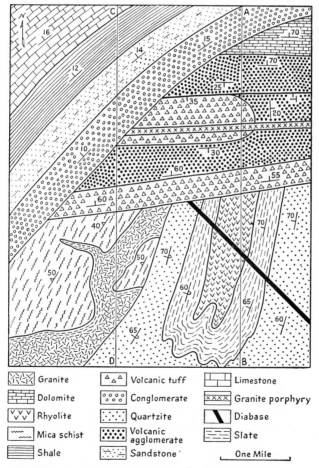

Fig. 380. Geologic map for use in Problem 2, Exercise 13.

489

cause of lack of data, this can be done for only parts of the map).[1] (b) Draw a structure section along the line *AB*. (c) What do you infer to be the structural relation between the pre-Cambrian and Cretaceous formations? (d) What do you infer about the structural significance of the line shown by the dot-dash symbol? (e) List in chronological order the geological history of this region.

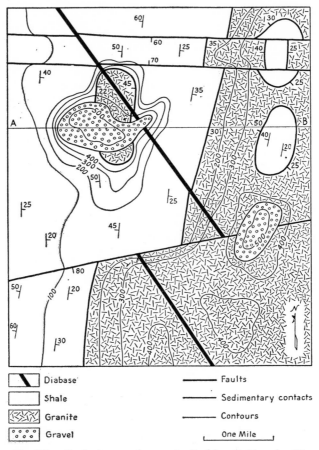

Fig. 381.   Geologic map for use in Problem 3, Exercise 13.

2. Assume that the region represented by Fig. 380 is one of no relief. (a) Draw structure sections *AB* and *CD*. (b) List in chronological order the geological history of this area. (The legend at the bottom of the map is intentionally not given in chronological order.)

3. (a) Draw cross-section *AB* in Fig. 381. (b) List in chronological order the geological history of this region.

----

[1] This work can be done directly on the map or on a piece of tracing paper placed over the map.

Index

Bold Face Type Indicates Principal Reference